NOGUCHI

NOGUCHI

BY

GUSTAV ECKSTEIN

Harper & Brothers Publishers

NEW YORK and LONDON

1931

CONTENTS

v

ILLUSTRATIONS

NOGUCHI

The Country from Which He Came

The youngest lifts his head and looks across the valley off toward his city and tears fill his eyes. Abruptly the oldest turns to him. "Would you dishonor your father?" The tears cease.

They have been fighting seasoned soldiers and making them give way, but glory is like the lightning. Now they are in this ravine half up the mountainside, alone, driven here, only nineteen left, behind them in every crevice rain and fog and soldiers—soldiers of the Emperor of Japan. The Japanese revolution is all but done. The oldest ruling line on earth is all but back in full power. This is Meiji 1, the year 1868, and only stubborn Aizu still holds out.

The nineteen had thought to make their way back to their castle, have got as far as this ravine. Too late. No use to make their way there now. The castle is in flames. "This then is the end." So says one. "Death is but what we expected." So says another. Suddenly one remembers they still have bullets left. Quick they creep down the slope of Iimoriyama and put to good use what they have. One receives a shot in the thigh. The others help him back to the ravine, then near the top of the ravine all arrange themselves in orderly formation. They face the castle. They fall to their knees, bow low, hands on the ground. "We, nineteen, bested in the game of war do now die here on this slope of Iimoriyama. But our spirits stay, still defend the castle. Farewell, lord of Aizu. Farewell, father and mother." Here and there then the stabbings begin. One cuts himself in the abdomen. One cuts himself across the throat. Two look into each other's faces then cut into each other. One and one the kneeling bodies topple. Leigemen to the lord of Aizu, they die without a sign of pain in their faces. Yet it is not the castle that burns. They are mistaken, alas, in what they see. It is only some houses between them and the castle.

Later, an old woman is picking her way up this slope of Iimoriyama. She is used to blood. These days have made her used. But boys? Not one older than sixteen. Dead, all of them. She turns each over, looks into each face, puts water to each lip. Ah, one lives! That one will tell the story. Aizu will know its story. Quick she glances toward the valley, draws the body over her back, stumbles off with it.

And the story is told and retold and will be for generations to come. The story is sung and resung, in the houses of the geisha, in the theaters, on the streams on summer nights. From it Zen priests draw questions for their disciples, Chinese scholars find substance for their teaching. The whole life of a countryside is run

2

through by a story. Children of Aizu are not like other children. All are touched, as will be the subject of this history—to be born now some eight years hence.

She Who Gave Him Birth

Eastward of the castle, near Bandai mountain, two miles perhaps from its base, in the village of Okina-jima is Omiyasan Choshozi, a very large temple for so miserable a village. One morning a child, a baby on her back, comes to the priest, holds up ten sen. "Give it to Kannon and pray for my house." Ten sen is much money and the priest is suspicious, asks the child's name. She tells him Noguchi Shika, then of her own accord tells about the money, sen for sen, how she got it, by what rough labor, ends with saying she saved it for Kannon all the last two years. The priest is ashamed, promises to pray, promises that with diligence Shika will lift her house back to where it stood five generations ago in the time of Noguchi Seitaro since when it has gone so steadily down.

Shika's father was the poorest, a sickly man, hated the life of the farmer, cold in winter and in summer from dawn to dark to have to keep his sickly feet in the muddy waters of the rice-fields, yet forever buried in poverty and suffering. Soon too he had slipped away

4

off to the town, become servant to a samurai, his wife with him, and soon too she had slipped from him, was gone a time, then came back, and he glad enough to take her. Shika they left with her grandmother.

Her grandmother is hired to a tea-room, all day must boil the water to wash the feet of the guests and in the twilight must walk to Inawashiro and on her bent back carry three sho of saki even though she was already sixty in the year of the coronation. But it is not this she complains of. What she complains of is that in her whole life she has not been able to lay aside money sufficient to make the pilgrimage to Zenkozi to worship the Buddha there. It is an existence to weep tears of blood. Then comes a night, it is between the 3rd and 4th, suddenly cold, and in the morning grandmother thinks she had better not rise. The neighbor brings a quilt. Shika is frightened, hurries from house to house, borrows ten sen, not enough to call the doctor from Inawashiro but enough to buy drugs and to bring two sen to the temple. She prays long. She prays fervently. Nevertheless a few mornings later grandmother is being sent to the fields.

So Shika is left with no one except the priest Uno Ura who is kind to her and offers to teach her to write. While he teaches her she rocks her master's baby on her back. To save cost of ink and paper she sprinkles ash on a lacquered tray and shapes the ideographs in the ash. She learns quickly. She is busy and happy, then the priest Uno Ura goes down with dysentery, and that is an end of learning. All the priest's family goes down with dysentery. No one in the village will so much as pass the priest's house, only Shika, and her they cannot drive away. She takes care of them all, lives in the contagion as if it could not touch her and it does not. Meanwhile her father, the sickly one, he who slipped from the town to work for the samurai, is back from the town and still is sickly, and she must get food for his mouth too and nurse him month after month then year after year. When the soldiers of the Emperor are filling the valley and the villagers are fleeing, taking their rice with them, Shika is sixteen. The soldiers burn as they go but the Noguchi house escapes. Presently the rice of those who fled gives out and Shika says she will return for more rice. The guards question her but let her pass. The soldiers occupy the house but she comes away with the rice, and with a kettle besides, her master's kettle, and he when he sees his kettle is so over-joyed he cries out it shall be hers, if ever she should marry. But a girl without a dowry, hard to think of a marriage from that.

Yet there is that farmer Sayosuke who lives on the way to Inawashiro, a good man, as everyone knows, but loves saki. His father loved saki before him, mortgaged all the property for drink. Sayosuke sits at the edge of Inawashiro lake, sits there often, thinking. True, she is a girl without a dowry, but a most excellent farmer, her eyes a little crossed, but most excellent callous in her hands, and most orderly hair, each hair rising from the nape of the neck parallel with each other hair. So firm a mouth too.

6

SHIKA'S FATHER WAS THE POOREST

A MOST EXCELLENT
FARMER

IN THE ZINJO-SHOGAKKO

Sayosuke the farmer marries Shika the maid in the 4th year of the Emperor Meiji, four years after the nineteen fell like cherry blossoms blown by the spring wind. He who arranges the marriage pours the san-san-kudo (the three-three-nine-times) and Sayosuke drinks what is poured, and that is only the beginning.

It Is Not for Daughters the Nation Celebrates the Nobori

He was born at the high-tide. They are strong when they are born at the high-tide. To-day is the 24th of November, the 9th year of the Emperor Meiji. How she must hurry from the rice-fields when the pains began. One neighbor has brought a squash and another a dried fish and another rice. "The forehead and the chin are Sayosuke's." That is what one neighbor said. "Nay, but this boy and Shika are as like as the halves of an egg." Not one infant wrinkle, and black hair, and much hair. Only when they are born at the low-tide do they die. She moves again to the sacred corner to give thanks to the ancestors for having sent her this male heir, later will go to the temple of Omiyasan Choshozi, and later will walk the twenty miles to Nakata Kannon, in each place will give thanks for this male heir who will help her lift the house back to where it stood five generations ago in the time of Noguchi Seitaro. Up to now the responsibility has been hers alone. Whatever has Sayosuke cared? A good man, a loyal leigeman to

8

the lord of Aizu, but neglects all for saki—no oil in the lamp, no rice in the bin, no millet, sometimes not even bran, house and land mortgaged like the house and land of his father, of late too has kept off somewhere in Hokkaido. Good riddance, perhaps. But perhaps not. Something there was in him to marry her regardless of dowry. True, she was the sturdiest virgin of the village, but he married her. She adopted him, but adoption is the custom when one is the last of one's house. He waited about till Inu came, expected a son and Inu came a daughter, yet was good-natured and made great guttural noises while he rubbed her infant belly. But when another came, it was too much, and he slipped away off to Hokkaido, off altogether of the island of Honshu. A villain. That is what the straight-laced missionary lady in Wakamatsu would say. A dreamer, really, a hero, marries the sturdiest virgin of the village then when he has had his fun and is growing weary slips away. Yes, some of him, some choice little of him let us hope has been left in this son. Seisaku is what Shika calls the son. And a fine name. It stands for a good make or here among farmers for an excellent crop.

[IV]

What This Act Really Means None of the Living Can Say

At the far end of the room, there where the kitchen would be if the house were divided, in the floor, is a hole, and in the hole a basin, and in the basin a charcoal fire to boil the water for the tea. That is the urori. By the side of the urori Seisaku sleeps. Shika has been leaving him with Inu of late. He is three. He is weaned. Sometimes he and Inu weep together because they are hungry, then a neighbor may come and feed them half-burnt rice from the bottom of the rice-pot, but sometimes Seisaku weeps alone, especially is afraid of thunder, and then Inu holds him in her arms and tells him not to be afraid. Inu can take care. Shika need no longer carry him over field and hill as she works. The work is hard enough. Nights the thongs that bind the warazi to her feet bear painfully into the flesh. She calls him pig-boy, which is the way the Japanese mother does when someone is listening. She says he is nothing to brag of. But when she is alone with him and the shoji are drawn she tells him he is strong and good, and that he must be, and shall be, for this is their house, not the house of Sayosuke, the house of Noguchi, and when the responsibility for the house rests on the mother alone the son grows strong, as everybody knows.

It is nearly June now, the busiest time of the farmer's year, and Shika has gone once more into the half-dark to do a little work in the rice before night sets in. To Inu it seems her mother stays out there long. Inu is hungry. Why should she not go to see what keeps her mother? It would be safe with Seisaku asleep. By the side of the urori he sleeps.

Shika is working in the rice. Inu is coming toward her. Then suddenly through the half-dark, through the stillness, a scream. Her heavy warazi stick in the mud. She pulls at them savagely, stumbles to the house. He has crawled into the urori, is trying to scramble out, is fighting with the hot coals. She snatches him up. The neighbor rushes in. The neighbor is not a doctor but knows. "The fingers of the left hand are mostly gone, and the left arm and the left foot and the right hand are burned, I know not how bad." That is what the neighbor says.

Twenty-one days Shika does not sleep, keeps open her eyes with bits of wood wedged between the lids. The left hand she does not touch, but the fingers of the right she presses back, timidly at first, then more and more boldly, hour after hour, gently, patiently straightens them out. Infection has set in and the burned places fester. He is very ill. She prays and prays. What will become of him? A farmer to face life without the use of his hands. It is the fault of her poverty. Henceforth she will double her effort. She has the responsibility for the house but she has the responsibility for this boy too. Henceforth she will carry him everywhere over field and hill, will hang his basket in the pines or set it at the edge of the rice where she can see. Strong he is, else he had been dead, and strength he will need. Kannon gave him that. Kannon knows best. What this act really means none of the living can say. He is brave. He is like the nineteen. He does not weep.

[V]

"Tembo, tembo. . . ."

In the zinjo-shogakko the boys point to the hand, then one whispers to the other. "What kind of a farmer will he be with a hand like that?" And if no one is about to stop them they chase him. "Tembo, tembo. . . ." That is what they shout. Tembo means hand-boy, and he flees ahead of them round the schoolhouse into the graveyard to hide behind a gravestone. The graveyard is next the schoolhouse, and next the schoolhouse is the temple, and behind all seen through every gap the pale cone of Bandai rises as if to carry the temple to a point in the sky. When the temple bell booms one thinks it must be in one's own head.

He hates his hand. Sometimes when he is alone with it he looks at it, sees how it is like a knot of wood, wishes he could hide it, or take a knife and cut between the stumps. But if he did and the stumps began to bleed and the bleeding did not stop, what would he do then? He weighs this many times, meanwhile misses a day at school, has found a boy glad to miss a day with him. Mornings they start from their houses as if for school

13

but go instead into the fields of lava that lie below Bandai and when time to return smear ink on their fingers, a little also on their faces, so it shall appear they have been working hard. Seisaku is not working hard. He is lazier and lazier, could read before he went to the school, now never reads, yet one day for no reason abruptly as if there were something had broken inside him has passed the others and gone to the top of his class. The others do not envy him on that account. Why should they? Still they are not quite as they were and he sees that they are not and works harder.

At writing he works hardest, bends far over the rice-paper. From time to time the others steal a look at him, or perhaps he only imagines they do, and to be sure he is not a pretty sight because while his right hand is driving the fude his left must steady the paper and the ugly stumps have a way of sticking up into the air. "What is the use of your beautiful writing when you can never be anything but a farmer?" Someone asks him that and he does not answer, edges away, takes a path that goes along the stream between the rice-fields, about two hundred yards till he reaches the shore of the lake, sits there somewhat as his father used to. It is always beneath a willow, always the same willow, does nothing particular, just sits, looks out over the surface of the water toward the dim mountains that encircle it. The others know about his willow but let him alone. Perhaps they scarce know why they let him alone.

His days have got very regular. In the morning he fishes, then sells the fish, which sometimes makes him late for school. After school he carries baggage often as far as ten miles and in winter through snow. But at least he can go to school. Inu works as hard as he and never has gone to school and never will. His mother sometimes reminds him of that. Nights he is at the bath-house, tends the wood-fire that heats the bath-water and his pay is that he may read by the fire's light. At home he never reads because it is always dark there, and he is reading again as he used to before he went to the school, only he covers many pages now. In the village the older people speak of how that boy is always reading. It makes those who jeered him because he was something to jeer hate him because he is something to hate. "What does a farmer need to know of books?"

Once when he is walking alone in the fields he sees smoke over the cone of Bandai. Bandai in eruption! Twelve hundred years ago when Bandai was in eruption the lava dammed a mountain stream, whole villages disappeared and beautiful Inawashiro lake was formed. In his own lifetime there was an eruption too, but he forgets. They tell in the village how his mother hurried back to the house to see that he was asleep then went again to her work and would not be made uneasy. This present eruption is but a little smoke and lasts but a little while yet he will remember it all his life.

If he comes late from the fields his mother is off fishing, goes every night. It worries him. He would go with her but she will not have it. Inu and he must sleep, she says. She has always gone alone and she always will, she says. She wades out into the shallow lake, draws

15

high her kimono, binds it round her waist, then begins to fish. Some nights she stays and stays and that worries him, did not last year, but now he feels it dangerous for her to be out there alone. As for her, she is afraid of nothing with her sickle under her sash. But three or four nights in the year he and Inu do go along. It is the nights the water is let into the rice-fields and if one is not careful some neighbor may turn the water into his own field. Inu always keeps awake. He would like to, but never can, always falls asleep in the fields and sleeps till morning. He did not mind that last year. This year he is ashamed. It is different now. It is not that his mother works so hard. It is not her responsibility for the house. There is something of which she does not speak, his burnt hand. She has taken that on herself. Nothing he could say would change it, so he says nothing, yet knows that he ought to be taking care of her, that they ought to be taking care of each other. It makes him work harder in the school and out of the school.

Ever so often their father drops in, is in the best humor, wants money. They do not like to give him money but do. Soon as he has the money he gambles and drinks and sometimes starts trouble in the village. Their mother has borrowed the neighbor's horse. Their father wants the use of the horse. A horse is a valuable animal and their father is drunk. He gets the horse though. He gets everything. He loads it with more than it can carry and it stumbles and breaks its knee. This is a calamity. A horse—no woman in a village like

As if to Carry the Temple to a Point in the Sky

this could ever pay for a horse. At first she does not tell the neighbor. She stays night after night with the beast to keep it from moving about. The knee heals but is useless. She goes to the neighbor. She cannot pay. But she has a son. "I taught this boy from the time I nursed him not to forget the kindness of others. He is still young and strong."

This is sad. But something good has happened too. There is unexpected money, only a few sen, but every sen counts, and it is Seisaku is earning the money. And the way he is earning it, that is the important thing. He is teaching in the zinjo-shogakko. Those he is teaching are taller than he. Some are older. They do not like it, this tembo teaching them, and ever so often one of them picks up a bench and slips with it through the open shoji and hides it behind a gravestone. They mean to start disorder. Therefore it is that the teacher's mother may be seen wandering round the edges of the schoolhouse. Then one afternoon from Inawashiro comes a Kobayashi-san, is to examine the boys who have passed the zinjo-shogakko, examines them all, is struck by one. And it is not remarkable that he should be. This one is poorer than the others. His kimono is torn. He is dirty. Kobayashi-san is taking note of these facts when he hears the voice. He asks the boy about his hand. He asks him what he means to do with his future.

"Since ours is a house of farmers, no doubt I shall be a farmer too."

"Do you read books?"

17

"Yes, honorable sensei, I read books."

"Then why do you not continue your schooling in the koto-shogakko?"

"I have indeed a mountain of desire, but we are poor."

"Come in three days to Inawashiro to visit me."

That evening Kobayashi-san is speaking with his wife. "At Okinajima I saw a very peculiar boy, a boy with a deformed hand, a very unusual boy who will have an unusual future."

[VI]

The Beginning of Seisaku's Rising Dragon

They leave Okinajima at daybreak, Shika with the shrimps in her hand. She caught the shrimps herself, has them wrapped in straw. Paper is expensive everywhere in the empire but straw is the cheapest commodity the farmer has. A few yards, then the road turns to the left and for a mile leads straight into Bandai, then turns to the right and Bandai lies to the left, and thus on into Inawashiro. Bandai is as beautiful as Fuji. Kobayashi-san's is at the far end of the town. It is a good-sized place with a pool in front and a garden behind, and Kobayashi-san has a maid. The maid admits them. An interesting place on the inside too. Above the shoji are writings in Chinese characters and on the shoji drawings in India ink. Kobayashi-san is waiting. In the corner of Kobayashi-san's room is an ihai, a small shrine, and immediately Shika and Seisaku see the ihai they fall to their knees and pray, do not stop even to greet Kobayashi-san. This is the first time Kobayashi-san is seeing Shika. It is but the second time he is seeing Seisaku. Naturally he is a little amazed, but

19

10806

he approves. He inquires as to their healths. They inquire as to his. There are inquiries on both sides as to the healths of both families, also inquiries as to the healths of both villages. Suddenly Shika remembers the shrimps, pushes them across the floor toward Kobayashi-san, who does not touch them but notes carefully they are shrimps, lifts his hand at right angles to his face, bows quickly several times, and Shika begins to talk of why they are there. With Kannon's help Seisaku ought not to be a farmer. His hand would make farming difficult. Kobayashi-san agrees. With Kannon's help Seisaku ought to choose work where he would not have to use his hand. Kobayashi-san hesitates. Kobayashi-san is a careful man with a long face and a long figure. He thinks Seisaku ought to wait, ought simply to enter the koto-shogakko, ought to leave to the future what belongs to the future. Kobayashi-san's face is dead when another speaks but when he himself speaks life passes over it like a shadow. He uses his hands too in a way to help very much the meaning of what he says. Shika and Seisaku bow to show they take his opinion, and for each detail that follows they bow to show they take his opinion. Then they go again the three and three-quarter miles to Okinajima, and these hours as the Japanese say are the beginning of Seisaku's rising dragon.

[VII]

A Whole Year and Not One of Them Knows

He has learned to hide his hand. He has learned how
not to get on close terms with people. What was wrong
about the zinjo-shogakko was that they knew him too
well, about his house, about his father, and used what
they knew to torture. So when he came to the koto-
shogakko he made up his mind they should not know,
not about his hand either. He has found a hundred
ways of hiding it. He drops his cap over it, or folds his
arms in front of him slipping the left hand under the
right elbow, or lays the stump on the back of his hip,
as if that were a habit. But mostly he simply draws the
hand up into the sleeve of his kimono. That is the best
way. Even when he sharpens a pencil and must hold
the pencil between the stump and the thumb he lets
a bit of sleeve slip between. The same when he writes.
Writing was the special torture of the zinjo-shogakko,
but now the sleeve almost of its own accord creeps down
to cover the hand that steadies the paper. He has
learned. For lunch he does not bring bento. Bento is
the ordinary loose rice, and he would have to hold the

21

bento box in one hand so as to have the other free for the chopsticks. He brings instead mushubi. Mushubi is rice packed into a ball with the outside toasted. That he can hold in his good hand. But the best way of all is not to eat with the boys. Best to eat with the servants. Best not to bathe with the boys either. And the boys do not think this strange, he is so quiet and natural. Then near the end of the year one boy finds out, stares, begins to ask a question, but before the question is out of his mouth Seisaku is on him and beats him. And every boy hereafter who asks a question he beats in the same way. In the zinjo-shogakko he had his bad half hours. Here he will not. He will not edge away either. He will fight. Sometimes in the middle of a fight he steps unexpectedly back, then leaps forward, grips the other boy's wrist, squeezes it, squeezes it, squeezes it till the boy is forced in pain to the ground. No, Noguchi Seisaku does not come of samurai. He comes of farmers. Farmers settle things with their fists. With one fist even. He laughs. Farmers were serfs only a few years ago and have not had time to learn fine manners. He laughs. The cloth of his kimono is rotting? Well, what of it? Farmers must weave the cloth of their kimonos, cannot sit about while others weave it for them. His poor mother has drudgery enough.

The months pass. In the school it is arithmetic and science and writing and drawing and geography and history and English. English he does not have to take but likes to. From gymnastics he is excused. Toda says that is not fair. Toda says it gives Seisaku an extra hour

22

of study. And so it does, and with that extra hour he
has pushed Toda down below him and is keeping him
there, and there never was anyone besides Toda. More
than twenty in the class. Three are girls. Girls study.
They are below him. One is of a wealthy samurai
family. She is below him. She even borrows his notes.
A girl of a wealthy samurai family borrows the farmer's
notes. He would be a fool if he did not see that in drawing, in science, in English he is as good as the teachers
themselves, and that is why lately he has been reading
the books of the middle-school. There will never be
money enough to let him go there.

Muto-san comes nights, always at 9 o'clock, even
when it rains, slips his hand under the hibachi to be
sure nothing will catch fire. Muto-san is much respected
for that. Muto-san is one of the teachers. Seisaku
laughs.

And now they have also made him kyucho, chief
of the class, and no one would dare be rude to him.
They would not dare anyway. They pretend to know as
little of his hand as they knew in the beginning. His
shoulders are overgrown, the right side of him is bigger
than the left, the whole body is too small, and they see
all this, but they show nothing of what they see. He
has taught them. Yet sometimes evenings when he is
on the road to Okinajima, reading as he goes, some boy
of the zinjo-shogakko will pass and when he is passed
will scream and run. Or perhaps the boy will only stare,
and that is worse. When they only stare there is nothing
one can do. There is nothing one can do anyway. It is

23

odd with those boys of the zinjo-shogakko, that he can be stronger than they and cleverer than they and yet afraid. They have some kind of hold on him. It is as if he could not get loose his arms. Should anyone in Ina-washiro look at him that way they would not twice.

[VIII]

The Man Before Him Is Like No Other He Has Ever Seen in His Life

This Watanabe-san they are sending him to must be the same brought sokuhatsu into the country. Watanabe-san of Wakamatsu, says the way the Japanese women wear their hair is a disgrace, says the great ancient shimada and marumage made up for a week at a time are unclean. Women should wear a knot and a roll and make up their hair every day like women of the west. As much a revolution as opening the ports. And women of Wakamatsu are not wearing their hair in the new way yet. A few, naturally. Watanabe-san's wife. But in Tokyo, many. Watanabe-san is a well-known man in Tokyo. He and Ichikawa, another doctor, have started the Sokuhatsu Society. No members are to use oil on their hair or stick paper flowers into their hair or put any but the faintest perfumes on their bodies. This has caused a great stir. Makers of combs do not know what to do. Should they or should they not make more combs? Some of those combs take months to make, even years.

25

Watanabe-san is one of the moderns. Even his house. There is a stone wall around it. There is a light above the door, and there are two stories, and yet there are tatami on the floor and the patients kneel as they wait. There are windows and doors like a western house, yet in the middle of the room is an hibachi, even a very large one, and the patients keep close to it, some because they are cold but most because they want a place to empty their pipes. A few read. They read Japanese books. Watanabe-san has books that are not Japanese, books printed in yokomozi instead of up and down. Even the little English of the koto-shogakko is enough to make out the titles. They are not all medicine. Watanabe-san has many interests. Biology. Physics. Heredity. He brought those books from America. He traveled in Belgium, in Germany, in England, was three months in London alone. He is not only a graduate of a Japanese university but studied at the University of California in America, got the doctorate there too. He would not have to stay in Wakamatsu. It is true that Wakamatsu has 40,000 people, but he could go to a place much larger. Yet perhaps if one is born in Aizu one wants to stay, and Wakamatsu is the heart of Aizu. Here is the castle. Here the battles were fought. Older people say the city is not much changed. It is just as it was before the war. They are proud of that.

Watanabe-san's drug-boy, the same who came for the other patients, comes now for Seisaku, and Seisaku rises, follows to the door, drops to his knees, slides

through, and only when he is well into the other room
lifts his head.

The man before him is like no other he has ever
seen in his life. Every doctor for a hundred miles goes
in kimono. This one has trousers and a waistcoat. He
has a watch and a chain. He has a beard and side-whisk-
ers. No doubt it is the beard makes the head look so
large. It would be hard to get on close terms with him.
He says to sit in the chair. He takes up the burnt hand,
looks at it carefully, makes some notes with the pen,
does not use the fude. He says much can be done with
this hand. He says that the doctor in Inawashiro who
said nothing could be done was in error. Would Seisaku like something to deaden the pain? Seisaku shakes
his head. "But if you have a book let me read it meanwhile." Watanabe-san works swiftly. No doubt there
is less pain here than in ordinary flesh because so much
of this is scar, but there is pain, and no doubt there is
less bleeding, but there is bleeding too.

It is a wonderful day. Yes, it is a wonderful day.
Seisaku's mind is made up. He will be a doctor. He will
be a doctor and be of use to mankind.

Indeed all is wonderful, from the very way Kobayashi-san came to tell him. That Kobayashi-san should
want to help him is natural, but that the fathers of the
boys of the koto-shogakko, that they should want to
help him, that just they should collect the money to
send him to Watanabe-san of Wakamatsu, surely that
is the most wonderful of all. It changes everything.
This morning he fairly ran the whole way from Okina-

27

jima and last night he and his mother talked and talked and for excitement could not sleep.

And this is not the only time he must come to Wakamatsu. There are many treatments. It is twenty miles each way. But that is nothing. Once one has made up one's mind to be a doctor it is well to see as much of doctors as one can, and Watanabe-san is a great doctor. What he has done for this hand is a miracle. He could not put back the fingers, of course, but the ends of the stumps that looked like knotty wood are gone. These stumps will be of use now. Each stands by itself. Each moves alone. And the scars that drew the hand to the wrist are cut through. The hand hangs quite like anyone's hand. The doctor in Inawashiro said nothing could be done and when he said it put black over everything. He said a boy with a hand like that would be fit for only the lowest labor.

So Seisaku's mind is made up. Shika says she always knew the injury must be for good. And Kobayashi-san agrees. Everybody now thinks Seisaku ought to be a doctor. But how to begin? Seisaku keeps worrying about that night and day. Then comes time for paying Watanabe-san's bill. Seisaku has the money collected by the fathers of the boys, but it is not enough. Instantly he offers to work for Watanabe-san to pay off the rest. And Watanabe-san seems pleased, says he does not think Seisaku ought to be a farmer, his head is too good. Why not be a doctor? Why not begin here as one of the drug-boys? He can if he likes.

That night Seisaku reads longer than usual in

28

the foreign book. It is a life of Napoleon. Seisaku has talked to his friend Yago about that book and to Yago has admitted that he would make himself like Napoleon. Not fight battles. Not kill people. He would be a doctor but with the will of a Napoleon. Napoleon slept only three hours a night. Henceforth he will sleep only three hours a night.

A Minute Spiral Organism

A tuft of something cottony prepared from plants is laid on the skin of a sick man's abdomen and the tuft set fire to. The skin burns with the tuft. If the man is sick enough there are several tufts and all are set fire to. That is Chinese medicine. Among the doctors of the countryside there are many Chinese practises. Burning is a cure also for stubbornness in boys, is indeed a much more powerful remedy than people know, and one of the doctors goes so far as to say that the burning of Seisaku's hand has put something into Seisaku's blood, and that it is that gives him the strength to stay up so night after night. For weeks, it is quite true, he has not so much as taken off his obi. When late Watanabe-san looks in where the drug-boys sleep he always finds this youngest still awake. This youngest is heaven and earth for learning. Drug-boys are supposed to bring their own bedding and Seisaku has none. But in Okinajima there were not even tatami, only scattered straw, and after all one sleeps but three or four hours a night and for that length it is possible to sleep soundly even under Watanabe-san's desk. Kobayashi-san of course warns Seisaku to watch for his health.

One of Watanabe-san's patients has a fever. It is a peculiar fever. For several days the temperature rises, then falls, then rises again, has done that twice. Watanabe-san does not know what to make of it. Seisaku does not know what to make of it either. It is a relapsing fever but could not be true relapsing fever because that does not occur in this part of the world. Watanabe-san draws a little of the patient's blood. How many doctors on this countryside would draw blood to find the cause of a fever? Watanabe-san is excited too at what he sees when he puts that blood under the microscope. He calls the drug-boys and all five come running. One after another looks into the microscope. There lying among the corpuscles in a minute spiral organism, a germ, a bacterium, windings in its body. The germ is not easy to see. Watanabe-san asks each drug-boy if he really does see. Watanabe-san never teaches, pays no attention to drug-boys, laughs when asked if a drug-boy ever examines a patient, says that he has his regular assistant and that when he cannot see a patient his assistant sees the patient for him, but this to-day is something remarkable. For it is just such a germ—spirochete is what Watanabe-san calls it—that is the cause of relapsing fever. But how ever did relapsing fever get up here in Aizu?

Seisaku stays long at the microscope. This is fate. He believes in fate. He does not care either who knows what he believes. His life was changed by looking into

31

that microscope, and when he steps back from it he says a few words that must strike anyone as queer. He says that he knows now not only that he will be a doctor but the kind of doctor—a bacteriologist. It is possible that one or the other of the drug-boys laughs, but Watanabe-san does not laugh, for Watanabe-san remembers how with the same suddenness this same Seisaku a little while ago made up his mind to medicine— as if he did not have to think, as if he knew directly what he ought to do. He asks Watanabe-san for one of his books, *Methods of Pathological Histology* by *C. von Kahlden,* would like to translate that book. He would learn something about laboratory method, would add to his English, and then some day the translation might be printed and that might be the beginning of fame. Watanabe-san gives him the book. Watanabe-san never teaches, but his books the drug-boys may use. They must ask, but he will always go to the case and take down the book.

Then something happens that makes this and everything else in the world seem trifling—Japan goes to war with China. Maybe they knew in Tokyo, but here in Aizu the declaration comes with an awful suddenness. This is Japan's first real war, and China is a big country, hundreds of millions of people, so every Japanese is for the moment stunned but burning too. The revolution has put something into everyone's blood. Watanabe-san is an army surgeon and must start at once for the front. He must quick arrange his affairs. He has never yet said one drug-boy was better

32

than another. Seisaku asks fewer questions, but that is because he likes to think things out for himself not because he is stupid, and the questions he finally asks always have sense. So it is without forewarning that Watanabe-san now puts Seisaku in charge. Seisaku is the youngest. He is the latest to come. Yet Watanabe-san puts him in charge. No, this is the greatest moment of his life. He is giddy. And the war in the air makes him giddier. If the country should be invaded? If the Chinese should win? The other drug-boys are jealous, and show it now that Watanabe-san has left. Since Seisaku is in charge it is they ought to be doing the work, or at least they ought to be doing the things he used to have to do, the things he never liked, hold the pan while the patient's ear is running. But they will not. First he thinks he can force them. Once even a letter goes off to Kobayashi-san saying that it is impossible to keep this up. Kobayashi-san writes back that he must. He promised and he must. And he does. He never really meant not to. The letter was simply one hour. He sees what a chance this is. This is different from being kyucho in the koto-shogakko. When the others are nasty he says to himself that the good Japanese swordsman does not keep his eyes on the other man's sword but on his own. He reads much. Watanabe-san's being away lets him free. If he once got into himself all that was in those books then surely he must conquer everything. Weeks, months go by. Victory is in the air. The war is over. Watanabe-san returns. Everybody surrounds Watanabe-san. Everybody is glad he is back.

At last when they leave him for one moment Seisaku slips up with the ledger. He has noted the smallest items—0.02 yen for stamp. Watanabe-san smiles, is pleased, asks Seisaku a number of questions, and is amazed at the way Seisaku answers them, is amazed at what he has learned, says Seisaku is ready really to stand for the first examinations. Seisaku's head swims. The first examinations! He had not dreamed of that. No, this now, this is the greatest moment of his life. If there were any way of doing it he would start for Tokyo to-night. Yet there would be something holding him in Wakamatsu too. He is bound to Wakamatsu by something he never thought of before.

[X]

*The Letter Is Not of My Friend but of the Man of the
Name of S. N.*

He has not so much as talked to the girl, not a single
word. She goes to the Aizu girl school and has to walk
down the same street every morning and he "looks
upon her at some shop window in front of Watanabe-
san's hospital on her way." People have noticed. And
it is an extraordinary thing for him to do. A distant
admiration, yes, but this young man is taking steps,
waits for her, looks on her. As for her, she never lifts
her eyes. Yone is her name. He has found that out.
Also he has found out that she does not come from
Wakamatsu but from the country outside, is only in
Wakamatsu for the Aizu girl school.

Yone has a friend, Kichiki, daughter of the Wakamatsu schoolmaster, and now Yone gets a letter from
Kichiki. It is the kind of letter no one would think of
putting straight into your hand, but if you just happened to have been in a crowd, or to have stopped for
a moment at the temple to pray, then when you got
home you might discover in the sleeve of your kimono

35

something that made you wonder how that got there. Mysterious anyway to receive a letter from Kichiki, but this letter is mysterious in itself too.

"Do not be scared. To send a secret letter, an act like that, who can blame the single heart."

That is how the letter begins. Plain that the writer knows that the sending of a secret letter is an unusual thing to do. The writer also knows a little English and is not ashamed of the fact, lets English slip between the kana and kanji till it is hard to make out just what the letter means. Yone is nervous, finally decides she will show her teacher "who is so frightened of it and gives me her advice to take care of myself, and so I know that the letter was not of my friend but of the man with the name of S. N." Scarcely decent of him. Were he thinking of marriage would he not have looked for a go-between?

Seisaku is thinking of marriage and he would not have looked for a go-between. Sixteen, dirty, poor, a cripple, it would be silly to look for a go-between, but not silly to think of some other way. "His love is not merely to gratify the brutal sexual passion, but to love her as his future half, so to speak, as his consort." To make a young woman love him, a remarkable young woman, for this young woman is remarkable, love him in spite of his hand, in spite of everything, the temptation is great. "There stands a female being behind success of man." Yone is only fifteen. He has found that out too. And she is dreaming of a career, his career, wants to be a doctor, plans to go to Tokyo, and no

36

trouble about money for her because her father is rich. It may be that her father's idea about Tokyo is not exactly hers. It may be he is thinking of rich friends who will introduce her to other friends and that be the beginning of a good marriage. At least it is clear what he would think about a drug-boy from Okinajima whose father was a drunkard who deserted his wife. Yone would no doubt think the same, and anyway any girl no matter how modern or emancipated in an affair so far-reaching would be guided by her father. Seisaku's chances are not much. He knows it. But he has never given up any desire easily. He writes another letter, all in English this time, and as soon as Yone receives it she hurries with it to her teacher "who was so kind to me to find out the man of S. N." That is how much she cares.

As for marriage, Seisaku has reached the right age and there has been much talk of marriage, not here in Wakamatsu but in Inawashiro. He is a much better bargain than he used to be, studying medicine, rumors all the time that he is going to Tokyo. He could easily have a certain Inawashiro girl, well-to-do, friends on both sides anxious, but Seisaku not so anxious. It is true that his poor mother works, works, works, still has nothing, the house as mortgaged as when he was born, and a good marriage would certainly lift the mortgage, and yet if he did marry an Inawashiro girl for her money he would of course have to live in Inawashiro to have that money, would grow old in a place smaller than Wakamatsu, be a big man in Kobayashi-san's little circle, a

37

Napoleon in Inawashiro. That is not the way he has been thinking things of late.

It has got to be August and there has come from Tokyo a Chiwaki-san, is to spend a month here in Aizu practising dentistry. Chiwaki-san is not so young as Seisaku, but still young, only last April passed his state examinations. In Takayama Dental College where he studied he never saw a patient, learned everything from books, therefore is coming here to Aizu for a bit of living practise. Chiwaki-san is a man of culture, knows science, is a graduate of Keio University, wrote for a newspaper, taught English and Chinese literature. And what is especially fortunate is that Chiwaki-san is here in Wakamatsu at Watanabe-san's invitation, every day now comes to call, and every day sees Seisaku at the same spot, reading. It is summer and there are not many patients and there is time to read. The book is a medical book and not in Japanese but in the original French. Chiwaki-san is impressed. He has somehow discovered too that the boy reads English texts and German texts, nights in winter goes to the Wakamatsu high school, then next morning before five is at the house of the catholic priest, a Frenchman, who is teaching him French. When the priest happens not yet to be awake the boy scales the wall. A number of people have seen him scale the wall and have spoken of it and praised him for it. Unayama-san who quizzes all the drug-boys says that this one is a genius. His thoughts are far beyond Aizu. And indeed he is forever bothering Watanabe-san with the same question. "How is it in America?" Chiwaki-san is much impressed. To him the boy talks physics and chemistry and often dwells on the fact that he ought to be getting away from Wakamatsu and on to Tokyo, that he is getting older and older and is wasting his life here, and once he bursts out and begs Chiwaki-san to be his *leader*. Chiwaki-san tells him that when he does get to Tokyo he must call immediately at Takayama Dental College. He, Chiwaki-san, will do for him what he can.

Chiwaki-san leaves, and in a few weeks winter settles over Aizu, snow covers Bandai, the labors of the drug-boy increase. Those labors are irksome now. He feels he has stayed in Wakamatsu too long. Only with Tokyo would he not be disillusioned. He talks to Watanabe-san. He talks to Kobayashi-san. Kobayashi-san warns him to take care for his health. He goes to Shika, paints the future, and she goes next morning to the temple to pray. Finally Kobayashi-san offers 10 yen, two weeks of his salary. And Watanabe-san offers 10 yen. There is also some vague offer of 10 yen a month after Seisaku gets to the capital. With 10 yen a month it would be easily possible both to live and to study medicine. But even if he cannot be sure of the 10 yen, the 20 yen he has, and Shika has perhaps a few sen, the villagers perhaps also a few sen. If he can but once get his foot into the capital he will not worry about the rest. Yone is already there. He has not so much as spoken to her yet.

It Is Drunk in Saki

He leaves Wakamatsu at dawn, walks to Okinajima, twenty miles, then to Inawashiro, three and three-quarter miles, then back to Okinajima, three and three-quarter miles. He is in high wild humor. The few things he is to take with him he has done up in a cloth, the four corners tied in a knot on top, and now, the second dawn, he and Shika and Inu come to the final rice and tea. Outside the house the children are gathering. All know this is the day Seisaku starts for the capital, a fresh generation of children that remembers nothing of the tembo. They look through the open shoji while he and Shika and Inu are drinking the sakadzuki, the parting cup. This is September, Meiji 29, less than a year since Louis Pasteur lay dead at Villeneuve l'Étang. The children walk along a short distance on the road then stand still, and he and Shika and Inu walk on alone. Then Shika and Inu stand still. It is told that a Japanese mother when her boy ran to her with an arrow in his eye said, pluck it out, and he did, and the eye came with the arrow. Perhaps that never happened, but whether it did or did not Seisaku on his side can scarce keep his enthusiasm down, tramps lustily away. He will catch the train at Koriyama. There are indeed two currents in him, as his friend says, the one boiling, the other cold, two currents that cannot mix and yet are forever trying to mix and look as if they might go on trying forever.

[XII]

He Arrives in the Capital

He does not call immediately at Takayama Dental College. Chiwaki-san said he should, but this is his first
visit to Tokyo, his first visit to any big city, and he cannot want an older man over him right away. Instead
he lets great Tokyo swallow him, and does not emerge
till time to present himself at the examinations for the
first two years of medicine, has not opened a book, and
so soon as the examinations are over lets great Tokyo
swallow him once more. In the interval he has made a
few friends. They show him the town, lounge with him
extraordinary lengths of time over extraordinarily little
o-cha and senbei, discuss everything. They address him
as Noguchi-san. He sleeps first with one then with the
other, keeps putting off the renting of a room and ends
by wondering why he should rent one anyway. His
money is nearly gone as it is, and who is there here to
loan him? Certainly not those he sleeps with. By November 1st he has nothing to eat. One cannot go on 20
yen forever. The 3rd—the birthday of the Emperor

42

and therefore a date easy to remember—he appears at Takayama.

He explains of course everything, how much Kobayashi gave him, how much Watanabe, how much the fare to Koriyama, why he did not call sooner, how economical he has been, yet has not one sen left, yet has passed the first two years' examinations, and has not eaten much the last three days, explains everything, details that Chiwaki will forget, but he will not forget the quality. What a roving imagination this Noguchi has. Now he is wanting work, any kind, is willing to be a rickshaw man. Chiwaki hastens to assure him that the rickshaw has killed stronger than he. The average life is about five years. Better to come here to the dental college to work. Chiwaki is only secretary but can arrange. There are always ways. There is no reason, for instance, for his not sleeping with Ishizuka. No one need know. Chiwaki himself sleeps here. Besides the place to sleep Noguchi will receive 2 yen a month, which is not much, but he must remember that the 2 yen will have to come out of Chiwaki's own pocket and that the work will be nothing so hard as pulling a rickshaw. Noguchi of course accepts.

He begins the work. He rings the college bell. He cleans the lamps. The cleaning of the lamps is nasty work, no soap, only bran and water, the grease hard to get off, and the lamps difficult to hold tight. They are round and smooth and his left hand keeps slipping. It has got him into the habit of wedging them into his left armpit, then polishing them with his right hand.

He does this on the sly, does not like the way it makes him look.

Soon he has begun neglecting his work, and not only the work that he does not like but all work. He even forgets to ring the bell. The lecturer overruns the hour. The students yawn. "Where is Noguchi?" They find him in the library with his feet on a heap of books, but hard to be severe with him. He is a queer fellow, works with great intensity when he works, but works less and less, stays out nights later and later, begins to look like the capital, wears his kimono long, as the other students do, has his hair cropped short, his body too shuffling along like the capital, and also, they say, his life. He has some strange companions, persons ready apparently for anything, not too particular even how they get their money. At least books have been known to disappear from private libraries to reappear on the shelves of second-hand shops, books borrowed sometimes with a learned solemnity. These young men mostly sleep when others wake. All carry canes.

Noguchi is changing rapidly, but still in some respects is not like them, still in spurts studies hard. An older man who stands by and watches them all says that he has never seen anyone who on the same afternoon could be so colossally lazy and so colossally energetic. Noguchi goes to Chiwaki. He has gone to Chiwaki again and again since he first visited him on November 3rd, talks passionately to Chiwaki, the details of this talk like the previous many talks Chiwaki will not remember, but everything once more is disillusion, even the capital is not much better than Wakamatsu really. He makes blood out of his tears, as Chiwaki says, blames himself for many things. But it would be different if he had a strong purpose. And indeed what did he come to Tokyo for? To study medicine, of course, but how can he with 2 yen a month? Will he ever be able to enroll in the Saiseigakkusha? It is an antique and a right feeling with the Japanese to help the student, to put the gifted where he can produce for others what they cannot for themselves. Chiwaki has that antique feeling and cannot help the present situation, and should in fact not have to be listening to these complainings—but if only the 10 yen promised monthly from Wakamatsu would come. Not one month have those 10 yen come.

Chiwaki listens. Chiwaki's friends are warning him against this young man. They say Chiwaki is a fool to give all he has to one who leads such a life, and they say they know too what kind of a life he leads. Nevertheless Chiwaki listens. This Noguchi is no usual human being, a strange phenomenon, passionate, dreaming, bragging. A temperament like that must be worth investing in, must pay back in some sort of way. It happens Chiwaki has had an increase of salary. Could the young man have gotten wind of that? At any rate Chiwaki promises him 15 yen a month, and next morning he enrolls in the Saiseigakkusha. It is odd that almost the same hour back in Okinajima his mother is enrolling in a school for midwifery, one of those temporary schools set up here and there in the

45

prefecture. She will add midwifery to her other drudgery. In Tokyo he is beginning his study. In Okinajima she will begin hers. Only one woman was chosen from the countryside. She was the woman.

[XIII]

Kikuchi Is Provident

The Saiseigakkusha has a thousand students. It is a private medical school, no part of a university, has a strong man at its head, therefore goes its own free way. The strong man wears his old kimono, lice in it, and when his wife, now that her husband's enterprise is firmly on its feet, as with a thousand students it must be, begs him to change the kimono he tells her that most human beings are parasites and that he means for once to give the other parasites a chance.

Even in Tokyo in this year 1896 there are doctors with every grade of schooling. In the outlying districts some still practise Chinese medicine, but the class is disappearing. Others got their license by apprenticing, a class also disappearing. Still others enrolled for a course of lectures like this of the Saiseigakkusha, afterwards took examinations for their licenses. That leaves a few, the elite, in many quarters the detested, the graduates of the Imperial University, licensed without examination. A story goes the round of the Saiseigakkusha that one of its graduates met in Germany a graduate of the Imperial University, both in Germany for study, and the graduate of the Imperial University asked the graduate of the Saiseigakkusha: "What can you be doing here?"

The Saiseigakkusha has two large lecture rooms, but neither with as many as five hundred seats, so a part of the students have to stand, sometimes stand all day, and in order to avoid this the ambitious come early, about five in the morning. The secretary of the college comes at four. The first lecture is on diagnosis. Five o'clock in winter is before daybreak, and the first lecture begins by lamplight. Tokyo has gas but not yet piped into any but a few private houses. On the colder mornings the students all press forward to the front benches because it is warmer there. Of course many of the students at the time of the first lecture are still stretched full-length with shoji drawn in some one of the countless boarding houses that dot all this bank of the river. Others are just leaving the houses of the Yoshiwara—a rough crowd, come to the lectures with geta on.

The lectures are rough too. The lecturers are brought from anywhere. A few are instructors at the Imperial University trying to earn a little by the side. A few are graduates recently back from Germany bringing to the Saiseigakkusha the latest in the world. Lecture follows lecture, hour after hour, no fixed order, when a lecturer gets through his course he simply starts the course over from the beginning again. The school is open all year round. The enrollment is any time. The student attends the lectures he likes and stays away from those he does not like, and graduates automatically when he has passed the state examinations. And there is blood in this too, though the student of the well-organized Imperial University may find it hard to see there is. The Saiseigakkusha creates the mass of doctors, they who will do the drudgery of medicine, all the high places closed to them, or if one single one should push himself up among the favored few he does it only because he has unusual strength. Now and then some one does, and that helps keep alive in the Saiseigakkusha the faith that all excellence is not yet housed in new buildings and that soap and water are not the infallible signs of civilization. Noguchi's kimono is dirtier even than that in the koto-shogakko. He bathes once every second week. He sees through much about him, shares some of the hard speech.

In his first zeal he attends all lectures, but soon gets over that, then attends only the clinical lectures. Why attend the others? He has passed the first two years. The clinical lectures are usually frank translations of German texts, the lecturer coming with the text under his arm and lecturing with it in his lap, the student since he has neither text nor German feeding on notes. But Noguchi never takes notes. Even in the beginning when he did he never took them in Japanese, always in English, this to the amazement of everybody about, and when the amazement ceased the note-taking ceased. As for living clinical material he does not see any. There are a few wards of a small hospital adjoining the

49

Saiseigakkusha and now and then a case is brought over during the hour on diagnosis, but that hour is too early. Indeed the small hospital mostly supplies material for the dissecting room. He never had dissecting, but dissecting is anatomy and anatomy falls in the first two years and he has passed the examinations for the first two years, so he does not profit by the hospital that way either. His zeal indeed began dropping from the day he enrolled. He never yet in any class has volunteered to answer any question. To a few he seems an unusual human being, but certainly to no one does he seem an unusual student. Not once has he had the coveted opportunity of assisting a professor at a demonstration. His practical experience is late nights just before his friend Kikuchi falls asleep when he percusses Kikuchi's chest and pays for the experience by having his own percussed. He arrives at the school later and later every day then fewer and fewer days, perhaps is not boasting when he says he enrolled for six months and attended two. When he does arrive he never sits, even if there is a vacant seat, prefers to stand off to one side where everyone must see him, his arms folded in front of him. He has the air of one who has taken the measure of all this below him, looks physically satisfied and no doubt is.

Yone is among those who sit. She can see him where he stands, if she likes. She is one of the good students, comes early and stays the fourteen hours. Now and then he and she talk, and now and then she asks him to explain a point, but not often, and this seems the extent of their intimacy.

The old despondent hours of course intervene, hours when he squats in front of Kikuchi, sighs, especially if he has been up all the night before, says no woman really cares for him. It is his hand. A few evenings ago he and several were playing cards, a game where half a poem on one card must be matched with half a poem on another. Games interest him, and he was cleverer than anyone there. He was able to match the cards quicker and more ingeniously. But did he get anything out of that? No, the girl who was his partner actually at the first chance took another partner. She did not try to hide either how she felt. She preferred the duller partner. Girls do not like him, and that is all there is to it. The same with Yone. Yone is bright, but she does not like him either.

He is not living on the Takayama side of the river now but on the Saiseigakkusha side. Once he was sure he had the 15 yen a month the Takayama side seemed too far, at least he gave that explanation to Chiwaki, said it was more economical to live on the Saiseigakkusha side, so found himself a boarding house in Hongo, a filthy place. Here at this boarding house Kikuchi comes to call. Kikuchi comes one night and Noguchi goes to Kikuchi's the next. Then from their respective boarding houses the two advance on the city and if there is money great things are likely to happen. If there is much money the two are quickly on their knees in a geisha house eating and drinking. Noguchi

51

always drinks till his money is gone, every sen. Kikuchi is more provident, thinks to keep back something for breakfast next morning. If they have advanced far on the city Kikuchi thinks to keep back also something to get him home by rickshaw. Never Noguchi. Noguchi spends all, then even considers spending Kikuchi's, but does not get far with that. Kikuchi is watching. Indeed the one is watching the other, the more so as they feel themselves growing tipsier, each squatting with his hand on his obi, his money having been carefully twisted under that while he was still sober enough to twist. Kikuchi is tall. Noguchi is small. They call each other brother. Everybody turns round when the two pass. Both want to be doctors. Both talk of America, will go to that country one of these days. Then Noguchi graduates from the Saiseigakkusha and Kikuchi remains behind.

It is October when Noguchi thinks nothing is lost by standing for the state examinations and, as he says, slips through. And that is the end of the Saiseigakkusha. He is glad to be done with the place, was anxious to get in, is anxious to get out. It was not what he thought it would be, and nothing is. He has been in the capital all told a little more than a year, is twenty-one, has the examinations behind him, has some difficulty finding the 6-yen license fee but finds it, and in November also has the license. He draws a breath of satisfaction, and is immediately downcast again. This state of things, as he says, will burst his strings of patience. What is the use to have studied to be a doctor? How

52

can he be? With a hand like his he cannot rightly percuss even his friend Kikuchi's chest, let alone some patient he does not know. Imagine those stumps lying on the patient's bare ribs. He could never win in the competition with other doctors. He has not the physique and not the manner, and does not want the manner. But what is he talking of anyway? Did he ever intend practise? That was not his idea from the beginning. From the beginning he wanted to be a bacteriologist. How he will manage it he has not a notion.

XIV

They Break Their Bones to Help Him

Juntendo is the big hospital. Tanaka is only a technician but perhaps could get him in there. That would be far from bacteriology, but one has to do something. He talks to Tanaka, and Tanaka makes inquiries, learns there is no vacancy at Juntendo, but there is a vacancy on Juntendo hospital journal, which is even farther from bacteriology. However, there is a salary of 3 yen a month plus board. Noguchi takes the place. He gets his first salary of a morning, keeps it till night, the following morning has not a sen. Not a sen for the rest of the month. To Tanaka this is simply mysterious. Tanaka has never seen anything like it. Whenever Noguchi comes back from one of his nights he is poetic and sad. Last night he followed a girl, talked to her, but she refused him. She had seen his hand. Even that kind of girl will have nothing to do with him because of his hand. He is very unhappy. He talks to Tanaka three hours on end. Tanaka tells him not to care, tells him to make himself into a great man, that that is better than following the women. While Tanaka is talking Noguchi sits there with his head in his hands, finally lifts his head. "I will." He speaks the words solemnly, two nights later is poetic and sad again, and two mornings later is penitent again.

At the same time he is always worried about money in spite of his knowing increasingly the ways of luring it. He sends a promissory note back to Inawashiro to his friend Yago.

"For four Chinese literature books the above sum because of urgent necessity I borrowed. As to time of return it will be June 25th. Then I will return, but if I in some way delay, then I will ask father and mother and arrange so you will not suffer."

And on January 8th, he writes this same Yago a letter.

"Just as the moon and the sun are flowing so are we receiving this year Meiji 31 and are welcoming the new spring light. Life is like dream and sky. Difficulty is the way of the world. Sometimes my body has been like the cave of a tiger. Sometimes I have been disgraced in the eyes of ten thousand people. Sometimes I have grieved for the length of the curse of heaven. . . . Looking back at the time when I parted hands with you I realize how I have always neglected letter writing. For one so affectionate as you that must have made you angry. However I have not changed fundamentally my heart. It is only the worldly duties gathering round me. . . . A letter arrived to-day from my mother. You have gone to my piggish abode, so miserable a place. I feel quite disgraced. I feel it a friendly

55

kindness and at the same time I feel my body cut to pieces. I will not forget this for a lifetime. . . . I am at Juntendo. I am studying practise and theory at Juntendo where there are three hundred patients. Besides I am editing bi-weekly magazine and I am sending a few copies for your laughing inspection. The fact is I am being used by biggest hospital in Tokyo, so please do not worry. As to university, as soon as I can find a way I am going to enter. But being a poor student I am sort of worrying. To-day what I need most is one European dress. Because I lack that everybody looks down on me and I feel my shoulders grow narrow. With this miserable attire you cannot stand in the society of heaven. Particularly in Tokyo it makes a big difference. If I have 50 yen I would feel so happy. And my monthly salary is just enough to feed my mouth with starch paste. But there is a future in this position. . . ."

On the 14th he writes Yago again.

"About the thing I asked the other day, please. I am very much embarrassed on account of empty hand."

And on February 1st again.

"As usual you are prosperous and happy and as usual I am destroying the day. So do not worry. . . . Although I have my new suit made, which is 30 yen, shoes and other apparel cannot be bought by poor boy who has no money even for daily bread. So I am much embarrassed. So cannot you please send me about 10 yen? And for the rest I will let my tailor wait till February 5th. . . . In fact in the early life of a doctor he

must have much money. Without it he cannot be anything. So please surrender to the idea that you have a
reckless young person, and then send me money. Is
Toke there? How about letting her come to Tokyo to
study? I am waiting for answer every day. So this letter
is only business. . . ."

February 23rd.

"It became terribly cold. . . . As I told you, on
account of indispensable circumstances I have made
new suit, and the tailor I have not paid, and have asked
him to delay to February 5th (old calendar). Now the
time is charging on me and I am much embarrassed
and for that reason I am asking wilfully this favor.
. . . About this I write in great haste. . . ."

April 21st.

"I just received letter and could not pick up fast
enough to open and read. According to your letter you
have suffered much loss by a certain party and I am
much surprised, and on account of this I am worrying
that you must have thought my letters in such circumstances a great nuisance. But they are due to my situation at present time, so I hope you will treat with your
usual generosity. When I got letter I was much revived
and almost crazy with rejoicing and peace. You may
think I have no small gut, to tell you this sort of thing,
but really I felt as though a question of life and death
had been satisfactorily solved for me. . . ."

What meanwhile he is writing for Juntendo journal
depends on chance. If there is a case of interest in the
hospital he reports that. If not, he invents a case with

the help of a book. Or he makes a translation from some foreign text. Or he goes to the bedside, himself does some work on a patient, knows very little about patients but may as well learn. There are several fine doctors at Juntendo and he listens to them when they talk. And all this occupies him, moderately, for a few months, then begins to weary him. What future can there be in it? He has no more money than when he was a student at the Saiseigakkusha and lived at Chiwaki's. He casts about for something else. He writes a few letters. He talks to a few people. He happens to think of that book he began to translate when he was a drug-boy. Perhaps if he finished it he could sell it? That night he goes to the Yoshiwara and takes the manuscript with him, lies there, translates somewhat in the spirit of Prince Ito writing state documents with his head in the lap of a geisha. When the translation is done he takes it to a publisher and to his astonishment receives 25 yen. Quick as he has the money he arranges a party. "My mother always says, don't send money, spend it yourself, father will drink it up anyway." He laughs, the party goes on, and next morning there is not a sen. He thinks of Yago.

"There is something I had in mind that I wanted to speak of badly. I am too busy to speak now. But I am much embarrassed. I hope you are coming to Tokyo soon. Meanwhile I like to know how you are getting along. This time I am particularly embarrassed. Could you not send 20 yen? This money I must have by the end of the month. This amount is so necessary that if you cannot give it to me let me know, but if you can, even half that amount would do."

He continues to cast about. He writes to Inawashiro. He goes to Chiwaki, describes his insupportable situation. How can he endure this state of things? No money, no future, and he has been here at Juntendo for a year! In his impatience he calls everything above a month a year. His friends simply must help him. He has done all that he can for himself. He speaks to Sugano. "Had you not better plan to be a scientist instead of a doctor?" That is Sugano's suggestion. Sugano promises he will do what he can to get him into the Institute. Yago receives another letter, a long passionate letter.

"I respectfully send you a letter. Since I came back to Tokyo the 7th of last month I have had much stomachache. I have been in bed and I have had great difficulty and I have scorned to take food. But with the kindness of my masters and my friends I begin to feel better. To-day there is a seminar and I have been able to be present. If that keeps on I will recover entirely, so do not worry. I ought to have written you before but because of the above I have lacked of my duty and ask your pardon. I am well all day now and am studying very hard. So be tranquil. While I was home I was always pushing my own self forward and I must have been a May-fly to you. But my mind is now more vigorous than fire and it is impossible to think of keeping my shoulder down to the level of my friends around, and I do not wish to be looked upon as a common per-

59

son of the mass. My will, that I cannot forget night or day, is to make it possible to return all to you to whom I owe so much, but my circumstances being what they are I cannot ever do that if I go into country practise. That is why I ask you who are so generous to help me. Your father and your mother know everything and I do not have to tell you more. At any rate consider this burning heart and this red spirit and please dip down and help me. Regardless of the great waves and whistling winds of this world I who vowed in front of your honorable face will show that my heart forced a way through, so please never give me up as an ordinary doctor of medicine. This may sound like a big word but I pray you to believe it. By the way, I am now speaking of the order of what I like to study. July Meiji 31 I will enter the Institute of Infectious Diseases, Shiba, of Kitasato, and I will stay there till the end of October to study microscopic science. The expense for this ordinarily is 130 yen, but I expect to do with 50 yen. That is, I will try to find means for self-supporting so I can graduate with less expense.

"During November Meiji 31 I will depart for America and I will go as member of the household of an American doctor and I will finish my studies and be a graduate of the university (receiving foreign title). Thereupon I will open the business of the doctor and make money. At my departure I should take with me 300 yen, more if possible, less if unavoidable. If I have not enough money I will work regardless of hardship up to the destroying of my body. My time of study in

America I fix from one to one and a half years. Toward Meiji 33 I will go from America to Germany to work for the German diploma. As to the expense of study in Germany for two or three years, I decided to earn it.

"Toward Meiji 35 I will go to France to visit the masters and the celebrated universities, and to obtain the French degree. I will remain there some time to buy the machines and instruments of the doctor. At the beginning of spring Meiji 36 I will return to Japan and will come to Tokyo. For the rest of my plans I postpone on this occasion and tell you only the necessary details.

"At that time I will be in the springtime of 27 or 28, with blood and spirit in vigor, and that is not too late to shake my arms around and to feel heaven and earth too small. There are few university graduates of medicine who finish their studies at the age of 27 or 28 and most of them are more than 30. I am not speaking too big a word. If I compare myself at that time with the fresh steaming graduate of the university I think there is difference between cloud and mud. This all I can open to you who are so close. It is not as if I was talking to one of those who had no relation to me. Between us two I do not dare cover my heart. Therefore be sure to listen to my sentiments. I am putting two hands together repeatedly.

"I cannot speak yet concerning my final purposes and desires, but once I go abroad and succeed I will speak again. If I speak before, it is forcing the bud unwillingly and there is no perfume, nothing. Therefore silence is the flower. Please be sure to cover this from those not concerned.

"The mountain snow heaps, heaps, till the spring water freezes.

(That is, I mean to accomplish the impossible.)

"Wait? If it falls before it blooms what is the plum blossom.

(If I stop now what has been the use of all this?)

"Especially I want to say I have so much debt I cannot look people in the face. In this need for money I am terribly uneasy, so cannot you send me 20 yen. At the present time I am full of plans and expectations, so please save me. In haste."

Talking later with Yago he admits to the nature of one of those purposes and desires. He will make himself physician to the Emperor. He would have told Yago before but could not put the name of the Emperor into a private letter.

The first step in this amazing plan he is now actually to take. The suggestion has already come from Sugano, and Sugano has talked to Sato who is Baron and director of Juntendo. Kawakami and Chiwaki are promptly drawn in, also break their bones to get Noguchi admitted to the Institute, and he is admitted, nevertheless reflects a bit sourly. "I am given to the Institute as you give a stray cat to a person who cannot but receive it." The Institute is the Institute of Infectious Diseases, at the head of it that man who not only in his own country but throughout the world is recognized as the greatest of living Japanese scientists, Kitasato Sibasaburo.

XV

Thirteen Guinea-Pigs

He goes to Kitasato. "You must study particularly hard," says Kitasato, "and if you do, for about five years, I may be able to send you abroad. However, you cannot leave before that time."

Five years! Kitasato is serious. And about this there is no discussion either. Kitasato is not a man one goes calling on day after day. There is nothing to do but to start work, so Noguchi starts, imitating the others, as he says. And there is nothing to do but to imitate. His research up to now has all been in a book. He has less actual experience than one of those liberal arts students who sit out the years on the benches of the Imperial University. He thinks he will like the laboratory life, made up his mind to it at Watanabe's, and as he says too does not easily change his mind, but really knows nothing, has scarce performed a single test-tube experiment.

Around him in the Institute are the graduates of the Imperial University. Kitasato himself has made discoveries ranking with the highest in bacteriology. Shiga has recently found the organism causing dysentery. The older are the strong men of Japanese science and the younger those with some hope of becoming the strong. Noguchi's friend Hata entered three days before him, is no graduate of the Imperial University either, comes from Okayama. "I am lower even than he." Noguchi speaks ruefully, would like to think he is looked down on for his education, and may be by some but not by Kitasato. Kitasato with his clear eyes simply was not sure that everything in the world would come from that mind more vigorous than fire, unless something happened to quiet it. Yet there is no denying that the Institute is an odd place for one who until recently sat under the oil lamps of the Saiseigakkusha and whose higher education was the koto-shogakko. In a few weeks he nevertheless feels himself much at home, is a bit surprised at that. "But I may say that despite I am a newcomer most treat me kindly."

He throws himself into the work, scrubs his apparatus, starts a number of experiments at once, and the days rush by. In one respect at least he is not imitating the others. He lets himself be driven by moods. He may be ignorant of what he is doing but his feelings are in.

"He enjoys himself very much when he happens to find some or other new fact or discovery, though they may be only the trivial data in science but he appears to be in ill humor if he happens nothing new for the day."

So says his friend Hata. Noguchi is put in charge of the Institute library, but it only goes as it went at

64

Takayama. A library is a place for him to read, and he is reading more and more and experimenting less and less. This being scientist is not what he thought. In the past he might sit up all night and read through a book and know next morning what was in it, but now he works day after day with nothing to show. One of the men describes to him a method for doing a thing. He tries the method. The method works. But what of it? No one will pay any attention to that. The making of discoveries is not at all like the mastering of facts in a book or the learning of a language. In school he may have been lazy, but when he did set to work and worked with intensity he soon was accomplishing something, soon had pushed everyone down below him. Here it does not go that way. So presently he is missing a day at the Institute, presently two or three days, presently does not come at all. And no one pays any attention to that either. The only thing that seems much to strike anyone is that he can read several occidental languages. He has been trying to teach them English, they him experimental method, and not much has been learned either side.

He has begun to think things over. Kitasato promised to send him to Germany, and Kitasato will keep his word. For that matter the Institute sends them all to Germany. It will send him too. But in five years. Five years ago he was still in the koto-shogakko. And will it really be five years?

"There are ahead of me Shiga, Moriyama, Sibayama, Tashiro, Murata. I realize that my turn to go could not come until I am more than sixty."

The sixty is merely a way of speaking, of course, but at least he will be middle-aged, because he is almost twenty already. But suppose he does not wait the five years? Suppose he does not go to Germany? Then there is no hope at all. Then surely he will have to keep his shoulders down to the level of his friends around. Till one has been to Germany there is no chance for one. Kitasato went to Germany. Everyone must go to Germany. And yet if one had wits enough there would be some short-cut through all this. Suppose he made a discovery? He visits Kitasato again. He tells Kitasato he wants to do animal experimentation. Kitasato answers that he ought first to do test-tube experimentation. And he answers that he wants thirteen guinea-pigs.

"Thirteen guinea-pigs! Why, even the heads of departments do not use thirteen guinea-pigs."

And there is the end of another interview. So he is simply to sit about month after month and let his mind more vigorous than fire die out. He is very discouraged, and when he has a chance temporarily to run away is glad of it. Kobayashi's wife happens to be ill with nephritis. Noguchi has had word of this and sees plainly that it is his duty to go back to Inawashiro to take care of her. Not much really he can do when he gets there. He knows no medicine. He stays a good deal with his mother. He talks a good deal with Kobayashi. He talks to Yago, goes for walks in the fields below Bandai,

66

picks up a novel by Tsubouchi, *The Life of a Contemporary Student*. The novel has been much discussed. What is odd, the hero has almost his own name. *Nonoguchi Seisaku*. What makes that odder is that the hero is also a student of medicine, and oddest of all is a person of highest promise who caught between women and drink comes to a bad end. It is only a story, of course, and at first Noguchi is mainly amused by the coincidences yet cannot help thinking of them and presently being annoyed by them. Have not his own affairs been going down of late? He was also a person of highest promise. He also is ruining his life. Why did he pick up just that book? He is more and more nervous, must talk to someone, and talks to Kobayashi. Kobayashi is the same careful man he always has been, says that if the name is a source of worry it ought to be wiped out, that there is no fairness in going through life with a name tainted by a novel, but what the new name should be, that must not be lightly decided, for the new must not only wipe out the old but must suggest something to the future. Kobayashi ruminates over the facts and after several days gives his opinion. *Hide* is Kobayashi's family name. *Hide* means *great man,* and *yo* roughly *world*. Thus *Hideyo* would be *great-man-of-the-world*. Kobayashi thinks there is even something divine in just this choice. The official change cannot take place till next year, but the decision to change is enough to quiet Seisaku's mind and he can go back to Tokyo. Kobayashi's wife happens also to be well again.

In Tokyo at the hotel are several Americans—this

67

is April Meiji 32—on their way to the Philippines to investigate diseases among the soldiers. One of the Americans is a Mr. Frederick Gay, another a Professor Simon Flexner.

"We requested permission from Professor Kitasato to visit his Institute and the invitation to do so was brought to the hotel by Noguchi."

That is how Professor Flexner sees the moment. He says it was at the height of the cherry blossom season and that the incident was perfunctory. And that is natural, a stranger in a country meeting a young native, as it is natural too that the young native should think the incident quite other than perfunctory. Shiga's discovery of the bacillus causing dysentery has made him the important man at the Institute, and Gay says it is mainly Shiga speaks to them. Kitasato as a matter of fact has left Tokyo for Osaka, had some business there. Noguchi describes the moment too, and from his own point of view, says that Kitasato speaks German and not English, and the American professor English and not German, and that he himself, since he speaks English, slips in to show the Americans about. To the Americans this English that Noguchi speaks can hardly be English, and Shiga remains the person of importance, which does not diminish Noguchi's importance to Noguchi. He sees what a chance this is, and remarkable if he did not, he who has grown so quick to see the men who may be useful to him. This is more than the chance to practise English on another American. This is the way to America. The American professor is the short-cut through the five years. And from America to Germany must be easy. America is so rich. What he actually does is "casually" mentions his desire to the Professor. "Oh, yes, that would be fine." That is the way Gay remembers the Professor to answer. Naturally the Professor is not expecting the young man to take the words too seriously.

"It is only proper to state that no particular encouragement was given to this request."

So writes Professor Flexner. Noguchi says that the Professor then asked him if he had any Arbeit to show.

"For one moment I am stuck. Then I recall two or three things I wrote for Juntendo hospital journal, something about foot ulcers in children."

He also recalls that translation begun as drug-boy and finished in the Yoshiwara and sold for 25 yen, and the Americans go on to Manila, and from Manila the Professor goes to the University of Pennsylvania.

"To avoid embarrassment, Noguchi was asked to write him there. In due time a letter, composed in English which under the circumstances must be regarded as remarkable, arrived."

Natural again. Noguchi has written a good many letters of late, and nothing so important as this visit of the Americans has happened in a long time, not since that summer Chiwaki came to Wakamatsu. It is one's fate pursuing one in the sunlighted street. That coming of Chiwaki meant Tokyo, the Saiseigakkusha, Juntendo, the Institute, and the American professor.

69

XVI

Noguchi Is Like the Wind and Will Find a Crevice

The government has opened a quarantine office and is wanting a quarantine doctor. It would be as easy to go to America from the quarantine office as from the Institute and the salary would be higher and nothing is happening in the American affair anyway. Noguchi has another interview with Kitasato, asks Kitasato to recommend him, which Kitasato does, willingly. Is it too willingly?

Nice to see the big ships come and go. But this is 35 yen, no more. The Institute was 13 yen, plus a future. For 22 yen he has traded a scientific career, but the realization does not prevent him looking very dapper in his white uniform, an occidental uniform with a cap. He talks leisurely to the officers of the ships, tries his foreign languages on the passengers, generally adds to his wanderlust. All he would have to do would be to step on one of those ships to be on the other side in sixteen days. The *Yokohama Maru* arrives in port with a Chinese in great distress. The man's glands are swollen and he has a fever. Noguchi guesses pest, makes a culture from one of the glands and finds his guess true and reports pest to the department. That was not bad. That has never happened in the department before. Pest is recent in Japan and everybody is anxious to keep it out, and everybody praises Noguchi, and he is pleased with himself, for a day, then knows there was nothing really to guessing pest. And, what is important, the American affair stands just where it stood. Chiwaki is sorry for him. "Noguchi is always looking for a chance to fly out." Chiwaki says too that in this boy's mind there is a mixture of fire and water.

And now pest breaks out in China, not an isolated case this time but an epidemic that must be a matter of concern to all nations. There is to be an international commission and fifteen doctors are to go from Japan. Noguchi wants to go. What use to stay here in the quarantine office? It would be as easy to start to America from China as from the quarantine office, and this Chinese business ought to have big possibilities, among others he could save and lay aside enough to pay his own way to America. The more he thinks of it the clearer it is that this is his opportunity, but before he can earn the money to get to America he must somewhere get the money to get to China. The commission refuses to advance passage money. However, that is simple. He hurries to Chiwaki. But, alas, the master has no money, has spent all on his marriage. Noguchi is immediately despondent. He is really a pitiful sight to look on. Chiwaki quiets him with telling him that somehow he, Chiwaki, will find the money. The way

Chiwaki finds it is to sell his wife's new bridal kimono. The sailing is for the following morning.

That night Noguchi has an appointment with Yone who is surprised to see him, but more surprised at his costume, so brilliant. "He put on the golden male uniform in contradiction to his common ugly one." He persuades her to go with him to have her picture taken. He talks, talks, talks, till daybreak. "I could not get in bed to sleep." It is no use. He cannot move her. He starts for the ship.

The other doctors are already on the ship. Each has his little Peking dictionary with which he hopes to make his way in China. There are fifty thousand characters in the Chinese vocabulary. A few thousand are the efficient minimum, so the more serious doctors are already at work. Noguchi instead goes down into the hold and stays with the coolies and by the time he reaches China is the most important man on the commission, because he can speak Chinese. It is he deals with the local Chinese government. It is he exchanges poems with the Chinese governor. And now that he has caught the idea of the language he keeps at it with passion, as he can when a thing interests him. There are many besides Chinese in Newchwang, French and English and German, and it follows that he adds to all his languages, knows none but uses all boldly.

As for the pest, when the doctors came the pest went. But there is enough other medicine. The poor flock from all the neighboring country, even the well-to-do, think this is a chance for skillful treatment. Only

72

the higher class Chinese women will not uncover their bodies to these Japanese, yet to Noguchi they do. Here in Newchwang he is a recognized doctor. Apparently all he has to do is to get away from his own to take a dominant place. At any rate he begins, boldly in this too, to practise all branches of medicine. "I do not know much, but that makes no difference. I remember a little from Juntendo." He delivers a baby. He makes observations on opium smoking. He starts a study of the effect of cold on the pest organism, writes a paper, and since the publications of the commission are in English sends a copy of the paper together with a letter to Professor in America, and with this feels something actual accomplished.

So by day. By night he is busy too, is already known to many parts of Newchwang. Around one part goes a stone wall and after a certain hour no more men are permitted in. Noguchi arrives after the hour, is curious, scales the wall, is caught, taken to jail, only freed next morning when it is proven that he is one of the Japanese doctors. But the intensity of this life does not imply that he has forgotten Yone. He forgets nothing. "He dispatches me the letter sometimes very sentimental." He buys two rings, has plenty of money now, on one has graven his own name, on the other Yone, keeps the one and ships the other and with this again feels something actual accomplished.

As for the pest, there is still no pest, and the commission has not so much as met to consider it. This is China. But the salaries are regular and large. He is

73

earning 300 yen a month. He estimates he would need 300 yen to get to America, has been in China six months, still has not the 300 yen, and now the beautiful opportunity is gone, for the Boxer disturbances have begun and the commission is leaving. First he thinks he will stay, will accept a place with the Russian sanitary corps at a great increase of salary, will save, but soon has followed the other doctors back to Japan. At Osaka where his ship puts in he is met by Hata. Hata feels at once how he has changed. These months in China have made him older. This getting out of the country has done him good. His genius is more visible and fewer would fail to see it now. But he does not drink any less whiskey. The two men pass several gay weeks.

"After returned from China he paid me the visit few times, but as I felt tiresome of it, I did not interview him on pretension of absence. He was so angry that he made no appearance since then."

That is how Yone describes the return to Japanese soil. This means of course that he has left Osaka and is once more in Tokyo, and as a matter of fact is finding Tokyo a more disillusioning place than ever. He has lost ground. The upshot of the Chinese affair is that he has frittered away another half year. People are losing confidence in him. Why did he not stay in the Institute? Almost two of the five years would be over now and soon Kitasato would be sending him to Germany. Or if he had saved in China he might be going to America. He goes to Chiwaki and as always is convincing. Chiwaki invites him, if that is what he wants, to live in the house, can sleep with Okumura and in return give lectures in the dental college.

The lectures are at night. The college has no building of its own and the classes are held in Taisei Middle School, a decrepit shack, the students having forever to move their desks about to get what they can of the one oil lamp, a mixed lot of students, working at trades during the day, thinking mostly of money. Noguchi has absolutely no interest, rushes through the lectures, talks so fast and so low that no one could possibly follow him. Everyone says he is queer. A few remember back to when their professor cleaned the lamps. But he can be interested when he wants to. A new book has come from France and no one knows French. "Let me see." He begins half absent-mindedly to translate. Much of the book is in technical French and there are no Japanese equivalents for the terms, so he invents the equivalents. A student takes notes, the notes make a text, the text gets printed, and thus do Noguchi's improvisations become part of the permanent vocabulary of Japanese dentistry.

But what is the use of that? What a botch he has made of things, to be teaching in a dental school. He has spoilt Japan for himself. He has cut his bridges, and still nothing has happened in the American affair. He is very disheartened. He comes home to Okumura's room at any time of night. No one seems to know exactly what he does. It is certain that now and then he practises the sword dance because Okumura goes with

75

him to a place in the neighborhood of Misaki Inaia temple. Often he does not arrive till morning looking gray. Or he may sleep awhile then get up again and leave the house, as one night Okumura remembers particularly, Noguchi pushing out into a thunderstorm, Okumura curious to know what this extraordinary behavior means, asks Noguchi. "A good night. Most men will keep to their houses." Then again he will be at the school trailing Chiwaki, begging Chiwaki to give him money enough to get to America. He also once visits Kitasato, tells him of his plan to go to America, and Kitasato thinks that it will not be so easy in America as this young man dreams, but difficulties make young men, and the difficulties will have to be great if this one is to be made, so he may as well go to America "where freedom reigns over everything and a man can push his way through hardship up to eminence." Watanabe too thinks Noguchi ought to go even if he can find no more than passage money. That is also Noguchi's way of seeing it. Once he has the idea of being a ship doctor, but the gentleman of the navigation company when he hears the plan only bows and smiles.

Finally Chiwaki offers 300 yen. Chiwaki has been talking things over with Kawakami. Noguchi is a natural subject for talk. Unpredictable though he is he has temperament and he puts the feeling of life into everything round him (a sort of decent way of repaying dead loans). "Noguchi is like the wind and will find a crevice." Chiwaki and Kawakami are discussing Noguchi's wanting to go to America. "Why not to Germany or France?" "Oh, things are too systematic there." "Well, why not Russia?" "But Russia, just Russia, is a trifle vague even for an adventurer like Noguchi, is it not?" "I suppose we'll have to be content with America then." Noguchi is overjoyed at the 300 yen, rushes off to Yokohama to buy his passage but is really in too gay a state of head, falls into talk ("dreams of how happy he would be to spend a part of his scanty fare"), suggests a party and draws in a crowd and before morning the 300 yen are gone— spends the whole money in a single night. Yet he has the face to face Chiwaki and when he comes away from him it is with an order for a steerage passage. Plainly he knows something about men, oriental men. Yone has not seen him since the night they quarreled.

XVII

But Now Sayonara

This time Inu does not go with him part of the way along the road, and the children of the village do not either, again a new generation of children that looks on him as the foreigner. Only he and Shika go, say nothing in particular, then after a while she stands still and he goes on alone. He goes about four cho then turns round and comes back, finds her where he knew he would, where he left her. Again they bid each other sayonara and again he goes. "But now after this I will not come back." He says he will write often, will address the letters to Kobayashi who will tell her what is in them, and that way it will make no difference that she and Inu cannot read and write. Except for Kobayashi they would be cut from one another indeed and therefore from this on he will call Kobayashi his spiritual father. But now he must start or he will miss his train at Koriyama. Of course if he were taking proper care of her he would not go to America at all, but then he could never give to the world what is in him. The world has changed since she was a girl. There are no more lords and no more serfs and everyone has a chance to rise, but there are more trying to rise. One must be as fit as possible. The three years in Tokyo were good for him, but would have carried him down had not she and Kannon stood always behind him. They will over there too. But now, sayonara.

In Tokyo it is fair weather. He leaves Chiwaki's house, Misaki cho nichome, early the morning of December 5th. Chiwaki may on and off have wished for this morning but now is not so sure. He has always liked to think of his nation as a great family where one helps the other not only with food and money and shelter but with faith, and it is that partly has kept him patient through so many an escapade, but it was his fondness too. His wife, however, is unmitigatedly glad to have this Noguchi out of the house. He may be a genius as her husband thinks, but she has had to have one eye on this genius long enough and is sick of it. She is glad too he is going as far as America. Never did she know what he would be up to next. That young man will come to no good end. The things he tried— but she is not one to carry tales. And for such a one her husband sold her bridal kimono.

At Shimbashi station the students are waiting to call banzai as the train pulls out. Okumura is among the students. To Okumura Noguchi looks gay standing there with the master Chiwaki by his side. Chiwaki is going along as far as Yokohama. The students bow till the train is out of sight.

At Yokohama the *America Maru* is loading her late

79

freight. Komatsu, a friend of Chiwaki, is sailing with her too, is on the way to Washington to take a place in the Japanese legation. The three talk for a time, then Chiwaki draws Noguchi after him into a cabin and closes the door and what he now says to Noguchi is written on his heart with tears. That is, Noguchi will remember. When the two leave the cabin there is a quick bowing almost perfunctory and the master hurries ashore.

Many hours later when the land has thinned away there comes a great storm that lasts three days and three nights, rails torn off the ship and lifeboats washed away. "By the kindness of the Great Shadow I did not even get sick." That is what Noguchi writes. Then the weather clears and Komatsu comes round to see Noguchi, as Komatsu promised Chiwaki he would, has indeed made it possible for Noguchi to travel almost first class though he paid for only a steerage passage. Some of the crew remember Noguchi from the time he was quarantine officer, and many others are friendly to him, but he does not on that account enter into the life of the ship. That is not his kind of life. Komatsu finds him always at the same place reading *The Merchant of Venice*. When Komatsu asks him why since he is going to the living country he does not read the living English his answer is prompt. "Shakespeare is the original and true English and it is better to begin at the beginning." Komatsu knows from this that he has on his hands either a blockhead or a genius.

After twelve days the *America Maru* puts in at

Honolulu. Steerage passengers are not allowed ashore at Honolulu, so Noguchi has himself transformed into Komatsu's assistant, has a trip round the town and a dinner and feels much better with his feet once more on firm earth. The passage eastward from Honolulu is in sunshine and seems full of the promise of a fine future. Soon he will be in San Francisco, and soon after in Philadelphia where he will live very likely in the house of the Professor as anticipated in the letter to Yago. Everybody in Japan knows how Japanese students have been taken care of by generous Americans. There is that celebrated case of Niijima, was practically given an American education. Komatsu listens to Noguchi's plans and is not convinced, just as Ishizuka listened in Tokyo and was not convinced. Noguchi reads quietly on in his Shakespeare. He knows that at the University of Pennsylvania he will be assistant in pathology, later will go to Germany and France, later still will return to Japan to be the physician of the Emperor if that is what he wishes.

On the 22nd the deck machinery is once more set in motion and at dawn next morning everybody is up and waiting for the pilot. Several hours later everybody goes ashore, Noguchi too, walks the occidental San Francisco streets, breathes the occidental air, is in the midst of occidental sights, and not till midnight climbs to his third-story room in the Palace Hotel to write Chiwaki a letter.

"The cold atmosphere is increasing severe, but I am thinking that my honorable teacher and wife must be in good health, and for this I rejoice. At my parting you showed me kindness like sea and mountain and I say thanks ten thousand times. . . . I wait every inch and moment to hear from you. Colds are source of every disease, so I hope the master will take care of his honorable wife. The purser of America Maru to whom I owe most is having toothache, so I take liberty of introducing to you. Please look over. . . . Please remember me to all who have eaten out of the same kettle. With bent neck. Midnight. December 22nd. Palace Hotel."

Of the new country not one word. Of the street he has been walking, of the masses of iron and brick, Gothic steeples, rows of ugly houses, not one word even to Komatsu who is with him. "His mind appears to be wholly absorbed in a different world." He has lived his life in the orient, by one flop, as happens from a ship, has been tossed into the occident, yet says not one word of what he sees. He is dreamy. He is silent. Then for five days he crosses the American continent, is drawn by huge locomotives, mounts the Rockies, rushes through the desert, leaves occidental cities behind him, and continues unperturbedly to read. Komatsu invites him to the diner at every meal but he accepts only once a day and Komatsu does not press him, feels some sensitiveness. Once Komatsu finds him with a set of costly playing cards, is surprised, asks him whether he wants to play. "No, these are not ordinary cards. On each card a photographic view of some place of interest is finely printed." So there is not much need to look out the window. The places are printed on the cards. "I paid three dollars for them. I am going to take them home as souvenirs." Komatsu knows how little money the boy has, suggests there would still be time for the buying of souvenirs. "No, I might not in future be able to find such precious articles." Three dollars, six yen. A letter to Yago has often brought twice that much.

[XVIII]

*In the Clear Foreign Sky an Embarrassment that Pierces
the Heart*

It is the close of Meiji 33, the year of our Lord 1900.
He has parted with Komatsu, for the first time is alone
in the great Christian country. Not that he is a Christian—he was baptized once in Tokyo but only because
the church was a good place to learn English and three
days after the baptism fell out with the preacher and
thrashed him for a difference of opinion—but even a
Buddhist or a Shintoist is likely to think of America
as the great Christian country and to think of it with
some simple veneration too. He is in the great Christian
country and all the way to Philadelphia. He appears
at the dormitories of the University of Pennsylvania.

The next days are bad days. It is true that he wrote
Professor from China, but perhaps Komatsu and Ishizuka were right in thinking that a letter cannot settle
everything and that all might not be as prearranged as
he imagined. "Your parting words are now useful to
me." That is what he says in his first letter to Chiwaki.
The words he refers to are those written on his heart

with tears there at Yokohama. Chiwaki well remembers the words. "The mother eagle three days after her young are born pushes them off the edge of the cliff toward the valley a thousand feet below. Each by its own effort opens the field of its fate. So now do I push you off into the strange country ten thousand miles away and the field of your fate you must open for yourself. From now on you yourself are the only one on whom you can depend. Remember that."

No, things are not so prearranged. There is of course no position waiting. He writes how it stands.

"My coming to America was dependent on one single Professor and he is a new arrival last year in this university, therefore his shoulder is not so broad before the dean and faculty. And when I arrived he welcomed and kindly took trouble and saying surely will hire me as assistant and so saying is working."

As Professor Flexner says, the university has no funds for Noguchi's support. The situation at the university seems even peculiarly difficult. Noguchi writes further.

"There is a rule not to employ foreigners so nothing can be done. That hurts my head. It is near the end of the year. I don't know what to do."

In the zinjo-shogakko when he was unhappy he would sit for a time under his willow. Here he may sit on the steps of one of the buildings, as he is indeed seen to do.

He writes to Washington, to Komatsu who by now is at the legation, wants Komatsu to send him money but does by no means state with clearness how things stand. "The statement of his real situation would imply, he would have reasoned, a complaint against either the unkindness of the Professor or fault on the part of Chiwaki." What he says instead is that the English of Philadelphia is too difficult to understand, and "as he does not think his further stay in Philadelphia to be profitable" he would like either to go on to New York or to return to Japan immediately. He wants Komatsu to send him traveling expenses. But Komatsu is no Yago. Komatsu promised to advance money only if Noguchi were ill or when his studies were complete. Komatsu thinks of Noguchi as assistant at the university, regards his letter as a caprice, and certainly it is remarkable to be laying all to an inability to speak the English of Philadelphia and yet to be wanting to go to New York. Instead of money Komatsu sends advice. Noguchi writes despairingly.

"It is a case either of biting on rock to go through with the original intention or to wait on starvation sitting still."

This all happens in a very brief space of time. If he knew exactly what was going on about him it would be nothing, but how can he know? In the past when he had difficulties he would pay a call on a man, would talk for half an hour, would come away with what he went for. But that man was a Japanese. What makes him so illogically grab at New York is perhaps not English language but Japanese people. He wants to be near his own kind. Here there are no Japanese. Here he is

86

alone. And how alone is proven by his readiness to return to Japan, he who for three years had thought of nothing but getting away from Japan. How alone is proven further by the fact that even as late as May 1902 he writes a note to students in Japan thinking of coming to America.

"No matter what you do, before everything is absolutely prearranged you must not come to America. In fact at that time when I came I was almost at the point of considering death, and such an event should not be repeated in another person again. In addition to that, if you are not careful, as a result of such a thing sometimes there is a danger of losing entire point of view (land to stand on). That is enough to caution you so I do not nag."

By the next letter the clouds have somewhat cleared.

"The other day I wrote you letter of great struggle and I am fearful shrinking because of. . . . When I told Professor I was not going to Washington he decided to let me study till money comes from my country."

To this Chiwaki adds a note.

"When I sent him one hundred yen I said it was the last."

But Noguchi knows only that he has the hundred yen.

"I have the hundred yen. It is like giving water to a fish washed ashore."

I Have Entered the Sweet Realm of Science

"Have you ever studied snake venom?" (This is Professor according to the pupil.)

"Moria did some work on snake venom at Kitasato." (This is the pupil thinking, according to the pupil.) "So I answer quick: 'Yes, I know.'

"And Professor says: 'Go, and investigate that.' "

Thus once more like the wind through a crevice he slips in, this time into what he calls the realm of science. He is given a room. Professor Flexner tells of the moment.

"A theme in bacteriology was chosen and work begun in the cramped quarters alloted to pathology in the old medical building. Providence was, however, not unkind, and before long a patron was found."

The patron referred to is Silas Weir Mitchell. Noguchi is given a letter to Doctor Mitchell. Mrs. John Mitchell remembers very well the night when Noguchi comes to the house on Walnut Street, a cold wet Saturday night, darkness fallen some hours back. The wet letter is taken by the servant to the second floor, then, after a little delay, down the stairs comes the distinguished Weir Mitchell himself. Extraordinary eyes Weir Mitchell has, eyes that see quite through human beings, at least so the young Japanese has been told. The young Japanese has eyes too. "See that pair of blue eyes and that pair of black eyes looking into each other." It is Mrs. Weir Mitchell to her daughter-in-law in the room upstairs.

Doctor Mitchell has immediately put out his hand, has begun to talk, talks straight into the young man, Doctor Mitchell's way, likes the young man, also makes the young man feel that he likes him, and even the following night, Sunday night, is still full of the young man. It is Doctor Mitchell's rule on Sunday nights either to go to the house of his son John or to have his son John come to his house, an absolute rule so the servants may rest assured of their free day. And on this particular Sunday night Doctor Mitchell talks of the Japanese student who visited him the night before, a most interesting person, new. His son John laughs, reminds his father that he is an enthusiastic man. Doctor Mitchell insists that he is serious, insists that this young Japanese has a most unusual mind, though of course one can never be sure of how far an oriental will go when he comes into an occidental environment.

The matter of salary has been arranged. There is some fund or other. At least that is the way Doctor Mitchell has explained it to more than one student, does not believe it good for students to feel they stand obligated to a single individual. Better to lay their for-

89

tune to some virtue in themselves or, well, some fund or other. Actually the money is coming out of Doctor Mitchell's own pocket, though there is a fund too, plainly labeled The Fund, for research and poor students, a separate bank book in the bank, now and then some rich patient at the end of an enthusiastic talk reaching into his pocket, but Doctor Mitchell very often also keeping up the level with his own. Noguchi tells how Doctor Mitchell pats him on the back and says: "This is not Professor Flexner's boy but my boy." Doctor Mitchell laughs. He has great gift for human beings, boys too, has made this boy much happier than he ever thought he could ever be again. For he has much that he did not have, a room, a salary, the sense of a strong man behind him. Later he will call the room a closet under a stairs, but not now. Now he shuts himself in in high content. A few hundred cubic feet of the new country are his. He has an address, a place to return to when he is tired, a key. The world is not so awfully, not so impossibly big as it had suddenly become. He writes Chiwaki.

"I am sorry I told you such a sad story last letter. Professor is very kind."

Professor Flexner seems almost immediately to have been called away.

"A week ago Professor was sent by government to San Francisco. It was regarding doubtful pest patient. When he left he gave me a certain responsibility and this may be the forerunner of a real position, but up and down is the way of the world."

The truth is that something, perhaps the afore-mentioned Providence, perhaps the prayers of Shika to Kannon, something is taking very good care of him to include a Weir Mitchell in the middle of Philadelphia, a Weir Mitchell who though never in a chair at the university is yet a pillar of it, a distinguished man in the world and in Philadelphia, something of Philadelphia in him very likely, Philadelphia the first capital of the country and not so long ago that Philadelphians have forgotten, moneyed New York growing exasperatingly big beside her. Weir Mitchell has a hobby—no, a real horse, he emphatically corrects—or, rather, earlier in life had a sober physiological problem that lately has settled into a hobby, enough life still left in it to become in turn the sober physiological problem of this young oriental dropped so oddly from anywhere into everyone's midst. It is this gives someone the chance to say that Doctor Mitchell himself is interested in venoms and will therefore have a personal good out of the young man. God forgive Doctor Mitchell the self-ishness, and it is certainly true that for nearly half a century, though a physician, a psychiatrist, a novelist, a poet, he has played and worked with this problem of the venoms of venomous snakes. His father played and worked with this problem before him, collected venoms all over the world and handed them on to his son who now in turn is handing them on to this young Japanese. For it would be well, as Mitchell in his doctor's English expresses it, to resume those studies along the line of

91

the new biological conceptions of toxicology and immunology.

Noguchi knows nothing of venoms, nothing of toxicology, nothing of immunology, but he knows something of work, forgot it a little in Tokyo, but lately had a great fright and henceforth will work regardless of hardship up to the destroying of his body as he said in the letter to Yago. He thinks as we all think at such a time that work will accomplish anything.

"I have no leisure morning or night and all night I break my bones writing the record of the day."

What is interesting is that even now, even here, he has no difficulty in regarding important what he does. Some months later Gay, now Doctor Gay, whom he met in Tokyo, comes to share his laboratory with him, and to Gay it is interesting how even at this early point Noguchi reveals his independence of mind. His experiments are of course directed, yet he will slip in experiments of his own, brings the tubes over to Gay, shows him, asks him to say nothing about them. The advance in these months is by bounds, as it is likely to be when one knows nothing to begin with, yet his hopes outbound his advance. In a letter to Tokyo he says that he expects to be through the whole subject of venoms by September. Weir Mitchell worked at that subject most of his life. Occasionally Doctor Mitchell drops in, talks a little of the art of Japan, especially of Japanese fans of which he has a good collection, then turns to the experiments of the day.

"Doctor Mitchell is to go next March to Japan, so

he told me when I saw him last time. He is known in the world as snake venom expert, also scholar in nervous diseases, also toward late years has published many literary works, and his reputation is very high in this city, no, in the whole medical world. If he asks for introduction to someone in Japan I expect to write one to you. Please be gracious to him. Considering the season, take care of yourself. With bent neck."

That is the changed tone in which the busy young scientist now addresses Chiwaki.

[XX]

The Field

When Doctor Mitchell spoke of the new immunity he spoke of something alive in the science of the time. Immunity is simply the defense of the body against what may enter and harm it. Some immunities we have at birth. Some come with an illness, as when we do not get the measles twice. And some are stuck into us with needles in the form of sera and vaccines, vaccines being dead bacteria, these dead bacteria generating in us something that will destroy their kind if later they happen to enter us alive. Besides immunity to bacteria we have immunity to the poisons or toxins given off by bacteria. Thus if a horse is injected with the broth in which diphtheria bacilli have been growing there is developed something in the horse that will neutralize the toxins of diphtheria, something that may be removed with the horse's blood, and if the serum of that blood (the yellow liquid that rises to the top when the blood clots) is injected into a child sick with diphtheria the poisons in the child also are neutralized and the child gets well. It is this diphtheria anti-toxin discovered by

94

Behring and Kitasato in 1890 that has had most to do with that reawakened interest in immunity of which Doctor Mitchell is thinking.

How the horse makes the anti-toxin, that nobody knows. And nobody knows how the anti-toxin neutralizes the toxin. There are many questions and many theories. It is hereabout that the genius of Paul Ehrlich has lately been shedding so much light, a good many others meanwhile talking and lecturing and writing and shedding no light whatever. Then again in Belgium, recently, light. Bordet has shown that if instead of bacteria the red blood corpuscles of one animal are injected into another there is generated in that other something that will dissolve such corpuscles. Plainly this dissolving is also an immunity. The foreign corpuscles may harm the animal so it dissolves them. The dissolving is a very curious phenomenon. Physiologists, pathologists, and even chemists would like to understand just how the thing takes place. In America no one is at work to find out but in Europe many are.

And this is the point where Mitchell's old problem of venoms touches the new immunity, venoms also dissolving corpuscles. Indeed it is partly owing to Mitchell's own work that we know that when a man is bit by a snake his blood will not clot and his corpuscles change. That there may be something similar between this change and that dissolving of which Bordet is speaking is a possibility of course not likely to escape a Mitchell. But Doctor Mitchell is past seventy. He cannot go to the laboratory and stay all hours as he

95

used to and is glad that this young Japanese with his mind more vigorous than fire has come under the guidance of Professor Flexner to take a hand.

Venoms in themselves are mysterious things. How is one to explain that frightful power to kill? The black memba, a deadlier of the African snakes, reaches down from a tree and as the dozen members of a visiting family of snakes walks underneath deftly puts its fangs into each, afterward scans them as they lie along the line of their promenade, the one touched first lying nearest, the one last furthest. Such a thing is strange. The fatality among men is strange, the death so quick the quantity of venom so small, a teaspoonful of rattlesnake venom dispatching well over a hundred men. It would not need the new immunity to make a Mitchell want to understand, to make him want to study, now that there is the opportunity, the exact action of venoms on such a system as the blood. It was Mitchell's earlier work, as a matter of fact, that threw the first light here, for it was he suspected that venoms had in them two factors and that the peculiar action of any one venom depended upon how much of each of these factors. The way he came to that idea is like him, and like him also to tell how not in his *Researches upon Venomous Serpents* but casually and entertainingly in his novel *Doctor North and His Friends*.

The doctor of the novel years before had studied venoms, then for some reason gave them up. Then one evening arriving at his door and putting his latch-key into the lock his eyes fall to the door-mat. There in the coils of the mat he thinks he sees a snake. Instantly a quite other idea springs spontaneously into his head, namely, that in venoms we are dealing not with one venom but with two, and that it is on the varying proportions of the two that the peculiar action of each venom depends. It seems that there was a black and a yellow thread in the border of the mat and that the two threads were interwoven, a circumstance that may of course have had something to do with the flash of the idea. At any rate the doctor of the novel goes back to his old problem and in six months proves his idea true. Thus Mitchell at the tired close of a day has made a discovery possibly more important than any Noguchi will ever make in this field.

Noguchi's labor is planned for a different point. He is to try to understand further the nature of the dissolving, that work done by Bordet, only will bring in venoms as a factor, but will study the dissolving for itself too, the problem no doubt presently leading him where it will. It happens that in the dissolving of the corpuscles of one animal by the serum of another there are also two factors, the one factor is called amboceptor, the other complement. Amboceptor alone will not dissolve corpuscles. Complement alone will not dissolve corpuscles. But amboceptor plus complement will dissolve corpuscles. Venoms also dissolve corpuscles. Do they act as complement, or amboceptor, or both, or neither?

All the Shining Stars Are There

Usually he does not get back to his boarding house till late. The boarding-house lady has a daughter and the two have been helping him with his English, but he is missing money, not much, but he has not much. At first he does not understand, now he does and hates too, hates to leave his homelike boarding house. He wonders how he will ever get up the courage to tell the ladies. He writes to Chiwaki, tells him.

"The University says I must leave in one one-hundredth of one day and night, so I am wandering in a five-mile fog. This emotional kind of decision I am most embarrassed by. I probably will leave after inventing an excuse but I don't know what is right and what is wrong."

Thinking in this manner on the ladies he is led to think on things in general, recalls how Chiwaki used to say that man's true education comes not from books and not from schools but from some more mysterious source.

"My several ideas must have been conceived in me

when I lay down my books, when stars were busy and skies blue, in Takayama nights, in the wink of an eye."

He remembers a poem, The River Tatsuda.

> If I cross wilfully
> the maple blossom will fall
> if I do not cross
> I will not hear the voice of the deer.

That means of course that he is still thinking of his landlady, still cannot make up his mind whether to move or not to move. Then the way he vacillates worries him. "Decision in this world must be in each man alone." That means of course that he is leaving his landlady. Having settled this he is free to let his mind wander where it wants to and it goes straight to Tokyo to the house of the master. "I see as in a mirage the happy family at Kanda." The mirage makes him warm toward all the world and when he climbs into his bed this night he has no fears and sleep comes easily. In the morning he tells the ladies his decision and they weep, implore him, move him very much till suddenly he realizes that they are not thinking of him really but of their good name with the university, which makes everything simple.

In the laboratory there is so much to learn. He has to bleed the animals. The larger he need not kill to bleed but can push the long needle of a syringe between the ribs into the heart and draw just as much blood as will not endanger the life. In all such technical proceedings he may bungle a good deal, but he is a

Japanese and that will hide him some, and he knows it. Gay is struck by the way he repeats and repeats a technical proceeding, does not, as most of us, try a thing once, perhaps blunder, see where he blundered and correct, but does it over and over and over. After the blood is drawn it must be centrifuged, swung round till the corpuscles because they are heavier settle to the bottom. Then he pours off the fluid top, rinses the corpuscles in salt solution, washes them, as the phrase is, many times, finally dilutes them and over the various dilutions pours the venoms in their various dilutions, watching all that happens both with the microscope and the naked eye. He is busier and busier. Tubes lie all over the place, and cigarette ends. He has been spoken to more than once about the cigarette ends, but nothing much changes. Now and then Doctor Kirk comes over from the dental school and stays a while. Gay's table is by the window, Noguchi's in the middle of the room. Much of the time Noguchi is standing before his table, in his right hand the glass pipette with which he makes the dilutions and between the stumps of the left the tubes, wedged between the stumps, often two tubes, sometimes three, even four. From the very beginning the more sensitive realize how sensitive he is about those stumps and avoid to look at them, one colleague even claiming he never once saw them though he always felt something was wrong.

The venoms are partly the dried crystalline venoms that Doctor Mitchell got from his father, but Noguchi also milks the living snakes. Sam, the animal man, comes whenever there is any milking to be done, brings a pole with a leather loop at one end and catches the head of the snake in the loop and pulls the loop tight, Gay holding the body of the snake, the body under the circumstances of course very active. Noguchi then pries open the snake's mouth and squeezes the poison glands, collecting about a dram of the viscid fluid in a watch crystal, a queer shininess in his eyes whenever he does it. Odd he should like to do it. But another side of the business he does not like. Before a snake has venom to give it must eat, and it is not easy to make snakes eat. They never will eat if anyone is looking, so what is done is to push live rabbits into the kind of showcase where the snakes are kept, and go away. When a snake has eaten there is one rabbit less, and which snake one knows by the bulge somewhere down its length. For this dinner the snakes are in their room off to one end, and the thought of that dinner going on over there is hard on Noguchi, but he says nothing for a long time, perhaps because he is afraid someone may laugh at him, then finally speaks to one man, and having once spoken comes back to the subject again and again, tries in his scant English to make plain what the rabbit suffers while waiting to be swallowed alive.

Presently he gives a report of his researches at a meeting of the Pathological Society, and that night shortly before ten o'clock a professor is seen coming from the meeting walking across the campus shaking his head. "We understand nothing, neither his English nor his matter." He himself feels that things are going pretty well.

"There is some good fate in how my affairs are, and my research is entering a sweet realm."

He is beginning also a little to look beyond his research, and beyond his new boarding house, not far, and only timidly at first, but even at public things. When McKinley is shot and on the 14th of September dies Noguchi appalled writes to Japan, tries to explain to the east how such a tragedy is possible in the west.

"Luckily in our country for several centuries there has been no confusion between ruler and subject, but with the strong father-son feeling there is no danger such as there is in these foreign countries where after two or three centuries of autocratic ruling anarchists rise up. I think the Japanese system peerless. Of course if another country conquered Japan I do not know what would happen. We ought to be grateful for this permanent and peaceful feeling in our people."

The eyes that were so closed that day at San Francisco have begun gradually to open. They turn to a number of things.

"Even the poor decorate their living rooms and adopt the plan to please man's sight. So by looking at the living room alone it would be difficult to tell whether rich or poor."

The eyes are of course not too open yet.

"The reception room is in the front of the house where passers-by might see in, therefore covered with curtains giving a fascinating appearance."

102

He sends the Sunday paper, thinks the supplement would be suitable for a Tokyo doctor's waiting room.

"It is necessary to get the attention of the patient for a big practise and they here are very good at it. But it is over-attention when you put in too many details."

Sometimes for one moment the eyes open wide.

"Here those who are the socially clever are those who have the smooth word. Of course there is no reason to lose kindness and honesty on account of the smooth word."

But mostly the eyes continue to keep well within the laboratory. When he began last January he knew not much more of research than as drug-boy at Watanabe's. In these months he has learned much, but there is much much more to learn, and he must labor every moment. Then again he worries that in the midst of so much labor he may be forgetting his inner self. He writes Chiwaki for a collection of classical poems and for some books to train the mind and heart.

"Since I came to this country I have learned besides science something of the ends of life, something about withering and blooming, what they mean. . . . In this whirlpool of confusion we should keep hope and virtue. If you realize those two it will be happiness. I have already realized one-half of my purpose in coming to America and the other half is fate and work. If I confess my ideal when I came it was narrow and small. It was largely, no, it was entirely to get glory. That was first with me. But this thinking has been destroyed

and now I want to consecrate my life to one great task."
He is just twenty-four.

He breaks the course of his experiments to write
an article on Japanese medicine for an encyclopedia.
"Thus I though only in a small way am representing
Japan." The publishers pay him twenty dollars but
want his photograph and that costs six. With the balance
he buys books and clothes. Meanwhile he has six
hundred pages of notes and says with satisfaction that
that would represent between two and three hundred
printed pages. "I feel very glorious about it." There is
no doubt that he will be able to stay in America at least
as long as he planned.

"But if I only published the results of my snake
venom study part of my object in coming to America
would be realized and I would be willing to accept hardship."

Then in November the name of Hideyo Noguchi
is among those appearing before the National Academy
of Science. Eleven months in this country and he is
appearing before the National Academy of Science.
Not as a member, of course, even Professor is not a
member, but as a guest and to give a demonstration of
his work. For that work alone he would not have been
invited. It is good work, but it is Mitchell's theme.
Mitchell is of course at the meeting. "All the shining
stars are there." Comstock of Washington. Remsen of
Hopkins. Brush of Yale. Professor does the lecturing
and Noguchi himself gives the demonstration. He sees
very well how everybody is interested in him, speaks

with excitement and happiness in his letter of how no one argues against his work, does not mention and possibly does not realize that no one except those actually having a hand in that work could argue, have any idea of what he is demonstrating. In the evening there is a banquet at the "famous" Bellevue. Weir Mitchell "famous" for many years of venom work presides and Noguchi sits next Doctor Welch who "being my teacher's teacher loves me like a grandson." After the banquet the older men talk of the changes in science. Osler is present. Chittenden "whom I admired in silence" sits on the other side the table. At the afternoon session Noguchi at the recommendation of Mitchell was appointed Bache Fund Fellow allowing him to push his research still further, and everything this evening is lovely.

"I accepted the fellowship with thanks. This fellowship is usually one or two thousand the money to be spent for research. By the way, it is absolutely prohibited to use for my own expenses." (He is writing to Japan and is thinking for a moment of his debts.) "I am going to continue snake venom research and these experiments are very expensive, as I said before, one or two hundred a month." (Has forgotten his debts again.) "Of course the fund has really no limits, so I can use freely. My laboratory is a large room and I have ten thousand things and ten thousand corners and everything from beginning to end is satisfactory, so I am quite pleased."

[XXII]

*But if I Have Not Been to Germany What Ever Will
Become of Me*

The present is safe. So what of the future? This venom research cannot go on forever, not more than a few months, then the money maintaining it will be withdrawn, and what will happen then? And even if it were not withdrawn he could not stay in this country much longer. If he does not get to Germany it will make no difference what fine work he has done here. Japan will not recognize him.

"As far as American medical world goes it has hopes in my future, and in my eye it is clear America will send me back beautifully. From American point of view study in Germany will not make a different person out of a man, and in fact there is no reason for thinking that it will. However, that is the present stage in Japan, and due to this belittling of American science they pour salt over whoever comes from America, and even if I am back with the flower I know nobody will look at me. So I am sacrificing my glorious departure from here, and must go to Germany."

But how to get there? He has worried much. And he has no one to talk with either. The only Japanese he ever sees, and him only occasionally, is Hajime Hoshi, also from Aizu, editing a Japanese newspaper in New York and having often to go to Washington and always stopping the night in Philadelphia, sleeping with Noguchi in the big double bed. There is no one else, so instead of talking Noguchi writes again a long letter to Chiwaki to see whether he cannot by writing get himself into the clear.

"Concerning the motion of my body after my period here at the university I am giving you my foolish view, so please look on scornfully."

He enumerates the courses he might take.

"First we will ask a certain powerful man for two or three thousand dollars loan, provided no interest."

This scheme does not sound very hopeful even to himself. It would be more hopeful to look for a job with a serum manufacturer. The serum manufacturer would pay him one hundred a month. Of that he would spend thirty-five, as much as he is earning now, which would leave him sixty-five. In order to be sure that he saved the sixty-five he would ask the head of the serum company to hold it back. That way the money would heap and soon he would have enough for Germany. But if this scheme did not work, and if no scheme worked, and if he could not get to Germany, then he would return to Japan without having been to Germany. And it is wasteful anyway to be debating such a matter.

"Imagine I am at the bottom of despair, then my grumbling and despair will only add to my inability to succeed and I will besides not have peace of mind. . . . I will do as much as I can and what I cannot I will consider beyond my power, and will not become miserable. To work continually without any carelessness through even the wink of an eye is the secret."

Here things are going very well. People are very kind to him. There is a snow storm, a big one for Philadelphia, very big if one is used to the winters of Honshu. He does not often leave his laboratory, but to-day he does. He has a cold-in-the-head. And it is not often either that anyone comes to visit him, but just this afternoon Doctor Mitchell drops in, is surprised to find no one and wonders what that means and immediately writes Doctor Flexner.

"If there is necessity for money at any time he should be told."

Then two days later Doctor Mitchell drops in again, says that the young man must not hide it if ever he is sick.

"I am moved by warm heart of the doctor. Up to this time I thought him to be only friend of my science and I did not think he wanted to help me also in this body way."

And that is how things have been, especially since the November meeting. He feels he would have no trouble to keep a position in this country, and certainly no trouble while this present research lasts. After that if he cannot get to Germany he can return to Japan.

Nothing is simpler. Some sort of work he would find, and he would not mind living in obscurity, at least not as he would have minded in the past.

"Up to the time of my departure I was in the middle of dream. I thought that if you succeed, that is to be a great man but when I came here and had so much bad time and asked fairly famous man for help and he said to another man that I had no spirit, when I heard this then suddenly I saw that man cannot stand up in the world by ability alone. Even if you do stand up it is like machinery. It is necessary to have virtue to correspond. And really I have awakened to realize that ability is secondary." He is twenty-four and six months.

It is about now despite all philosophy that he paints a big picture in blue-black ink, star on one side, crossbones on the other, *Success or Suicide,* and puts the picture where he can look at it now and then.

"I reflect and I find I have a simple heart and brain, easily boiling, easily settling, and if I get work that is truly responsible I will not be of two minds. I have never yet got tired of a thing. In the end if I go back to Japan and am not received, why, the leopard can change his spots. In this worldly world there must be as many chances of work as numbers of heads."

Woods Hole

When summer comes he does not as last summer stay in Philadelphia. He goes to the sea, works with sea animals instead of land animals, works, but Woods Hole is a vacation too.

The last time he was in such a place was before his departure for America, at Atami. A thing happened at Atami. A lady high in Japanese rank noticed how nights when he got back from his pleasures there was always a light in his paper window and he would be kneeling there for an hour or two over his books. An admirable young man for her daughter, thought the lady, made inquiries, found he came of poor farmers and decided she would adopt him. Adoption is one of the very few ways of his rising in Japanese rank. Nothing came of the adoption, but that was not the lady's fault, someone on his own side interfered, some friend of his, he too far away to do anything about it, much galled at first, but rather glad now. That all seems so far behind now.

Woods Hole is very different from a Japanese

watering place, yet not so different, young people everywhere, young women, also unpaved roads and straggling paths. They ask him to go swimming, but he never does, never was much for anything like that, any deliberate exercise. However, he is very willing to sit on the beach and watch the others. There are several Japanese, and Sundays he and they go on long walks, can start any direction because any direction there is sea and forest and dune. They do not return till late night, and if there is a moon Noguchi leaves the others, stands alone awhile. The moon has some odd effect on him. Even on work nights he will tramp over to Penzance Point, stand there a long time, then moodily turn his back on the moon and tramp toward the village again, enter the dark streets, and if it happens one of the others is with him will talk loud in Japanese filling with suspicion, as he says, the hearts of the simple Americans, who pass them by.

He has been in Woods Hole about a month when a letter tells him of the death of Kobayashi's old mother. He quick writes the teacher. "Death is nothing." Easy to say that, but not so easy to put the old lady out of his thoughts.

"It is only the divine will to remove us from this world of suffering and none can slip either to right or left."

He tries then to comfort the old teacher with fancying they are both her successors as they themselves will be succeeded by the coming generations and thus the old lady's virtues run on into eternity.

"Your aged mother has realized gracefully and well the life of the world which is temporary, and now she is going down the road she formerly took and in the glow of Buddha's light is meeting with her ancestors and is happy to wait for us till we too have finished our lives round and full."

All this reminds him of his own mother, whom he is unable to help, or when he is able forgets, and he grows so sad that presently he is wondering why anyway he was ever born. Then he brightens again.

"In such time faith is the only light. Faith is an influence going round and round, and real happiness and unhappiness cannot be judged by to-day."

He reflects how his own life has changed, how different he is from him who enrolled in the Saiseigakkusha, how different even from him who came to this country, and he says again to Kobayashi what he said to Chiwaki.

"High honor, high rank, which I have been desiring, to-day in my eye give no impression and what I hope is to become a real man and to resign myself to things without grief, and when I come back to my native country I want to be near my great teacher and want to help the poor and the suffering and give rest to my old mother so she can go in peace out of this world." He is nearly twenty-five.

The great teacher's troubles are not over yet. In the late summer his wife falls ill and again the pupil writes.

"Of course worry of days past and intense work

112

and helping everybody, these are nine of the ten causes."

Suddenly he remembers he is a doctor.

"According to my diagnosis it seems proper to use diuretics and heart stimulants."

But if he were an utterly just man, would he not return to Japan and take care of the case himself?

"For one who is beyond waves of ten thousand miles it is not easy to come directly and wait on the sick bed and this gives me unbearable pain and I blame myself for my unloyalty and have to ask forgiveness."

He thinks over that a while, then decides it is not yet excuse enough.

"What is to be regretted is that the experiments that I am following belong entirely to the public duty and the circumstances are all so entangled that no one could stop all of a sudden. In a way I am in a position to compel me to become jealous of the man who has the freedom to study with his own money. . . . Medical science to-day is infantile, only half-explored, and of all the sicknesses the curable are few and to find more cures for others we must depend on the progress of pathology and the responsibility on us pathologists is great and we ought not to waste a single day."

Clearly then he ought not to run from Woods Hole to Inawashiro to take care of Kobayashi's wife. Is he not himself responsible for the discovery of some of the cures?

"I am developing a serum against venom of American snakes and when the serum is manufactured it will be distributed to all the world. Also I wish to use the horse for this. To get facilities for such big experiments is difficult even for the highest Americans. The expenses even of a goat are about 10 dollars. It is 40 or 50 dollars for a horse. That would be 200 dollars for five horses. That makes altogether 300 dollars, or 600 yen. If I were to find snake venom cure the expenses for Germany would be a simple matter and there would be no trouble about a world tour for you. But there is a saying that on this earth there is a devil in every happiness and therefore I am keeping my enthusiasm down so as not to give disappointment. But the chances are eight and nine in ten."

This is as to Kobayashi's tour. He has promised the master Chiwaki a tour too, the whole of America, all expenses paid.

"Ah, the boy born in Inawashiro and discovered by the teacher in the small village, this boy in the country of America, very active and busy in the scientific world and meditating upon the universe, please think over this thing. I put Inawashiro school above Tokyo university and my teacher above the university professor, and I will not stop till I make this true. The future has no hope if we measure things by the usual typical person. . . . I positively declare we must break with the prestige of scholastic autocracy in Japan. . . . Each time I remember your mother I weep. Everything is empty. Past, future and present are like dream and like real, and I wonder what divine yen is between us. Mysterious yen, even life of father and son could not be so deep as this."

[XXIV]

Except for Eating and Drinking there Is Only Experimentation

Bunting feels that Noguchi ought to have more recreation. Bunting, Pearce, Yates, Gay, all are in pathology. Noguchi ought to see an American circus, and Bunting invites him to a night performance, but he says no. He has too much to do. "To-day library, to-morrow interesting experiment." That is the way he expresses it to Gay, and it sums up his life. He writes a family letter to those in Tokyo who ate with him out of the same kettle.

"Except for eating and drinking there is only experimentation. . . . The manuscript I have not begun there being so little time and I so much driven. . . . To-night I am so busy I am not able to write, but please my regards to the master and next Sunday I am in hopes to write."

Now and then nevertheless he does take off a night, usually the night of a day when he has been particularly spoken to and feels bad, thinks he needs the lift, so as to get where he can work again next day. One colleague says he must answer back when unfair things are said to him, but he seems frightened at that. "Oh, no, in Japan the student never does." Yet he is very frank about the way he suffers. "Many a night I go home and weep." One colleague says he has a way when he is spoken to of drawing like an animal into a corner. Another colleague drops in, breaks, as he puts it, the poker-face reserve, slaps the Japanese on the back, calls him Yellow Peril. The Japanese grins, likes it.

Leo XIII dies. The younger men of the laboratories create a college of cardinals. Whoever wants to belong must contribute five dollars, also his guess as to the next pope, the money to go to him who guesses right. Noguchi comes quick with his five, is earning only thirty-five, but always wants to pay as much as anyone, a little more if possible, laughs much about the college of cardinals, perhaps does not see exactly why. No one guesses the lucky cardinal so the money goes for a dinner. Later at the announcement of Dick Pearce's wedding there is another dinner. Yates is present at this dinner too and another society is born, the Society for the Liberation of Captive Balloons, toy balloons having been tied to the handles of steins and no one permitted to release his captive with the hot end of a cigarette till he has drunk off his stein. At each pop Noguchi is convulsed. He is very funny with that beer in him, but also is having fun, wants so much to be part of the life. "His face gets red as the Rising Sun." Someone says that. Someone recites a limerick and everybody laughs, Noguchi too, then slips over to him who calls

116

him Yellow Peril, whispers something, has something whispered in return, laughs again, and hereafter is forever wanting limericks recited, as many as possible, says there is no better way of learning English, especially English slang, and English slang he wants especially to learn.

The truth is that after more than two years in this country he is having trouble in the simplest conversations, and next his hand what hurts him most is his English. Cow's English. That is how one speaks of it. And when he gets excited, demented cow's. The one who says the last is perhaps the most careful of all that Noguchi should not overhear and not be pained, also the quickest to make out that Noguchi never understands your English if he happens not to like what you say. He practises on everybody, even on the occasional Japanese visitor, has made some kind of rule about speaking nothing but English in his laboratory.

One day he botches an experiment. A mongoose was brought from Jamaica by Doctor Gay and got through the customs with much difficulty. The mongoose is interesting because it is known to kill poisonous snakes, and there is the natural question whether its corpuscles like other corpuscles are dissolved by venoms. Noguchi was told to chloroform the mongoose while still in its box because it might otherwise bite him, and he has chloroformed it to death. He does things like that. He is exasperating often, and then afterward he is miserable, and when he is miserable then sometimes the friend who calls him Yellow Peril drops in, sees how awful he looks, invites him to a hole-in-the-wall where pig's feet and drinks are to be had. He prefers such a hole-in-the-wall. He takes a whiskey, maybe two, talks a little, the little loosens a little more and soon everything flows out. At such times he may not wait till he gets to his room to weep but may weep right there in the hole-in-the-wall.

Of late he drops into other men's laboratories, invites them into his own, wears his white laboratory coat, still is not used to coats, still looks uncomfortable and rigid. In the outside pocket he has for several months been carrying a white rat, and some say they have heard him talking to that white rat and that the white rat understands. He explains that it is a very special white rat, that in the beginning there were about a dozen females and this one male which becomes thus the father of all the white rats in all the laboratories, too old to be a father now, and therefore *pater emeritus.* He himself has given it that name. He has christened it. He grins. He talks to a young lady, has bought a camera, takes her picture. He talks to her a good deal as a matter of fact. But he talks to everybody. And when he goes in and out of the medical building he nods to everybody. One or two begin to see in him the delicacy of Japanese manners, even the delicacy of the Japanese physical world, all that of late they have been reading in Lafcadio Hearn. If he happens to be crossing the campus and someone he knows is coming toward him he stops at a good distance ahead, always the same way, lifts his hat, bows profoundly, advances, then puts out his hand and shakes the other's hand, stiffly, like a child beginning to learn. Hajime Hoshi drops in for a night and sleeps in the big double bed. Then one Monday the druggist at the corner reports a Japanese having moved in a few doors west. That makes two. And when a distinguished Tokyo gentleman on tour through the United States reaches Philadelphia it is Noguchi shows him round the university.

With this expanding scene the work is also expanding. The notes are heaping. The discoveries are no doubt still only the trivial data of science, as Hata called them, nothing that will much change prevailing conceptions, yet Noguchi is learning more and more about venoms, more and more about laboratory technique, and as a serologist, a class only lately born, he has had enormous experience.

Are there or are there not substances in serum that will dissolve cells other than red blood cells? Are there or are there not substances that will dissolve kidney cells or liver cells or brain cells? And may there not be such substances in venom too? That is the kind of question for which he is seeking an answer, about which he is writing pages and pages, staying up whole nights.

One looks in at the laboratory door, does not cross the threshold but most emphatically looks in, a gentleman from another department of the faculty of medicine, a professor and among professors a distinguished man. "His English is execrable," says the gentleman, "and he is the most disorderly worker I have ever seen." The gentleman is speaking with reserve, is much more upwrought than he gives out, feels the disorder as if it were his own, as if there was something personal, an affront, and directed at him. "Neither I nor anyone could anticipate any greatness from a worker as slovenly as he." Others also say the Japanese is messy. The gentleman is himself the neatest of workers. "And I have no doubt either that once he has begun slovenly he will continue slovenly to the end." The gentleman takes for granted that the young man had some formal training before getting his degree, does not realize that all he knows he learned right here at his first actual problem, thinks perhaps, as does one other professor, that he ought to have stayed a longer time in Japan, learned more, trained more, stilled a little more of his youth in a school. However, the gentleman is perhaps right in thinking that order and disorder are matters of character and that training makes no difference. The gentleman has been orderly too long to realize that a great orderliness of mind may go with a truly great quantity of unwashed glassware. He could not possibly imagine, for instance, a great neatness representing a deep laziness, and that the having things orderly in front of one may at least not discourage a slipping into the illusion that the order is inside one, or exactly to encourage one to force upon things in nature an order that they do not have. Ehrlich once advised a very orderly and gifted young scientist to spend the rest of his life answering the question why nature when she

120

may just as well have created one neat variety of oak created indiscriminate hundreds. That a certain reckless character in the outer scene may actually help all but methodic discovery, that is of course too much to expect the professor to see. Yet it should have struck him that in the heat of an idea, or even in the heat of the hope of an idea one may not feel it worth while to wash the test tubes of yesterday.

Late nights when the building is quiet and the other laboratories are deserted and a "stimmung" fills the few hundred cubic feet Noguchi plans next day's experiments, writes down the plans, red pencilings all over them, and keeps the plans, knows how a thought may flit but once through the head.

"To-night my mind is confused, the sentences are disordered and I am in a rush. My regards through you therefore. 2 a. m."

His letters are marked any hour up to 5 a. m.

"When the plum blossoms scatter and the cherry blossoms smile this will reach you. Since for long I make no sound I know not how to excuse myself, but all of you without change must be studying hard. As for me I am performing experiments with a pleasure beyond sleep and eating. On account of preparations for experiments of the next day often I have pierced through the night and omitted food. Anyhow, my brain and spinal cord are many times stronger than of old, probably due to dropping smoke and wine and women."

He speaks more of his likes and dislikes than he did

last year. This bringing of enormous chunks of roasted flesh right on to the table, that he does not like. And when all one's life one was used to having rice three times a day suddenly to have no rice at all! Of course there is rice but boiled so differently. However, he is quite used to the occidental food now. He talks too of his own country as he would not last year, says what a fine country it is. Gay happens to know some Japanese, and Noguchi is "tickled to death" at the idea of anyone trying to learn his language. To Doctor Kirk he describes the best way of raising Japanese plants on this side the Pacific, and several times on a Sunday goes to Doctor Kirk's and shows by practical example how the thing had best be done, also eats one meal away from the boarding house. He even feels so free as to attempt an occidental joke, puts a large blue-lettered card behind a test-tube rack:—

No-touchi
No-guchi

And when he writes to the same-kettle people back home there is a levity there never was in his Japanese letters before. The same-kettle people have moved.

"Alas, how sorry I, when you are hungry hereafter the noodle-stand will be so far away."

Then, as when things begin to go they go faster, he is one day given what for all scheming and worrying he never yet was able to get for himself. He is given Europe. He is given a Carnegie fellowship for study abroad. And more, when he returns to this country a position will be waiting for him in New York. Mr. Rockefeller has allowed a million dollars, and Professor Flexner is to head a new institute for medical research. Noguchi is going as part of the staff, but first he is going to Europe, sails via Paris and the continent for Copenhagen, will work at the Staatens Serum Institut under Thorvald Madsen. That is, he is staying in the occident permanently. He is not returning to Japan. He is expatriating himself. It would seem a decision of some importance. He does not make much of it.

"In fact I will stay in America for a long time. The reason is that it has much more future at every point than Japan. The venom experiments are coming to an end and for preparation for publication of book I am squeezing brain power immeasurably. Two or three days ago I sent some manuscripts. Early this summer Carnegie Institute wrote me that they would spend five thousand dollars to publish my research, also eight hundred for illustrations, but this work will take much time and so I think I will postpone till I get to Europe."

He writes another letter, this to his old friend Kikuchi. It is the second in a short time. In the first he told Kikuchi (Kikuchi is Yone's cousin) of his growing reputation and of the scholarship to Europe. Kikuchi answered, mentioned that Yone was married to a doctor. "A jewel in the hand that someone has snatched away." That is what Noguchi answers. "The shooting star no one can catch." Noguchi is writing poetry. A

123

few years ago the announcement would have knocked him down. "Brother be happy and enjoy your life." He is patting Kikuchi on the back, and it is the last of the letters to Kikuchi the cousin of Yone who is another man's wife.

*I Have Never Been So Happy or Had It So Good in My
Life As Now*

He reaches Paris in the humor that goes quick buys an
afternoon coat and a silk hat and has its picture taken,
starts at once for Copenhagen, and when he arrives
there calls at once on Doctor Madsen. Doctor Madsen
did not expect he would be so young, wonders how old
he really is, but does not like to ask, speaks instead of
the difficulty of guessing people's ages from their faces.
How old, for instance, would Noguchi think him to
be? The question embarrasses Noguchi but he must
answer something. "Sixty-five!" Madsen is thirty-two,
thought he looked younger. It is only many months
later that he feels he can ask.

"Of course I knew you were much younger, but
after the Japanese fashion it is the greatest courtesy
to state a man for as old and as wise as possible. I considered to say one hundred, but then I thought I could
not bring it up higher than sixty-five."

And with this begins the life in the country of Hans
Christian Anderson. Twenty-nine years since Ander-

son died. Copenhagen continues so visibly the place where he lived. One looks up and sees a steeple of twisted tails of dragons and down and sees a sea with tongues of land like a map, and flower boxes bridge the houses. "Last month was like a dream and I could not work at all."

In the Institute are only a few and their research unfolds in a quiet like the country. Doctor Madsen comes to each each morning, looks over what each did the day before, may sit the longest time, even as long as an hour and a half, almost as if he had no work of his own. But he has. He works very hard. Only there is no outer drive. The drive is inner. It is a society of men not a factory with an office, a place where there is time, where by-paths are worth the following, where for days one may forget there is ambition and that science has material application. And if this is part illusion, and it is too much to hope that it is not, in the beginning it feels true, and the ideal is there. It is an ideal of scientist new to Noguchi. He was not ready for it at Kitasato, if it existed, and there was no chance of it in Pennsylvania. He needs it. He says that he has never been so happy or had it so good in his life as now. He says that not till he came to Copenhagen was he finally sure within himself that he would spend his life at research. He tumbles into the learning of Danish, wants to speak freely to this dear people, loves them, Doctor Madsen particularly, possibly even already someone else particularly too.

His laboratory he shares with Famulener, another

student. The laboratory is good-sized, tiles round the wall, the stone floor rubbed smooth every morning, the brass pipes polished bright, servants plentiful and cheap. Doctor Madsen likes drawers and benches neat and sometimes brings visitors, shows them Famulener's drawers. Once Noguchi loses some irrevocable work by an untidiness. Nothing is said. But Noguchi knows. But Noguchi will not change. In the first months he cannot keep his mind on his experiments at all.

"On account of the strangeness of the place my mind floated and I could reach no interesting result."

Then his mind settles somewhat. Doctor Madsen is working directly with him on a problem of toxin and anti-toxin, a problem in immunity, and he is learning that even in that kind of problem there may be exact quantitative work. He will say many times in the years to come that it is Madsen taught him accuracy, and he will never say it as if it had been a painful thing to learn. He brought with him from America several hundred grams of dried rattlesnake venom and he and Doctor Madsen produce now for the first time a serum against this venom. The venom is injected in repeated doses into a goat, the goat later bled and the serum separated from its blood. If now an animal is bitten by a rattlesnake and quickly treated with the serum the wound heals as if there had been no venom at all. Noguchi is "straalende" happy when things go like that. It is just as Hata said it was at Kitasato. Noguchi is never cold, but always has the feelings of a feeling man in his work. When an experiment is succeeding he will work the whole night through, and a bad day is the end of the world.

One afternoon the royal family of Denmark visits the laboratory, brings along Queen Alexandra of England. The royal ones behave like ordinary people, watch him while he works. They want him to have the feeling of home in Denmark. Their sea-walled town has much of the seclusion of a university campus, and a man may stop in the street and lift his hat and let the young foreigner pass by. Copenhagen is allowing him to come close, also allowing him to keep his apartness, and he sometimes feels things very differently from those about him. Again and again his teacher will try to draw from him a criticism of Danish conditions but never can, yet when the two go to Oxford to give lectures so soon as Noguchi touches English soil he speaks with a most critical frankness of all he sees. Doctor Madsen asks him how that is. He explains that in Denmark he is the pupil and must not say what, without his meaning it, may give pain either to Doctor Madsen or to Doctor Madsen's family, the more danger because Doctor Madsen's father is Denmark's minister of war.

In the midst of all this, everybody kind to him, experiments succeeding, maybe in love besides, in the midst of this comes a thing disturbs the whole world and him in particular. On the 4th of February Japan goes to war with Russia.

Ten years ago when Japan went to war with China he was at Watanabe's. There he could give vent to his feelings, but here he cannot really. Here he must worry as one may about what one is not near. He is afraid for his country. He sees all this present as revenge for the previous war and prays that his nation may be unified. Why does he not receive the Japanese newspapers? He sent for them long ago. To have to stay here and have the flame there, how sometimes that frets one's passions. He waits every hour on the dispatches, can only with the greatest will keep his mind on his work, is far from that oriental calm that the occidental has so largely invented.

"At every report the whole Europe is as if electrified. Each victory is mixed with a thousand feelings of surprise and suspense and envy. Russia everybody thought strong and so Europe was unwilling to say anything concerning. I am reading English, French and German newspapers. I buy all and this city's too. The dispatches are the same but the editorials are quite diverse. I have fairly clear notion how the different countries feel. The French are pro-Russian and the official newspapers publicly urge helping Russia, call the Japanese half-civilized savages, report Russian victories as stirring the nation. Germany cunningly declares perfect neutrality but underneath she is communicating with Russia, is helping Russia to win, and the German press is no better than the French which is full of blame, sarcasm and bitterness. The English quite contrary are trying to help Japan both in open and in shadow and people's sympathy is flowing. Recently on account of

Tibet question England is on a critical footing with Russia."

The Russian Black Sea fleet has been ordered to return, but he does not believe it. It is bait. There is a report of two regiments destroyed by Cossacks round Port Arthur. The report is French! It is the personal quality in the taking sides that galls him most.

"In general Europe is praying for Russian victory because of racial feeling. They cry out that Japan is barbarian, look down on our country, sneer at our ethics."

Ethics reminds him of something else in the thoughts of these westerners, something it needed no war to make him hate.

"They denounce the sex relations in Japan. But what do they do themselves? They have concubines, commit adultery, and what are the relations before marriage? Smile-sellers everywhere. They think the Japanese do not know but we must be truly blind not to see."

Two months more roll by. He cannot get to his work with a single mind. There is so much to learn from Doctor Madsen, and here is this war, and before the war it was the strangeness. He is working, but with so much energy going into another channel surely he must be cheating that work. Yet he cannot help it that he only wants more newspapers. Why do the Japanese newspapers not come? He long since sent fourteen yen to Zizi Shimpo.

"But I hear nothing from them. I think day and

night of battles and experiments are not satisfactory. Navy battle at Port Arthur has knocked the whole world down with surprise and the name of Admiral Togo is known to every three-foot boy."

He recounts the recent victories for the excitement of recounting them, as if Chiwaki who is in Japan might not know. Suddenly he boils over once more at the neutral nations.

"French and German newspapers speak of Yellow Peril and I cannot bear their faces. They are so shrewd, and the French like prostitutes are tempting Russia. The French are unexpectedly nasty. Denmark, the size of the palm of my hand, with no political influence, being human, does not keep still. As you know the Russian empress is the second daughter of Denmark. The English queen is the first. But nations and houses are quite different in Europe. The other day the brothers of the two emperors of England and Russia came to the institute and next day we were invited to a banquet, me too. That is how democratic it is, common people mixing with royalty, and we had a fine conversation lasting two hours. While I am writing the newspapers are announcing that a Russian flagship has been mined with six hundred dead, only twenty-three saved, including the Prince seriously wounded but taking charge. Eighteen Japanese ships are bombarding Port Arthur, so its fall comes soon. The glory of Japanese navy is so bright. In this mail I am sending Japanese-Russian war record in European languages. If you find war magazine send me."

Weeks go by. He is working better than he was. His intelligence is fine. Despite this war he is learning many things, especially that a scientist may be a complete human being, and perhaps that is more important even than to learn accuracy and the refinement of the technical process. He feels very close to Doctor Madsen, and Doctor Madsen feels very close to him.

From Hamburg on the 15th of September while waiting for the ship that is to take him back to America he writes to Chiwaki. A sad thing has happened to Chiwaki. His little daughter has died.

"Already a week since I heard the gruesome bad news. It gave me great shock followed by growing feeling of uncertainty. And thinking it over since it leaves me quite dazed and I have not courage even to send you words of sympathy. The night I received your letter I could do nothing but read it over and over, and in the days that followed I did not know what to begin, could not think how to comfort you, and ended by gazing steadily into the lonesome nine heavens. As you say, for man who has never bent, this first feel of real loss is indescribable. I think I can put myself into the place of the childless father. Even I unmarried though I am can understand. The road of life is full of mysterious cliff and mountain. The pleasure of to-day is the misery of to-morrow. The sorrow of this year is the rejoicing of next. These are facts of human life, but they are sad.

Madono ana itodo minishimu akinokaze

Through hole in paper window
sadly to body pierces
autumn wind

(the hole made by the finger of the child now gone.)

Tombotsuri kyowa dokomade ittayara

Dragon-fly catcher how far to-day
(child chasing the dragon flies, how far have you gone
to-day?)

"Are not these the sentiments of past masters concerning fathers? There can be no difference between poor and wealthy, noble and humble, old and young, in feeling for the lost child. Alas, it is sad. Steal silently in, steal silently out. And your love only five stars and frosts, yet cruel fate did not permit to continue. Is there any meaning? Or is there just no meaning? For earthly us there is no meaning. It must be command of heaven. Master most reverend and respected you can no longer catch by chasing so be content with heaven's command and believe there may be a deeper thing which human mind cannot comprehend. Believe she has not died. The image which she has left for her mother and father will not disappear for a thousand old. You cannot cut the thread of love. The life of the flesh is independable but the life of the spirit is eternal. Let her go where she wants to go and let us not keep her in this world against her will. . . ."

[XXVI]

The New Institute

He is in New York. He wanted his boarding house close to the laboratory at 50th and Lexington, and has found what he wanted, one room, a long table in the middle of it, and on the middle of the table a photograph that he carried carefully from Copenhagen. The lady has a round face. Japanese like round faces, he says.

Not till November 13th does he get to writing Chiwaki again.

"About myself, both body and mind are much better than they used to be. I am first assistant which corresponds to head of department and am studying hard. Came back September 22nd. During October I made preparations, on November 1st began experiment. The present laboratory is a temporary place but the new building is progressing. Its completion will take a year and a half."

He is being paid $1800. If he had not borrowed from Famulener in Copenhagen he would be rich, but how would he have got back? What folly to have gambled away the extra on the ship. However, there will be money enough after this. He buys a good many cigars, the kind he has always wanted to buy, the black kind, sometimes fifty cents apiece, buys at several tobacco shops, runs an account at each, will pay when his salary comes. He is introduced to several Japanese. He is introduced to Takamine. "But I do not associate with any Japanese, though there are a few students." He is introduced to several Americans. One of them thinks he has no sense whatever. One thinks he is delicious just because he has no sense, buys a post-card album for a lady, a cheap post-card album, the lady a New York lady, she having remarked that her husband was away and she receiving post-cards from him, naturally a little astonished when the gift comes, and the gift astonishing in itself too because in the package carelessly, as if it were part of the wrapping, a beautiful and old and precious print. As to the wrapping, any Japanese might have done that, but what a satisfaction not to have to think of what the old print costs. And what a satisfaction besides the money in one's pocket to have all this money behind one's work, this great new Institute, a million now, millions hereafter. At Kitasato he could not have even thirteen guinea-pigs and was to wait five years then go to Germany and get thoroughly trained, and here it is five years and he is only waiting on the finishing of a great new laboratory in the great new building that is building at the head of 66th Street, and his future is the future of American medical research which, as he says, is like the bamboo, nicked a

135

little at the top it will split quickly all the way to the bottom.

"Flexner is head. There will be six including me, of whom two are professors, and they are thirty years up in age and they are above me, but their departments are different. The remaining three are below me, and, if I say from age, I am the youngest, because the rest are above thirty with wives. So the future is bright—if it goes as now."

A telegram from Philadelphia. It is from Okumura, Okumura with whom he slept in the same paper-walled space in Chiwaki's house, who got up in the middle of the night to find him pushing out into the storm. Okumura has reached Broad Street Station somewhat as Noguchi himself four years ago, only it is five o'clock in the morning and raining. He runs down to Philadelphia. It shows how life has changed, telegrams, visitors from Japan, he just back from Europe running down to Philadelphia, and money to do it with. Yet when one Japanese meets another ten thousand miles from home some simpler feelings are likely to come to the top. "When I saw his face I remember I had tears in my eyes." He stays with Okumura all day, and part of the next day, takes Okumura to the old boarding house. The lady is German. That ought to make the place ideal because Okumura will learn German besides getting his meals and bed. Okumura thinks so too till the next morning when he wakes and finds himself covered with bites. He shows Noguchi the bites. Noguchi is immediately severe. "You can't study in America if you can't stand bedbugs." In New York there are fleas, and scientists amuse themselves picking up fleas with pliers and dropping them into alcohol. But poor Okumura can't. He leaves the German lady, considers it his first defeat in America, and that afternoon Noguchi returns to New York.

"My research is still snake venom and I will continue till the book is finished. I am finishing with great success."

He carries part of the manuscript to the American whose wife is the lady to whom he sent the cheap album and the precious print. She will help her husband straighten out Noguchi's English, plumps the English dictionary on one side of her, a medical dictionary on the other, thinks that between those two surely everything ought to be manageable, then looks for a verb where a verb should be, follows down the page, turns the page. There is no verb. His language is as elaborate as his courtesy, but his courtesy is understandable, especially to a woman, has made many a woman move a little nearer the edge of her chair when he is passing, bowing, smiling, for instance, through a door out of a doctor's waiting room into the street.

One afternoon there is a caller at the Lexington Avenue boarding house, a Japanese, eyes like the devil in a show, come lately to New York to complete his medical education, Miyabara his name. Miyabara happened the other day to meet Hoshi, Hoshi who used now and then to share the big double bed in Philadelphia, asked Hoshi if there was not any "famous" Japanese in New York, and Hoshi told him to go to see Noguchi, a nice person, was in Pennsylvania, then went to Denmark, now is at the Rockefeller Institute. Miyabara's first thoughts are what a poor sort of place for the richest man in the world and what a poor sort of room for Noguchi to work in. Miyabara goes round the room touching things, asks what all the tubes and bottles are about. Noguchi explains that he is using them in his venom work, has a book in preparation but somehow cannot get it done, invites Miyabara to dinner, likes Miyabara and tells him, tells him too that there are not many Japanese in New York that he does like. He shows Miyabara the Lexington Avenue boarding house and the photograph. Miyabara thinks Noguchi one of those who likes things neat, is the first ever thought that. They see each other often after this. Noguchi sees someone else too, a single time, a certain young woman, a very stately and striking and beautiful young woman, a Miss Mary Dardis, the meeting conceivably of some importance.

*I Am Working On B. Tetani and Anti-
Complementary Bodies of Various Organs,
and So Forth*

On December 16th there is a letter to Madsen.

". . . Indeed I am ashamed myself of such a long negligence of writing letters to you and I only beg your forgiving for my impoliteness. . . . I was working pretty hard and my brain was someway affected so that I lost my readiness of writing any letter. . . . I was writing a part of Doctor Osler's New Edition of 'System of Medicine' (on venom), then was translating our French Manuscripts into English. Beside, I was working on 'Trachoma' and also on 'Syphilis.' I worked on Syphilis with Doctor Flexner and confirmed the presence of Spirochaeta pallida in the primary and secondary lesions. The work on Trachoma was begun in April, but owing to the presence of numerous microbes in such inflamed lesions of conjunctiva I was led to clear up these non-specific bacilli before I can go on further. I am still working on this rather resultless subject. . . ."

139

He is finding for the first time unidealized what a bacteriological problem is. He is learning what a mess of bacterial tribes live in a wound, for these trachomatous eyes are wounds, infected in the beginning very likely with one species of bacterium, but soon other species coming in, secondary invaders, as they are called, and these increasing till the species with which the infection began may have the fewest representatives of all. The eight months since April have been spent among these secondary invaders. Now it is December and he is sour.

He takes another problem. "I have made some observations. . . ." Observations are printable, hence good, especially when everything, oneself, one's institute, is new and in need of reputation, whereas the cause of trachoma is not printable till it is found, which may be months or years or never, hence risky, better to have papers, keep one's name in the journals.

"I have made observations concerning the photodynamic action of certain fluorescent substances upon snake venom, tetanolysin and tetanospasmin."

Eosin the dye is one of those substances. "What on earth is Noguchi doing in there?" Doctor Sweet has just gone into Noguchi's laboratory and come out again. "How did he get the dye on the ceiling?" The letter to Madsen goes on.

"I found a peculiar fact . . . rats or guinea-pigs inoculated with spores of B. tetani can be saved from suffering tetanus by means of eosin injections at the same spot."

Peculiar, yes, but nothing compared with the finding of the cause of trachoma or the making of a discovery in syphilis. He is already altogether out of the problem of syphilis.

"Doctor Flexner is still working on Syphilis, with his new private assistant. I myself withdrew from this work."

Withdrew from syphilis to study the effects of a dye on the spores of tetanus! On the 5th of April he writes Madsen again.

"I am most pleased to hear directly from you that the wedding has taken place. . . ."

So Madsen is married too, Noguchi's own affair in Copenhagen meanwhile broken off, and all the other men at the Institute have wives, facts to be gay over when one is gay.

"As to the manuscripts you kindly sent back to me this time I wish to inform you that, after reading through a couple times . . ."

The letter goes on, but incomprehensibly unless one is stirring in the same pot, then grows comprehensible again. He has begun to talk of the new brick building.

"Was opened last week and we had moved in in the same week. . . . The first floor is used for the business purposes (office) and the library." Then a description of the second floor. "In the interior of each room the floor is not concremented, but so is the corridor. My room is upon the third floor and confronts the East River and Blackwell island—a nice

141

view! The Institute is on the extreme edge of the bank of the East River and is isolated from the town buildings and reserves quite a large area of ground open free. Dr. Flexner is on the same floor and occupies the northern side (three rooms—one for his official purposes, the second for the investigations) with his private assistant." Then more about rooms. Then—"Dr. Flexner's Private Assistant is Dr. Houghton, a graduate of the Johns Hopkins."

Noguchi is a graduate of the Saiseigakkusha. The letter goes on.

"The Library is fairly well provided, and I am the Librarian by name (because the work is practically done by a young clerk)."

Very wise, remembering the library at Takayama and the library at Kitasato and knowing that human beings do not change.

Meanwhile print continues important—twenty articles now. He writes those articles as readily as a professional, it is said, yet somewhere between the time they leave his hands and the time they appear a little of someone's labor slips into them, for when they appear they might be anybody's while his letters are nobody's all-adorably but his own.

A strange concentrated personality—that is the way Hideyo Noguchi strikes one who meets him for the first time now. It is in the Institute dining room, perhaps a dozen at the table, Doctor Carrel among them. Noguchi rushes in, a long white laboratory coat covering him, holes in the coat big enough for Noguchi to push through his big little head. But he would not. There is no playfulness in him. The quality of his concentration is such that it is difficult to talk to him. In his letters he sometimes seems free, but in his person he has again lost some of what he had at the close in Pennsylvania, seems sensitive, harassed, is still far from making anything very clear of the circumambient occidental world, still takes very literally what people say to him. Two are coming into the Institute as he is going out. His face is grayer than usual. This is the middle of the morning. He was in the laboratory through the whole of last night, through the whole of yesterday, through the whole of the night before. One of the two looks at him, possibly a trifle hard, remarks something about his leaving that early, something about banker's hours, something certainly not meant for criticism, yet the gray in Noguchi's face goes grayer.

The 18th of October he writes Madsen again.

"I am delighted to hear that my venom paper appeared from the Royal Academy and wish to thank you for it. . . . The neutralization experiments on venom and anti-venom (by you and me) is coming out from the Journal in January in English language. It was pity that it was kept back so long time, but many anticipated articles. . . . From October 1st the appearance of the Institute resumed its usual activity. There were about six men added, and one out."

He names the six, still places himself fourth in line, and mentions among the recent fellows Alexis Carrel for experimental surgery. The letter goes on.

143

"I am working on B. tetani and anti-complementary. . . . Something about trachoma is also being done, but very discouraging so far."

Later he gives up trachoma altogether, in one letter says he has stopped trachoma, in another that he has stopped because he has exhausted all the methods. To Doctor Martin Cohen who has been working with him on the problem he says that he must let it rest awhile, that he has lost his freshness for it, must work on something else and bring what he learns with that to the trachoma at some later date. Where he goes instead is down into one of those dimly lighted places.

"Very recently I was working on the so-called complement a alexin of blood serum. . . ."

The question is, which of the substances in blood serum is the complement. Professor Kyes has shown that it is perhaps the lecithin, but Noguchi is not satisfied, and for months now the question whether he or Kyes is right is the center of Noguchi's increasingly muddled universe. He puts off buying clothes because he cannot afford clothes, then buys in quantity, thirty-six dollars at once, suit, hat, shoes, straight wears all in the laboratory and in three days looks as he looked before, scowls when reminded, continues worried about money, buys a ledger, will write down every penny, never makes an entry.

If he could but find a chemical that would combine with serum and the serum act like complement, and that would combine with lecithin and the lecithin not act like complement. He experiments with innumerable chemicals. He follows one path, gives it up, follows another, gives up that. Then——

"I wish to communicate to you some of my results. Blood serum (or any organ, especially certain glands) yields, upon hot alcoholic extraction a fraction of high lytic activity. . . ."

Then follow parentheses, parentheses within parentheses, quotations, dashes, and one thinks of that professor back in Pennsylvania who felt bound to go to the meeting of the Pathological Society though he knew very well he would come away understanding neither substance nor language. Natural that in the midst of such science Noguchi's thoughts should often go to Copenhagen.

"It was nice and so grateful that the King had reminded of me. It recalls my warm and happy days of Copenhagen and Serum Institute. I certainly remember the Princess Ingeborg. To such high personnels I am at loss how to greet and to return my most cordial appreciation of their kindnesses. I will be extremely happy if through you I could express my thanks to the King, wishing him the best of health, and congratulating him upon his brilliant reign full of men of arts and sciences of international fame."

[XXVIII]

$1800

January 7th he writes Chiwaki:—

". . . have been examining my finances. Every month there is no balance, and particularly from this year that I have become independent I want to prepare for emergency. . . . Since October last I can't get good sleep on account of piles, and as the moon goes this condition is getting worse. Yesterday and to-day walking to the Institute, which is one or two blocks only, is quite a handicap, and I have decided soon I must go to the hospital to be operated on. And this is my first reason for preparing financially for the unexpected. I am to-day received as a gentleman and therefore I must maintain feature and face of a gentleman, and especially when I am near Americans I cannot be unguarded. Hereafter to ask for loan from stranger becomes impossible. Flexner already gave me warning on that point. The fact is that I am living in this country of unknown four faces and have not enough money for a little illness. The daily life is just like day labor, full of things should not be done by independent person

. . . I have every year before received clothes, but since last October I have become independent man and must pay for my own. Especially due to sea voyage and other incidents I have much debt which I cannot repay. I am ashamed to speak of but I have no winter coat, not even from last year, and I am using a raincoat in place of. Expenses in New York are two times Philadelphia, mainly rent. I have not yet found out instalment places, so I feel very inconvenient. As you know, since I came to America it is already five years, and first three years, though you may call it salary, it was only maintenance. First year I got a month $25. Second year $35. Third $50. Fourth year $2000 for expenses for study abroad. The first year I could not tell real amount because it was so disheartening to say to you $25. But since that was only for living expenses it was not so bad. . . . So from last September I have become like ordinary man, and with that there are many new things for which I have no experience, and I have been very careless and result is I have not one penny left and my unhappiness is maximum since I came to America. Even if I try to be economical the habit of long years of dependent life became a second nature to me and is indeed painful. . . . My brain is not clear because I can't sleep and ten thousand things are bothersome. So I am anxious to get to hospital as soon as I can. My piles are due to non-bathing during sea voyage. . . ."

And on April 23rd he writes again:—

"Three times I read your letter from far country

from which I have been separated so long. And even though in the middle of this confusing big city I was able to go back and find many affectionate threads. Since I came to New York I have not had one day leisure, and even if I had had on account of being in midst of common earthly things and crazy insanity my mind would not settle and therefore no chance of deep and distant ideas, and that is terribly to be regretted. In the boarding house were I to stay half a year I could not recognize my landlady's face, such is the inhuman state. If you leave a thing a moment there is worry of robbery. Life of human being at that level is just like animal life. Such metropolitan life is lowest form. Then my piles are torturing me and I am much depressed. In the past month I was asked by a professor (Osler) to write a chapter on snake venom. There is a time limit for and I have taken the pen forcibly to hand. There is no spare moment. In addition I go to the Institute every day to begin my new experiments. So in my heart and mind there is no peace. Then I am worried about navy battles and am aroused at the injustice of the different countries and I think of conditions at Inawashiro about which I have been so careless. Of course such a thing as a letter, if you become lazy once it becomes a habit, and the second and third letter is easier not to write, and then the embarrassment. . . . I will tell you a little of my experiments. I have stopped snake venom problem because I have solved the more important aspects of, and have launched upon the more difficult problem of trachoma. I have connection with a hospital and can get all materials at will. This that I tell is a scientific secret and it is important to have it kept so. Although I use many animals the chief ones are monkeys. . . . As I think over carefully I am no longer of the age which should depend on others. Indeed if I were a proper man I would be able to help other students. For this I am very disappointed and am blaming myself. But, master, look at these things with great eye and be patient for a few years and there will come a time when I can lift up my head. . . . Perhaps I have no excess to help others, but I can take care of myself and for unexpected I will save. I will take 20-payment life insurance policy for 6000 yen. . . ."

He is twenty-eight and a half.

Another Minute Spiral Organism

The same month, April, from Germany comes news of the discovery of Spirochaeta pallida. Few discoveries have been more stirring both to bacteriologists and common men. The cause of syphilis is found. In the centuries since that disease first struck Europe false hope has followed false hope, but more than once in this recent bacteriological era has the finding of a cause been the finding of a cure. And the cause of syphilis is found, Spirochaeta pallida, the pale spirochete, another minute spiral organism. It was a spiral organism he saw that day when Watanabe called the drug-boys and all five came running.

Amazement too sits on the manner of this latest discovery. Schaudinn the discoverer is no bacteriologist. He is a protozoologist, not a deep distinction but interesting because as so often in science someone from without with fresh eyes has stepped in to point to what no one within with tired eyes was able to see. A protozoologist has found what all the bacteriologists missed. He has found with the microscope, of course, but not even that in the usual way. The usual way is to cleanse the patient's wound, then squeeze a drop from it, spread the drop on a slide, heat the slide, kill whatever is on it, then pour over a dye, stain the field, as it is said, and with the microscope search the field. This however is not the way Schaudinn did it. He found the spirochete in a so-called fresh specimen, did not heat, did not stain, but spied the organism alive, pale, disappearing in the murkiness through which with a screw-like motion it drove along. And this is a feat. He had not the help even of darkfield illumination, but used the ordinary microscope with the ordinary illumination. Indeed, many an able bacteriologist even after he is acquainted with the organism might not find it too simple to so much as repeat Schaudinn's slender discovery.

Quickly the discovery has been verified. Schaudinn announced it in April. Already the next month Metchnikoff and Roux, who were the first to infect the monkey with syphilis and so to supply an experimental animal for the study of that disease, and so also to keep alive the search for the cause, report that they likewise have seen the same pale spirochete. And from other places come further verifications. The new Institute is prompt to fall into line. On June 17th Flexner and Noguchi announce that they also have found Schaudinn's spirochete, in five cases.

Schaudinn is thirty-three years old. Natural that Noguchi should think of how he is only thirty. The whole world has its eyes on Schaudinn. Many will half dismiss Schaudinn's achievement with saying he is a genius. Anecdotes are already told of him. But maybe he, Noguchi, is a little queer too. That is what they said in Tokyo. And more than once since he is here he has heard someone say "funny Noguchi," the person not thinking especially of his genius either. "There is no such thing as genius!" Noguchi loses his temper when one of his Japanese friends uses the word. "It is hard work. That is genius. To work three, four, five times harder than anyone else, that is genius." Schaudinn worked. Schaudinn paid not what he decided in advance he would pay but what the thing cost, and he, Noguchi, can work too, harder than Schaudinn, harder than anyone. He has a strong body. He is young, the age when the old ones say that discoveries are made. He needs almost no sleep. But perhaps the work must also be happy work?

[XXX]

A Certain Daughter of a Certain Gentleman in Tokyo

A little while back he wrote Chiwaki, asked Chiwaki to speak to a certain well-known Tokyo gentleman, a gentleman with a daughter, Chiwaki to say that Hideyo Noguchi would marry that daughter. Plainly then something has gone wrong with the affair in Copenhagen. And at least it would not be hard to imagine, especially on the side of the girl, America only all too clearly the absolute other side of that water from Copenhagen, and Japan on the other side of another water, a broader water still. Suppose he were one day to decide to go back to Japan? Where everyone speaks Japanese? English was hard enough to learn. If one were married to him one would go with him of course, all one's children Japanese, because that is the way they come in a marriage of that kind. There is much to consider. One does not consider when he is close to one's side, but when he is three thousand miles away one considers. But, however this about her in Copenhagen, what is sure is that Chiwaki speaks to the gentleman in Tokyo, wins from him his consent, quickly writes the glad news to Noguchi, who does not answer. Chiwaki waits weeks, months. Noguchi does not answer. Noguchi does not want the Tokyo marriage after all? What has happened? Copenhagen changed her mind once more? Hardly. Some Copenhagen in New York? Possibly. Decided not to marry at all? Maybe. Felt confident that he could make arrangements without Chiwaki? Through some Japanese in New York? Arrangements fairly well concluded when someone comes to Noguchi's room, knocks at the door, is met by someone, claims to be someone definite, throwing an odd light that frightens off Tokyo? Some rumor like that. Anyway Noguchi does not write Chiwaki any letter of any kind for more than a year and when he does it is as if there had never been any question of a certain daughter of a certain gentleman in Tokyo.

[XXXI]

East 65th Street

Okumura comes from Philadelphia, is through his studies and ready to go to Japan, is visiting Noguchi at Noguchi's invitation but does not see much of him. For though he pays board at the Lexington Avenue boarding house he does not turn up there often and almost never to sleep, arrives usually just before breakfast looking somewhat as he looked in Tokyo just before breakfast, gossips awhile then disappears till the next breakfast, says Okumura can sleep in the boarding-house bed as long as he likes because if he does not no one else will.

One night they go out together, Noguchi showing Okumura the town, (fourteen years now since those two or three showed Noguchi Tokyo), visit eighteen houses, Okumura counts them, drink two dollars worth of beer in each. Noguchi seems well-known in all. Everybody likes him. When he is out he is all life just as he was in Tokyo. But thirty-six dollars! Okumura is of the opinion that it is rather a disorderly existence Noguchi is leading. That photograph that was on the table when Okumura was here before is not there now, but Noguchi says nothing so Okumura cannot ask.

This is August. In September Noguchi moves to East 65th Street and not into a boarding house but into a five-room flat with two beds and in the kitchen a gas-range. Noguchi has learned about instalment places, buys where he has twenty months to pay. The gas-range ought to save him a little because he can eat some of his meals in his own flat. The rent is only five dollars a week. Miyabara will do the cooking. Miyabara is coming to live in the flat too. However, nothing can be saved if Noguchi is always eating somewhere else. Noguchi works hard but does things besides work, still many nights does not come to his own bed, arrives just before breakfast as he used to at the boarding house, sometimes not even then, Miyabara catching sight of him about 8 o'clock hurrying across the street in the direction of the Institute always a little careful about the automobiles and warning other Japanese about the automobiles. Better to ride in taxis, he says, and does.

But whenever Noguchi is home Miyabara cooks. Noguchi writes, writes and smokes, and with equal energy. What is peculiar is that Noguchi has energy even when he was up all the night before. It is hard to understand. He has energy even when he is in the most disillusioned, the most exasperated, the most demoralized state, only his face then gets green. He talks much to Miyabara, hot talk often, both feeling the same about things through which they are living at this particular period of their lives. What helps the friendship

156

is that Miyabara is one Japanese from whom Noguchi can have no hope of borrowing. If anything, Miyabara can have the hope, so Noguchi in a way pays for his right to pour out all that delights and troubles him. They talk a good deal about the women. One must to someone, and to someone one does not fear, someone to whom one loans money is very good. And better if the someone is a Japanese. In the Institute it would be impossible to talk about the women. In the Institute Noguchi is a flat wall, as one there who sees him well says, a flat oriental wall.

To Miyabara he lets out also his vexations, talks often of one colleague who comes with silk gloves and a cane, pronounces the silk in a particular way, as if the whole colleague might be made of that commodity. Which is certainly no reason for being vexed at the man, and perhaps no one is vexed. The man uses perfume. When Noguchi speaks Japanese he may emit the oddest bitterest puffs of a scalding vitality, but quick forgets, five minutes later may be in the best humor again. Presently he is himself wearing silk gloves and carrying a black cane.

"Look at my body. It is little. But every organ in it is powerful." He is naked when he says that and about to get into the tub. He struts back and forth. Miyabara loves him. Miyabara may gall him and he may gall Miyabara but they gall each other as two people who love each other. Sometimes Noguchi dances around the room, not often though, mostly he is cranky, but when he is happy he has the lightest of fig-

157

ures, especially when he talks and grows excited. Miya-bara likes to listen then. He likes particularly this talk of the life of the softer sentiments. Hero loves color. The Japanese all say that.

There is a third floor Lexington Avenue flat where a number meet. Noguchi comes too, usually in some mood of his own, often a heavy mood, and if so it is impossible to draw him out. Invariably he smokes a cigar, big, and looking bigger because of the way it droops from one corner of his mouth. Some say he smokes fifteen in the twenty-four hours. Some say more. Every now and then he puts down his cigar and takes up his whiskey. He drinks the whiskey very slow-ly, very slowly, and if someone tries to push him fur-ther than he cares to go laughs and recalls to them his mother's teaching. "Drink, but not so much that you begin to sing." He has a habit of looking at one spot of the ceiling and not letting his eyes off the spot. Someone puts him a question. He may answer *umh* or *ah* or nothing at all, but other nights expresses himself freely, the talk flowing, then suddenly his eyes seeking the ceiling for the spot they lost. A loud party is not his kind. He and a doctor go off into the next room, the kitchen, where another, who likes to drink whiskey alone, drinks it out of a bottle.

In a place he does not want next day to return to he loses his pocket book, or has it stolen from him. It has his personal card. He worries much about that, about who may find it, about what they may say, about what they may do. Suppose they telephoned the Institute?

The Institute is still a formidable creature all new brick, hard to know at the heart, as well to reveal as little of one's happiness and unhappiness as one can, *be* the flat wall. A number are together, someone reading a newspaper aloud, sees Noguchi's name, reads that aloud too. Noguchi grows pale. Everybody looks at him. He is so timid about the big world, officials, gossip, scandal. The Noguchi in the newspaper is another Noguchi happens to be in New York at the same time.

To the 65th Street flat no one comes, or seldom, two or three times a lady, carries a dog. She has a pretty face, Miyabara thinks. Some other lady marries. Her brother favored Noguchi, thought he had the bigger future, but she, a Japanese who had been in America a long time and had gone to an American high-school, knew a thing or two about men, had heard a thing or two and had made an investigation on her own. Noguchi is jealous. When Miyabara tries to tell how jealous the outer ends of his eyes start still further up and out making him look yet more diabolic. To Miyabara Noguchi admits that he is jealous. "My mind understands, but my mind don't like."

His fate is a bad fate, he says. Miyabara is lucky, will not have to stay in New York, can go back to Japan. His future is in the practise of medicine. Suppose he were a bacteriologist, forced to be because he was deformed, also because he had ambition, could he then go back? No, he would have to stay here because the opportunities are here, and he would have to carry in him the thought of having forever to stay here. "I

159

will work but if I do not succeed, then I will commit suicide." A healthier note quickly supervenes. "But I would like to show these occidentals what the oriental mind is like." Miyabara says that of all the Japanese who want to leave the new country Noguchi wants to most. For a while the two of them play with the idea of starting practise right here in New York, even get so far as putting an advertisement into a Japanese newspaper, but nothing comes of the scheme. Noguchi's friend Takami urges him against the scheme, feels it would lower him.

In March Miyabara sails away and Noguchi is alone. "Five rooms and two beds." He returns to the five rooms and the two beds as little as he can.

And if I Have the Flower in My Hand it is Not Particularly Pleasing

Lately he got an honorary degree from the University of Pennsylvania, had a promise of it before he went to Copenhagen, already then wrote Doctor Mitchell.

"I am extremely pleased to have this prospective honor and will work hard to bring back enough results in order not to blame such a high academic title."

Perhaps Doctor Mitchell was nevertheless surprised when a little while back he had a letter reminding him. Noguchi writes Madsen.

"The other day I was given the honorary degree of Master of Science from the University of Pennsylvania and in the fall I am going to be an associate or an associate member of the Institute."

All this time he is piling up his bibliography, twenty-five papers now. And he has two new subjects. "I am working on Tuberculosis and Rauschbrand." He is driving at the same time to finish the venom book. Once he thought he would be done with venoms by the end of 1901, put off to the next year, then to the next, planned to write the book before he went to Copenhagen, instead only further expanded his materials in Copenhagen. That was 1904. He put off to 1905. He put off to 1906. It was not all his fault that he put off, but at any rate the book did not get done. Now it is 1907. Now he means to finish it. He means to have credit. The master Chiwaki receives a letter.

"I am now suddenly recalling the bathing in hot springs Hakone that we had together. That is now seven stars and seven frosts as I turn back. Since then there has been the passing of scalding summer six times, and not once have I opened my collar and chest to free the spirit and heart. From morning till night without a single time losing the feeling of the strange country, it is a miracle that I have not gotten sick. Sometimes there are uncontrollable things in the work, but even without that my irritable temperament produces seven rips and eight smashings in my bag of patience. As years go by I realize that my lack of smoothness of nature and lack of perfection of common sense are not sin of man himself but of his environment."

The letter goes on to its real point.

"But this world is flower only when dreaming and when you actually get it is not pleasing. You wish once and if you receive you wish once more. So now I wish from Japan the hakushi degree."

He names those who have gotten the hakushi degree.

"I do not know what my merit to Japanese science.

In Europe and America I am better known than anyone except Kitasato and Shiga."

His mother will work too. She will hear of his wish through Kobayashi and will walk the twenty miles to Nakata Kannon to pray. The letter to Chiwaki goes on, Noguchi enumerating his works, stating the character of his present research, referring to the fact that all recent publications mention his name.

"Although slight feeling of slow maybe it is a fact that I am the highest among the young ones."

In twelve days, on the 31st, he writes Chiwaki again. Often he has not written Chiwaki for months, once did not for a whole year.

"Forgive the long silence. . . . My summer vacation starts to-day, but when one is in the strange country there is no pleasure. Very urgently next summer I am hoping to go back to Japan and to scatter there the worried thoughts of many years. I am waiting for. Since light and shadow are like arrow it won't be long. . . . Was informed of conditions in my native village. The hardship of the living there is like mountain. I expect to send mother a little money, and this I will send to you and though inconvenient please change to Japanese money and send not to her but to Kobayashi who will take to her. This is mainly because in the village the needle small is exaggerated to the size of a rod. Kobayashi is a careful man and will arrange perfectly. I have come to realize that road of life is not smooth. As to science I am a great success but as to financial condition I am below zero point. Since I did not have any mind for saving, things are as they are to-day and I repent a great deal. For human being it is necessary to cultivate mind for saving from very young. Without this there is great hardship in late years which they have to meet. . . ."

And in less than a month he is writing once more. About the same time he writes Miyabara, tells him about the honorary degree from Pennsylvania, about the hakushi degree from Japan, about how well everything is going, ends with saying that now he has the degree and the gown and henceforth will be able to have all the girls he likes.

[XXXIII]

A New Room-mate at East 65th

For a time after Miyabara sailed no one shared the flat, then for a time there was someone, then again there was no one, and now Noriwo Araki, a young man, a boy almost, here in America to learn what he can of the craft of porcelains. Noguchi likes him. "You won't have to pay any rent."

Araki is another slept at Chiwaki's and studied at the dental school, thinks Chiwaki's wife especially remarkable, a wonderful woman, would never let him eat the rice that he brought along for lunch because it had got cold, always made him exchange his for the servant's. Araki did not meet Noguchi in Tokyo, but felt he knew Noguchi, there had been so much talk of him both at Chiwaki's and at the dental school, no one quite sure whether he was a genius or just crazy. Chiwaki said Araki must be sure to look up Noguchi in New York, and here is Araki living with Noguchi, and certainly Noguchi is queer. Araki does not see him the way Miyabara saw him, and maybe Miyabara is right, and maybe not, Miyabara's eyes are a little more on the level maybe, while his, Araki's have to look up. Not that he does not catch sight of the teacher mornings hurrying to the Institute looking green, but he does not let his mind wander over the teacher's affairs. He calls Noguchi sensei, which means teacher. The teacher is a great scientist and his life is his own.

The teacher is especially queer about money, has the hardest time laying aside even the smallest sums, spends everything right away he gets it, naturally then has to borrow from Araki, not much at a time, nevertheless it adds up finally to $2000. Not that Araki lets his mind wander much over the $2000 either. Araki can earn money when he needs to. He is an excellent porcelain worker and has a strong body and is young and can keep going day and night, so when he complains to Noguchi it is not the debt he is thinking of. Noguchi does not owe that money really because he has given more than that amount in good advice. But what of Noguchi's character? Is it good for Noguchi not to pay what he owes? Araki asks Noguchi that. Noguchi grumbles but says Araki is right. "You come each time when I get my money. But if you do not come at the exact right time, that is your lookout."

Sundays Noguchi takes Araki to dinner and after dinner the two go for a walk. Noguchi is a different man on Sundays. Other days he is cranky. He is not so cranky as when Araki first came. He has changed, but still he is cranky, often says that he is not satisfied with his life, which is surely odd for a great scientist like Noguchi. Sometimes he says he is not happy at the

166

Institute, but seems afraid to say that. Nights, those nights when he does stay at the flat, it is much as it was when Miyabara was there. Noguchi smokes and writes or if he is reading never once lifts his eyes from his book. He uses every minute. He never knows what is going on around him, or what Araki is saying. Araki does the cooking just as Miyabara did. Sometimes it is necessary to ask Noguchi to watch the boiling rice. Araki does not like to, but Noguchi is always willing, brings his chair into the kitchen, puts the chair in front of the gas-range and props up his feet, and continues to read. Suddenly he turns to Araki. What is the smell? He seems never able to grasp that the smell could come from the burning of the rice that he is watching. Araki snatches the cover off the boiler. Noguchi looks in. He shakes his head. "Yes, it's gone. We go out to eat." He always uses the same words, and both get their hats, leave the kitchen as it is, go always to the same Japanese restaurant, a cheap place. As soon as the waiter sees who is coming he begins to serve, never asks Noguchi what he wants because Noguchi always wants the same thing. Sometimes Noguchi does not say one word, not even in the beginning for politeness, right away opens his book, puts it next his plate, and Araki does not disturb him. Yet Araki cannot help noticing how Noguchi eats, because that is peculiar. He pokes his fork toward his plate, has no idea what he is poking at, but whatever is at the end of the fork he puts into his mouth. And when he is using chopsticks

167

it is remarkable—to carry rice with chopsticks from a bowl that you do not see.

Ever so often there is one night when Noguchi is sociable, asks several Japanese to the flat, talks and laughs and helps prepare the dinner. Maybe he will tell over again about the first time he prepared chicken soup, how he gave instruction to stick the whole chicken into the boiling water. It was back in the Philadelphia time. "We ate a good soup." That is what Yatsu said. "But soon we found that the chicken still had viscera in it. That was a great joke. And very likely the neglect of taking out entrails was the cause that the soup tasted so fine." Noguchi always laughs loud as if he were telling the story for the first time. Of late he laughs more anyway. He is not nearly so cranky. He also puts a little perfume on himself—lilac. And he has silk handkerchiefs, sometimes forgets they are silk and wipes his pen on them. On some nights too he takes Araki with him to the Institute. He is working at a new problem. He has been at that problem a good many months now—syphilis.

[XXXIV]

*A Man Who Knows Something About It Is Likely to be
Turned to as a Person of Worth*

The first infection of the monkey with syphilis by
Metchnikoff and Roux, followed two years later by
Schaudinn's discovery of the spirochete, followed the
next year, 1906, by the Wassermann test, all that has
put something into the air. Men in the streets speak of
a positive Wassermann, and more scientific words have
been poured over this one test than over all previous
discoveries in immunity put together.

Before now the diagnosis of syphilis was made on
the story of the patient and on his symptoms. But
syphilis is often hereditary and the patient has no story,
or the patient wishes to conceal the story, or there are
no symptoms, or the patient is thought cured. The
doctor does not know whether to begin treating, or to
keep on treating, or to stop treating. All this cannot be
decided with the Wassermann either, and has always
been decided pretty well anyway, yet there can be no
doubt that the diagnosis of syphilis will henceforth be
more certain than before. And here in this Wasser-

mann Noguchi sees his chance. He can get away now from the heaviness of these last heavy years, can get away from venoms, can bring his work to human life, a stimulus that he felt for a few months once before, that time in China, and not really since. And the reason of the chance is that the Wassermann test is serology. That serology at which he has spent the best of the last seven years has suddenly come to the fore. What he is doing is trying to modify this Wassermann test. Everywhere there are efforts to make the test more sensitive and accurate and simple, and whoever can is taking a hand, as always when a discovery is the kind that gets the public eye. At least Noguchi may feel that if anyone has the right to make profit out of the Wassermann he has, for the test involves that very dissolving of corpuscles that he has studied on and off ever since that rainy night when he took the wet letter to the house on Walnut Street.

This turn to syphilis is what has made Noguchi a different man of late. Noguchi has always worked but now works like mad, reveals how capable he is not only of intensity but of patience too. Araki calls him a twenty-four hour man. He needs scarce any sleep and when he does sleep it is like the dead. Sometimes he is so tired that coming from the cool outer air into the warm room, suddenly exhausted, he drops limply back into his chair, half an hour later lifts his head, goes on with the page where he left off, and this is night after night, week after week, then whole months pass.

He is finding things too. He looks on the original

Wassermann as a rough test that can be made exact and logical. He sometimes gets very excited, speaks of a time when all substances used in the Wassermann will be painstakingly prepared in one central laboratory and from there distributed throughout the country. The diagnosis of syphilis will be absolute. His writings on the subject begin to pour forth. *Some critical considerations on the serum diagnosis of syphilis. The fate of the so-called syphilitic anti-body. The relation of protein, lipoids, and salts to the Wassermann. A natural and simple system of serodiagnosis of syphilis.* And so on one after another, and these are papers will be read. This is not as with *On the influence of the reaction and of desiccation upon opsonins.* Every doctor everywhere wants to know about syphilis. This is a science puts money into pockets, lures endowments from the rich, builds buildings, is visible and comprehensible, and is sure to bring the attention of the newspapers both to Noguchi and his Institute. Men from all parts of the country visit Noguchi's laboratory. He is a great man to more people than Araki, people possibly scientifically naive, but numbers of them, and numbers count. Noguchi is coming in touch with organized medicine, is invited to societies to read papers, is beginning that teaching of serology to the American physician which may one day prove his most lasting work in this field. It seems to have come all overnight. The sudden interest in him is like his splitting bamboo and shows once more how working in syphilis, even without important discovery, magnifies the size of a man.

Two of his discoveries stand out. In the original Wassermann the corpuscles used are sheep's corpuscles. Noguchi now replaces the sheep's corpuscles with human corpuscles, works out the test on that basis, an anti-human as against an anti-sheep system, and believes his test more logical and more sensitive.

His second discovery has nothing to do with the Wassermann. It is an independent test for detecting syphilis of the brain and spinal cord. He has repeatedly of late had to visit the hospitals of the insane, has talked to neurologists, has seen some of the terrible consequences when syphilis attacks the nervous system. Besides the membranes which wrap the brain and spinal cord there is a fluid called the cerebro-spinal fluid serving still further to pad these delicate structures from the bone around. This fluid is watery like the fluid of the eye and contains small quantities of protein. In disease this protein is increased, and what Noguchi now finds is which protein is increased and a simple test for detecting that increase. It is a comparatively easy matter to push the long needle of a syringe into a patient's back till it enters the spinal canal, draw out a little of the spinal fluid and test it for the quantity of protein. The test is called the Noguchi butyric acid reaction. On March 29th he writes Chiwaki. This is now 1909.

"During the last year I made one discovery, a method of diagnosing tabes dorsalis. . . . Between last winter and early part of this year I have discovered a second method of diagnosis much praised in America,

172

Germany, Italy, even in a South American corner. Especially the head of the Pasteur Institute has translated my work and introduced it to the French medical world. At present time three or four men every day are sent from different universities and hospitals to learn my method and over ten letters in the mail. The other day I was invited by the State Hospital for the Insane where I gave lectures for a week. I will send four articles about these things. Please read laughingly, then send to the Department of Education." (That is, he still is thinking of the Japanese hakushi degree.) "Snake venom book upon which for several years I have worked distressingly and hard is finally coming out as a big volume in June. I have already finished proof reading. Also pass to Department of Education if chance. At present preparing to publish book on diagnosis of syphilis. I will send. During June there will be a meeting of the American Medical Association at Atlantic City and I will read three papers."

A few years ago scarce anyone knew what a serologist was, and now Doctor David Kaliski, Noguchi's friend, is organizing a Serological Society of New York, wants Noguchi as its first president. *President Noguchi*. Noguchi smiles and bows and declines.

The book on the diagnosis of syphilis amasses with great speed. This is not as with that on venoms. This will not be put off seven years. Noguchi has no secretary, writes the manuscript long-hand, writes at night. Araki cooks the supper. The writing begins between eleven and twelve and leaves off toward six in the morning. "You have to do it while it's in you." He lights cigar after cigar. Except during eating Araki keeps off in one of the four empty rooms. Noguchi is in a bristling state. "To-night I finish another chapter." A chapter a night, drafts the whole in two weeks, and it comes out accordingly, but better a good deal than that first draft of the venom book. At the making of charts and tables and the drawing of apparatus, at all that he is very good. The manuscript he gives to Doctor Lewis who rewrites it and gives it to Doctor Kaliski who rewrites it again, puts it into the English of that doctor up the side street whom it is to serve, then returns it to Noguchi, all a little as George Moore and Lady Gregory and Yeats did their Irish drama. Noguchi is in Boston when the galley-proof reaches him, sends it to Kaliski, wants Kaliski's help, at the same time wants the manuscript to look as if it were all his own, would like even that some of his Japanese-English be left.

"I have a few alterations made in order to convey my thoughts more completely. The sentences may have lost the original smoothness and eloquency through my changes, but this I was hoping then to have you straighten up in proof reading. . . . There are many words of description or detailed description, etc., in the original. I substituted them with certain other words or sentences meaning the same thing."

But the Japanese-English goes, Doctor Kaliski finally typewriting the whole manuscript with his own hands.

The Spirochete of Syphilis

Meanwhile the cause of syphilis is found and not found. Sch udinn found Spirochaeta pallida, and whoever has looked has seen what Schaudinn saw, but no one yet has been able to cultivate the organism by itself, to grow it unmixed with other organisms, and until someone does, grows it in what is called pure culture and with that pure culture produces syphilis in an animal, it may justly be asked whether after all some other organism, some organism carried along with Spirochaeta pallida, some still unknown, still unseen, even unseeable organism is not the true cause. No one much doubts Spirochaeta pallida, but a doubt remains. And indeed from one part of the world and another there have been reports of such a pure culture, each time false. Certain spirochetes have indeed been grown, spirochetes that under the microscope might easily be confused with Spirochaeta pallida, and with impure cultures animals have been given syphilis, but that only leaves the problem where it was. Again Noguchi sees the chance, and again has begun work.

The first technical difficulty is where to get his syphilitic material. He might always go to some syphilitic human being, but it would be less bothersome to have a syphilitic animal, a rabbit, for instance. If the testicle of a rabbit is inoculated, three or four weeks later there are enormous numbers of spirochetes, and the infection may be kept going by passing it from rabbit to rabbit. The testicle will of course at the same time have other bacteria, be contaminated from the bacteriologist's point of view, but one real advantage of the testicle is that there is a gradual purification of the spirochete from those other bacteria. The testicle does part of the work that the bacteriologist would otherwise have to do. So the testicle is the reservoir Noguchi uses. "A man must make his foundation before he is forty." That is what he says nights when he comes home to Araki. He says he has something bigger than he ever had, perhaps even a great problem. He is not at all the man he was.

The second technical difficulty is the medium. The medium is some food or mixture of foods upon which an organism will live and multiply. He experiments with many such foods. He tries the plasma of rabbit blood and the plasma of horse blood. He tries serum. Serum he finds inconstant. Organisms will grow on one serum and not on another. He tries serum water, which is serum with three times its volume of water, and that he finds more constant. Then one day talking over his difficulties with Doctor Theobald Smith the latter suggests that he add to the serum water a bit of fresh animal tissue. Such tissue keeps alive for some time after it is removed from the animal, for some time breathes, and in the breathing uses up the little oxygen that is dissolved in the medium, and this may be imperative for there are bacteria that cannot survive if there is present in the medium even that small amount of dissolved air. The fresh tissue is of course also a food. Noguchi tries several such. Liver he cannot use because liver itself often contains bacteria that contaminate the medium, also because there is sugar in liver, and sugar turns to acid, and some bacteria die in acid. The tissues he finally settles on are kidney and testicle.

He has then the source of his syphilitic material and the medium. He takes now tall test tubes, taller than bacteriologists commonly use, fills them four-fifths with serum water and drops into each a bit of the fresh tissue. The tubes were sterile before he began, the serum water is sterile, and the fresh tissue is sterile, nevertheless he incubates the tubes for two or three days to be sure they are sterile. If nothing grows in that time they are sterile, and he may go on.

He prepares hundreds of such tubes. He inoculates hundreds with the syphilitic material from the rabbit's testicle, hundreds where the ordinary worker inoculates tens. These tubes he places in a jar of such device as to exclude all air, then puts tubes and jar into the incubator. And such tubes containing the serum water and the fresh tissue and covered with paraffin oil and placed in this jar of his own contriving constitute the Noguchi method, and nothing else does, he insists.

It is a method like most methods made of many men's methods, but the total is his own. Then every day he takes jar and tubes from the incubator to see if anything has grown in the tubes. He examines every tube every day. This rule is strict also for anyone who works with him. No matter how the tubes accumulate, and accumulate they must if every day he is adding new tubes and still examining the old, and no matter how weary he is, or what the hour, every tube every day, for the likelihood is that if the spirochete will grow at all that growth will occur but rarely in any of all tubes inoculated, perhaps in one. And if that one should be overlooked?

For not much can be calculated here. Too little is known of the nature of organisms. Too little is known of the amount of oxygen they need. Too little is known of the correct composition of their food. Or of how acid or how alkali that food must be. It is simply a matter of modifying, modifying, modifying, of persisting, of understanding enough about oneself to keep one's head alert despite the monotony of the business. One must not only have tubes enough and patience enough and ingenuity enough but there must be a nervous vitality behind it all, and if there is, and if one have the tubes and the patience, and possibly also something else, then the spirochete of syphilis will grow in one tube in thousands as amidst trembling and enthusiasm he now finds that it does.

"It must be emphasized that to obtain these six cultures almost innumerable series of unsuccessful cul-

178

tivations were carried out with each strain before one suddenly started to grow for the first time."

That is the quiet way he states it in the published article. But when he gets home to Araki he laughs, shouts, dances round the room. What a changed man, Araki keeps thinking.

Up to now Noguchi has not been able to grow the spirochete on a solid medium and the fluid medium is always contaminated, spirochetes in it, but other bacteria too. He tries filtering this fluid medium. Filtering is in general use for separating the so-called filterable viruses from bacteria. The spirochete is of course a bacterium, visible, very long though it may be very thin, and what he now finds is that while it will not pass through a filter quickly it will *grow through* in about three days, weaves its way very probably in and out the pores of the stone. And those spirochetes that do weave their way through are correct in form, remain motile for weeks, and have the power of starting syphilis in the testicle of the rabbit. The first strain he cultivates in October 1910, the second in March 1911.

The task is done, "I am the first to cultivate the spirochete of syphilis." What was begun by Schaudinn is completed by Noguchi and the end compares with the beginning. He too will have the eyes of the whole bacteriological world. His Institute too. His serology already brought those eyes. Even brick buildings glow when vitalized thus from within. For syphilis is like cancer, the worried eyes of millions follow every fluctuation in our knowledge of it. Someone has the grace now to say that Noguchi's fame is out of all proportion to his achievement. Had he for instance got a similar pure culture of a cattle disease the report would scarce have caused bacteriologists to cut the pages of their journals. But the point is exactly that he did not culture the spirochete of a cattle disease. The point is that it was the spirochete of syphilis, that it was something big in human life that exalted him till he was able to do what others could not. Furthermore, he turned to this problem deliberately. It is one thing to make a discovery in the course of one's daily laboratory life, stumble on it, have it pop up in front of one, and another to choose to settle a certain question and settle it, a question over which many in the world are at the same moment tense, to make that very tension count, to lean on it, to lean on life. A colleague says he is all ambition. Easy to say. And at any rate his fame is certain. Here is a discovery of which the newspapers will know. He is so afraid of the newspapers, grew pale that day when his name was read aloud. Perhaps he will get used to them now. The Japanese bacteriologist at the head of 66th Street will be known not only to the scientists of New York but to scientists pretty well everywhere. Something has come into his gait. A few see it and speak of it.

He sees something else. He sees as never before how he must work. He wants to, but he also must. Weak to the weak so soon as anyone threatens to get strong. That is what he speaks of in the flat on East 65th Street, and he works in these months prodigiously.

"His intenseness no American can approach." Thus proudly one of his compatriots. And an American, one of the world's greatest bacteriologists, says the same differently. "No occidental I think could do it. He works twenty-four hours on end. It is something in their philosophy, I suppose."

If he could but make the pure culture count in the treatment of syphilis. If he could but cure syphilis. Metchnikoff and Roux already had the hope of developing some sort of vaccine or serum. The discovery of the spirochete brought the hope nearer, but still no one was able to obtain the pure culture with which to attempt the development of such a vaccine or serum. Now Noguchi has the pure culture, but with a chronic disease like syphilis the chances are none too good, and he makes no headway. In another direction he does make headway. It has been found for tuberculosis that if a small amount of the broth in which the tubercle bacillus is grown is injected into a man sick with the disease his symptoms flare up. His temperature rises. And so one has a test for hidden tuberculosis. A number of bacteriologists have sought to develop a similar test for syphilis but never succeeded because they had not the spirochete in pure form. Noguchi has it and quickly evolves a product, calls it luetin, the other being called tuberculin. He tries it on syphilitic and healthy rabbits then on syphilitic and healthy men, and in his hands and with his product the results seem clear-cut. In the healthy rabbits and the healthy men there is little or no reaction on the skin where the injection is made. In the forms of syphilis called primary and secondary the reaction is infrequent or mild. But in tertiary and hereditary syphilis the reaction is severe. He is in a beautiful heightened state, runs on for months that way. He fancies he has found something will supplement the Wassermann, possibly go further, the name of Hideyo Noguchi being identified not only with the cause of syphilis but with the diagnosis and perhaps one day with the cure. "In investigation the same problems can be attacked by any other worker therefore one must finish as soon as one can." That is what he says nights to Araki, and he drives in these months as if he thought the other worker just outside the door.

To his friend Thorwald Madsen he writes freely touching all these great matters.

"I beg you to pardon me for not having answered your very kind letter of March 27 which reached me in due time. I had been away from the Institute during the latter part of April and was overwhelmed with my work and correspondence accumulated during my absence." (A sentence like that makes him feel almost a stranger, he has gone out so into the world.) "And I did not want to answer you without sending you at the same time the luetin which was to be tested out before sending away. This has been done now and I am forwarding you enough material to test, at least, five or six hundred cases. . . . I find that to obtain a good growth of the pallida in fluid media to be much more difficult and slow than in solid media. However, it is possible and I will do it." (Nothing shall resist him now.) "I read somewhere that Dr. Boas had succeeded in cultivating the pallida in Schereschewsky's gelatinized horse serum. I cannot understand why I never could get any strain by that method." (What he means is that he does not believe that Dr. Boas got any strain either.) "Even my pure cultures (altogether 12 now) do not grow in that medium." (Neither did Dr. Boas'.) "Again I am firmly convinced that the pallida never produces any offensive odor in culture and I often wonder why the cultures obtained by certain Germans produce the odor." (Certain Germans think they are dealing with pallida and are not.) "I have now several varieties of spirochaetes which resemble the pallida in morphology and produce odor. Could that be possible that their strains were some of these varieties?" (Exceedingly possible. There is not even the slightest doubt in the world, or in Noguchi's mind.)

He is working now to the exclusion of all else. No, not quite. Lately he has informed Araki that they can no longer live together in the flat. He Hideyo Noguchi is going to be married, a lady by the name of Dardis, met her a single time just after his return from Copenhagen, then did not meet her again for years, then ran into her in the street, had a rose in his hand, held it up to her, the rose that keeps him company when he studies (that is what he told her). He calls the lady Maizie. It is to be a double marriage, his friend Jacques Grünberg to marry at the same time a lady by the name of Myrtle. But Araki must say nothing. No one must know. Especially no one at the Institute. "They might not be so quick to give full membership if he had a wife and they had to figure on her pension for the future too." He warns also another Japanese, writes him a note, does not want the news out among the Japanese of New York. Maizie is an American.

It is a bright April day, the 10th, a Monday, out of the state, over in Jersey City, where they marry, the four. There is sunshine and wind. Noguchi has the papers. He is so gay.

[XXXVI]

1 Manhattan

Maizie and Myrtle have begun immediately looking at apartments and have found what they like, a fifth floor, 1 Manhattan, the roof just above, the rent thirty-two a month. Thirty-two seems a fortune to Myrtle and Jacques who are having to live in one room downtown. Hidey's salary is big. Myrtle and Jacques call him Hidey, just as Maizie does, because he wants it, says he will not have them calling him Doctor or Professor or anything like that.

On moving day Myrtle brings the sandwiches. The furniture is modern American, not a great lot of it, but enough, a round durable dining-room table. There will also after a while be this or that, so utterly different, out of the east. Myrtle and Maizie are standing in the front room when Maizie happens to lift her head, happens to look through the half-open door across a hall and through another half-open door into someone else's apartment, and there, in stocking feet, a gentleman, a Japanese gentleman—remarkable there should be two on the same floor. That gentleman's name is

185

Hori, Ichiro Hori. Maizie will tell Hidey as soon as Hidey gets home.

Regular married life begins. Maizie sees to it that Hidey pays more attention to his clothes. He must not wear his best in the laboratory and he must be careful what he buys, not overlong shoes that turn up in front and not a too big hat. It is now his Japanese friends recall how slovenly he used to be. Of course that was partly their idea of clothes, and Hidey never did wear a gold chain across his waistcoat as Watanabe did, but always kept a recklessness about him, even back there in Pennsylvania when he was not yet quite at home in coats, knew almost from the start that a Japanese if he is too spick and span only calls attention to a kind of clothes that he has to wear and cannot quite. Maizie tells him too that from now on he must not use perfume—a man can't, and especially not lilac.

Plain that there is to be very little leisure in this married life. Hidey is always at that Institute. How he loves that place. And he has not enough with working there but must bring it home with him, is filling the kitchen. That kitchen is a sight. He takes pictures of germs and develops the pictures and slops water over everything. Maizie complains. He answers that she must come and see. "Oh, it's lovely, Maizie, it's lovely." He shows her the picture of a germ.

Sundays he stays at the Institute till 1 o'clock, then Maizie had better call him over phone or he may lose track of the time. Evenings it is usually 7 o'clock. He enters always the same way, rushes a little. "Where are you? Where are you?" He likes to be in the kitchen and cook around a bit. Maizie is frying a steak and what does the fool do but crack an egg and plump it all over the top of the steak. He is quick as lightning. Hori comes from his flat, likes to be in the kitchen too, and once both together show Maizie how to make sukiyaki, grease the bottom of the pan, dump in the mushrooms all to one side, and the onions, and the tofu, and the celery, and the thin slices of beef, and always pouring over shoyu—with sugar! Sugar with onions and beef! And everything stewed together. Still the taste is good, and Hidey says sukiyaki is also good for the health, all those different kinds of foodstuffs in it.

When it comes to the actual eating, Hidey likes that over quick. To begin with Maizie has always to be pushing the microscope and papers off to one end of the table so as to be able to lay the cloth half-way, and before the meal is over he is slipping round to his microscope, sharpens a pencil and spreads his yellow note paper around, lights a cigar. Presently Maizie has the table cleared and the dishes washed and is back in the dining-room. She would rather Hidey were at his microscope than writing. If he is writing and she talks, suddenly he will throw down his pencil. "I can't write." And then she has to be still. But if he is at the microscope she has got into the habit of reading to him. He looks into the microscope. She reads. Sometimes it gets very late and he listens and listens, and certainly it is astonishing how he will remember everything that happens in those old tales. Only rarely do the two leave the house, sometimes to the opera, but not often. In the beginning Hidey found it hard to make much of occidental music, but lately he knows a melody when he has heard it before. Sometimes they go to the Grünbergs. And Christmas dinner Hidey goes alone to the Flexners, then in the evening comes home and eats a second dinner, says it would be hard to lead a double life. What that means is that he is still keeping his marriage a secret. Araki knows, of course, and Hori, and of course Myrtle and Jacques.

Myrtle and Jacques drop in evenings, early usually. If there is some supper left they help finish it off. Then perhaps Hidey and Jacques settle to a game of chess. Hidey plays Japanese chess better than American, learned it lately from Hori, does not play either game well yet. Some nights he may play very concentratedly, may not even hear what the women in the next room are saying, but other nights walks around while Jacques is making up his mind, does some little thing for the women, picks up something, looks at something, perhaps lights another cigar, the place reeking of tobacco and by the end of the evening his stubs lying all about. If the game languishes the two men talk, often of death. Jacques leads the talk that way. "Life go on? Perhaps, a spark out there. Perhaps not." Hidey may say something like that. Jacques is a musician, talented, moody often. There may be a drink or two. Hidey likes Sparkling Burgundy. What would they say at the Institute, or what would Kobayashi say, if it were known that at the Noguchi's they could afford Sparkling Burgundy? The truth is Hidey cannot stand much alcohol, is likely to say things he regrets, or the alcohol may make him sad and he may weep, or it may make him gay and he may sing. Sometimes when he comes back from somewhere he will say that he wishes he could drink like those Americans. One night Maizie hears him singing long after she has gone to bed, wonders about that, finally decides she will get up and see, but he is only working, the eternal tea-pot in front of him. It is unbelievable how much tea that man can drink, pot after pot, would never stop if someone kept bringing it. And water he will not drink at all. Soon he is singing louder. Maizie has gone to bed again but decides to get up a second time. He is so graceful in his movements, such an actor. Sometimes he mimics his colleagues, one especially, works so neat, so accurate, so fine, if he had to paint a wall would do it with a camel's hair brush. Another walks so daintily. Hidey will take his cane and show how, and Maizie cannot help laughing. But it is easy to see that he is hiding something. Maizie looks around, finds it, a bottle of sherry next his feet. She empties the bottle into the sink and he will be grateful, to-morrow. One night he meets a German who lives in the neighborhood, and Hidey likes so to talk German, and the German has good beer, and Hidey comes home without his watch and pen, only has left his six dollars. He is such a child often. She sees an old drunkard cheating him. She warns him. "A man with a lot of children cannot cheat. How bad-minded you are." That is what he says.

This is all a happy time. Presently Myrtle and Jacques go off to Europe for a year, and really only Hori is left because no one knows of the marriage yet. Many things happen. There is some extra money, a check for royalty for the book on syphilis, money that perhaps ought to go to the grocer, but they have "tick" at the grocer, and why should they save? They will do their saving later on. Both feel the same about that. So Maizie has the whole twenty dollars in her purse, passes a shop, sees a pup in the window, likes the pup, buys it —four dollars. Then she remembers that Hidey likes birds more than pups and thinks how nice it would be for him to have an animal of his own, so buys a nightingale. And even that is not enough. She thinks how nice it would be for him to have finches too, and buys a pair of them, and a cage for the nightingale and a cage for the finches. The twenty are as gone as if they had been sent to the grocer. But Hidey will be pleased. He loves birds. He also loves cats, but not dogs so much, anyway not big dogs. The nightingale dies next day, something about the feeding that neither of them understands, and the finches escape from their cage, no one seems to know how. The cages are empty, then one night Hidey brings home a bird that someone at the Zoo gave him, a wild tropical thing with strange eyes. Just that day Maizie read something of Ella Wheeler Wilcox about caging a wild thing, so when Hidey is away she slips over to the cage and lets the wild thing out into the free city air.

Sometimes Hori stays after supper and the two

play chess. Or Hidey goes over to Hori's. Often Mit-suboshi is at Hori's and if Noguchi does not play with Hori he plays with Mitsuboshi. There may be other Japanese at Hori's, many of them, and late at night when they go down the stairs they talk loud in Jap-anese, and all the way from the fifth floor to the first floor, sometimes stand about on each step and call back to someone on the landing above. What must the peo-ple on the other four floors think? Maizie complains to Hidey and he tells the Japanese clear.

On chess nights Hori and Noguchi begin about 9 o'clock. Noguchi plays a crazy way, has none of the patience of a so-called good game, believes in mass, not two games an evening but forty-two. If he plays forty-two he may win twenty-two and that way have the vic-tory. Victory is very important. "Move, move, move." He is always pushing his partner and when his own turn comes moves instantly, his head darting across the table after the chessman. Early in the evening Hori often wins. Hori explains this by saying that Noguchi has not yet had time enough to get to be a good player and that no one can hope to play as fast as he plays, this perpetual activity, and so many hours on end. Noguchi never will stop if he is behind in games won. He pretends not to care, yet he will glance half-secretly into the note-book where he is jotting down the score. Hori gets very tired. Noguchi literally physically wears him down. Then, abruptly, he will rise, will take out a cigar, run it back and forth under his nose, likes the smell of it, lights it, walks back and forth in the room and says that he is extremely sorry that he has had to beat Hori again. He is very awake now and in the highest good humor. If he has been playing in his own apartment Maizie has perhaps called him several times from the other room, has been wanting him to go to bed, has been hearing the continuous tap-tap-tap of the Japanese chess, the tap-tap-tap dropping way down each time she has called and then gradually rising again. But if the two have been playing at Hori's, Noguchi will usually say that he still has something to do and go back to his own apartment. Maizie can tell from the way he puts his key into the door that he has won. And if she could not tell from his key she could surely tell from his step in the hall. But she asks him nevertheless. "Yes, I beat the hell out of them." She does not ask him if he comes in quietly and slow. He says that he must win, that he must beat his man, but that he wants fight in his victim. Hori says that if Noguchi has won he may not come to play for as much as two weeks, but if he loses he comes the next night, continues coming night after night till he wins, at the same time says he does not particularly care for chess, at the same time goes to the brother of a doctor friend who studied chess in Germany and practises. Hori is one who understands Noguchi a little, has something real in common with him. Noguchi may get out of patience with him. Something may happen to hurt or irritate one or the other and they may not see each other for weeks, yet something sensitive remains. Hori is an artist by profession, and by instinct, has a short broad body,

192

very living eyes, wears his derby to one side, carries a cane, and when on Saturday nights he walks against the lights of Broadway is as like Broadway as ever anything foreign-born. He knows Tagore, Ibanez, reads Oscar Wilde and the Bible, loves Isadora Duncan, or perhaps not, Isadora having the habit of taking hold of the lapel of his coat, picking at it, saying: "Why don't you wear your kimono?" Very disturbing that to one who wants to be like Broadway, to a painter who wants to paint the occidental scene, says he has no feeling for the Japanese scene, finds it beautiful but cold. Hiroshige is the master of the Japanese. But, no, there is no romance in the Japanese scene.

When Noguchi has returned to his own apartment he carries the microscope over to the dining-room table. He goes to the kitchen, gets a few things from there, takes a few things into there. He has some test tubes in a rack in the oven, just the littlest flame underneath. He takes out one tube, holds it to the light, looks at it a long time. He starts still another cigar. Maizie gets out of bed again. He asks Maizie to look at the tube too. They sit down for a time at the kitchen table. She gets a pot of tea. That kitchen is full of things. This house is more and more a workshop. Maizie looks at him—at times he is such a happy little fellow.

[XXXVII]

Pure Cultures

The pure culture of the spirochete of syphilis he has. That was the discovery. That gave him the method. It is almost easy now to grow other spirochetes, and he grows them one after another. There are a number live in the human mouth. He grows them. He grows a strain of the spirochete of syphilis that will give syphilis to a monkey, interesting because Metchnikoff and Roux showed the monkey subject to syphilis somewhat as man is. He grows Spirochaeta refringens, the spirochete that Schaudinn found so often to be the companion of Spirochaeta pallida. He grows a spirochete that lives round the teeth of persons with pyorrhea. He grows a spirochete that produces mucous. He grows several that produce odors. He grows Spirochaeta novyi, kochi, recurrentis, duttoni, the last the spirochetes of European and African relapsing fevers, one of them that very spirochete he saw that first day at Watanabe's. He grows Treponema calligyrum, also a spirochete. Spirochete after spirochete. A right method is often a more cutting tool than a right idea. It is nothing to pile up a bibliography now. The danger, of course, is that it will go with him as with so many who in their youth discover a right method, then apply the method over and over, try it on everything, repeat and repeat their first triumph, think they consolidate their victory, actually sleep on it, henceforth make no more true discoveries, have the satisfaction of growing powerful where they might have had the satisfaction of being great. Perhaps, though, he is working so fast, so pas·sionately, so happily at last, that he may yet escape.

His method of course is slowly changing, slowly changing, each spirochete differing slightly from the one before, each cultivation differing slightly, small but innumerable changes, the removing from the medium of some bit of this constituent, the putting into it of some bit of that, trifling changes but made so many times that when now he makes a new one he often hardly knows exactly why or even how. It would take almost another person, an accurate other observer to stand by and note just what he does, and men in other parts of the country who read his papers and try to do over again what he has done think sometimes he is keeping something back, is not telling quite all, to the end, for instance, of adding as many pure cultures as possible to his list before too many men have had the chance to come into the field. And altogether imaginable. But it is not true. He is telling all he knows, some secrets no doubt sunk into the very muscles of his hands, as into the muscles of every exquisite worker's hands. "Funny, I show them what I do, show them step for step, even hold their hands while they in-noculate the tubes. Same tubes, same medium, same way of inoculating, then, it sounds crazy, my tubes grow and theirs do not. I don't understand."

He says a thing like that, looks at you from under, something almost apish in his face. Is he acting again? Is he trying to create a mystery? Some honest per-plexity there must be because the person he is saying this of is annoying him, delaying his work in these bounding weeks. But actor too. He does not fool Maizie. He does not fool his friends, at least no more than he fools himself. Sometimes he even makes de-liberate use of that awkward English about which he is so sensitive, lets the awkwardness heighten an effect, lets a wrong idiom go for a charm, then again is strangely pained by a blunder, a wrong use of shall and will, those two that he can somehow never get straight.

The pure culturing of the spirochetes goes on. He will make himself master of the whole field of spiro-chetes. It is inevitable that that should become a self-conscious intention now. He has had the most intimate experiences with these spiral lives, has watched them hour after hour, night after night has sat there at the dining-room table, Maizie reading Anna Karenina, the eternal pot of tea before him, the eternal yellow paper, making drawings of the various forms, then drawings of the various forms as they vary when he varies the conditions of their lives, those lives that the experts worry their heads whether to place among plants in the class of bacteria or among the lowest forms of

196

animals. "I live so much with the infinitely small that I do not always know how to live with men." Possibly he looks from under as he says that too.

He has turned again in spite of all work to the old problem of trachoma. Evenings he goes past Doctor Cohen's office and Doctor Cohen gives him a few slides with smears that he got that day from sore eyes at Ellis Island, Noguchi putting the slides carefully into his inside pocket, then taking out his notebook and telling Doctor Cohen what kinds of bacteria were on the slides of yesterday. Noguchi was in a bad state of head when he laid aside trachoma in 1906, but is in a confident state now. "He never begins maybe-I-can-maybe-I-can't." There have been some additions to the knowledge of trachoma since 1906. Certain minute bodies have been found in the diseased eyes. Many bacteriologists regard these as the cause, and for the present Noguchi also leans that way. What he does is pure culture them. He also cultures the rabies bodies, very like the trachoma bodies, found not in the sore eyes, of course, but in the brains of the mad dogs. And one more labor—a search for the cause of poliomyelitis or infantile paralysis that to everyone's dread has sprung up again in epidemic proportions.

"I am now working on Poliomyelitis and Rabies although my work on spirochetes is going on at the same time."

That is what he writes to Madsen. Everything is going at the same time. He is living as never before in his life. How incomprehensible he must be to those who

197

relax two hours at luncheon and go home at five so as to have their minds properly rested before beginning at eleven next morning. He wants to do everything with his very own hands. Seven weeks ago a monkey was inoculated with his culture of the spirochete of syphilis. To-night he is removing the organs from the dead animal, is trying to find in which organs the spirochetes elect to live and what the relative quantities in each. So he is grinding each separately in a mortar. Some of the tissues are sinewy and the grinding is slow work. Araki has come. Araki now and then visits the teacher nights in the laboratory. To Araki this grinding seems merely mechanical, so he suggests taking a hand. "Oh, no, thank you. I must do it alone. I can trust no one." Can trust no one even with the grinding. At least he has not learned the wisdom of the factory that accomplishes most by giving over to someone else whatever someone else can do.

[XXXVIII]

The Two-hundredth Slide

And now a new problem. This new one is again a big one. He is going to try to find the spirochete of syphilis in the brains of those who have died of general paralysis of the insane and in the spinal cords of those who have died of locomotor ataxia. He is going to try to prove those two diseases syphilis, those two common and terrible diseases. Both very likely are, but no one is able to prove it by finding the spirochete, and many distinguished workers have tried, and the fact that none of them can, even now when they know how the spirochete looks, has much encouraged those who have all along doubted that it is there. Noguchi has some hunch about all this. Hunch is the word used in laboratories. While making his pure cultures he noticed that sometimes the spirochete changed its form, seemed to roll up into a minute point-like body. Perhaps that is the form it takes in these diseased brains too. Perhaps that is what has balked the previous workers. Perhaps they were looking for spirals where there are none.

This time the technical problem is to collect the

brains of the dead paretics, sufferers with general paralysis, and to put those brains into solutions that will harden them, and when they have reached a certain hardness to cut them into sections, then section the sections and section the sections till these are no more than fine shavings, stain the shavings, mount them on slides and study the slides under the microscope. Here again there are innumerable chances of trifling variation and yet the many workers in many parts of the world who are trying to do this thing are following roughly the same plan. And he is not departing from this plan either, perhaps hardens the brains a little harder, but nothing fundamentally new. He has his hunch, of course.

Soon the laboratory is full of jars, brains in the different stages of hardening, sections all over the place. The gentleman from Pennsylvania who thought, once a disorderly worker always a disorderly worker, would feel he were a prophet could he look in here. Noguchi hates at any time to throw anything away. He thinks always he will want a second look then never gets round to it. The old rule applies too. Every brain once begun must be studied through. Every slide once stained must be examined. It makes no difference that every day there is a fresh increment of slides, and that the work can only gather as it advances, and that he must have before him the vision of this gathering, the sense of being perpetually driven, not by a human being as sometimes in the past but by his own rule. He looks bad. But he always looks bad. This person and that has warned him to take a rest, and he has promised that he will, will go on his vacation next week, or the week after, does not know the exact date yet, but they need not worry about him.

When he gets tired in the laboratory he takes a batch of sections home with him. Hori comes over. Hori also knows Noguchi needs a rest, but knows too that there is no use speaking of it. Maizie brings the pot of tea. The day was hot and the night is hotter. After a while Maizie leaves the room, and the two men take off their clothes and play chess in their B.V.D.'s. Shortly after midnight Hori returns to his own apartment, tells Noguchi to go to bed, and Noguchi says he will, just has a little that he still wants to do. Maizie also knows that he ought to go to bed and knows that one way to get him to go is to keep at him. He tells her that he will. "Maizie, just start the bath water for me." Maizie nods her head, has had that played on her before.

Out of doors not a sound. The nearest street cars are off on Columbus Avenue and they are infrequent and too far really to hear. It is cooler than it was. He brings the high piano stool, likes it because he can twist on it, also the microscope, also the batch of two hundred slides that he has stained for the day. He always stains them in batches of two hundred but must examine them one by one. He has been examining such a batch every night, sometimes in the laboratory sometimes at home, never has been able to find the spirochete. But the spirochete is there. Those who think the spirochete is not there are wrong. He has not the slightest doubt. So he looks confidently and carefully at each slide, moves each back and forth, then advances it a little, then moves it back and forth, and so on till every corner of every slide has been scrutinized. One after another. One after another. It is very good to do this kind of work at this hour of the night, the best hour of the twenty-four, nothing likely to escape one, as in such a monotonous business is always possible. His long experience with spirochetes is very helpful now, for in the brain there are many tortuous fibers and among these the eye might easily lose a spirochete. It is past 1 o'clock. He has examined the first hundred slides, has entered on the second hundred, presently has examined the hundred-and-fiftieth. The hundred-and-ninety-ninth. Nothing. Then he examines the two-hundredth, the last for the night, examines it carefully like the others, back and forth, back and forth, and they are there. And in the two-hundredth slide. Who would believe it? They are there in numbers. He calls Maizie. "I think I've got them." He lights a cigar. He is terribly excited. He looks again. "Yes, I've got them." There is no possibility of mistake. But his hunch was wrong. They are not the minute point-like bodies but the ordinary spirals. He looks back over the other slides of the batch, finds spirochetes in a number of them, and in the weeks that follow establishes firmly what he has found. He proves the spirochete in all the layers of these diseased brains. It has a way of wandering out into the substance of the tissues, does not as in

202

syphilis elsewhere keep near the blood vessels. Perhaps that is why the other workers failed. Perhaps they were looking too much in the usual places.

"I thought at first that my luck in finding was due to the modified technique, but now I am convinced that the regular Levaditi method gives a good result in many instances. I am improving the technique to obtain more uniform results."

But perhaps it is mostly that his eyes were better. Perhaps his patience was greater. Perhaps his genius —but he does not like the word. On the 13th of April he writes to Madsen.

"To-day I am sending you several slides from different cases of general paralysis. They all contain some pallida, although in some slides the number of the organisms is very small. I do not remember whether I told you already that I found the pallida in 48 cases of general paralysis (examined over 200 different cases) and in only one case out of 12 tabes dorsalis (locomotor ataxia). It is much harder to demonstrate it in tabes cases. I was to stain them repeatedly before I could make any use of the preparations for this purpose. As I have not any good preparation to spare at present I am not sending any to you. Later, if I get many beautiful specimens I will present some to you. . . ."

He has then clinched the cause of syphilis by pure culturing the spirochete, has shown that general paralysis of the insane is syphilis of the brain, has cultivated a horde of spirochetes that no one could before, has cultivated the trachoma bodies, has cultivated the rabies bodies, has even possibly discovered the cause of infantile paralysis. So his name runs round the world. The Versammlung deutscher Naturforscher und Aertze is held this year in Vienna. Noguchi is invited to address it. The Germans are inviting him. He thinks of the past and smiles.

XXXIX

And How Many Years Have You Studied Bacteriology

He reaches France September 10th, stays five days in Paris, then travels on to Vienna, registers there at the Hotel Imperial, leaves his luggage and wanders into the street. Kaichiro Manabe, also attending the Versammlung deutscher Naturforscher und Aertze, spies a fellow-countryman going at a little distance in front of the administration building. That same instant Noguchi spies Manabe, rushes toward him.

"Who are you?"

"I am Manabe."

"And what are you doing in Vienna?"

"Studying to be an internist."

"An internist? Why then are you not with Friedrich von Mueller in Munich? Do you not know Friedrich von Mueller is President of this Versammlung? When you are once studying, why not with the greatest?"

"But I have. My first semester was in Munich. Mueller is my oldest teacher in Europe."

"Ah, so. You have finished with Mueller then. You are a far-sighted fellow."

The two bow like orientals and shake hands like occidentals and together enter the administration building. Toward evening Manabe meets his former teacher, President of the Versammlung, and next morning before Noguchi is awake is knocking at his door. He has news for Noguchi. Friedrich von Mueller is wanting to call. Noguchi has no clothes on, nevertheless leaps out of bed, runs round the room, says he must, he must, he is so excited.

"Friedrich von Mueller wanting to call? You are sure? But no, no, Friedrich von Mueller cannot call on me. I must call on Friedrich von Mueller."

When Noguchi appears in the hall where he is to lecture the crowd gathers round him. He likes it. Everybody is, wanting to see him but he is so much shorter than these Germans that only the nearest can. The place is full of loud talk, the gentlemen all are in frocks, the crowd is so great that the excess is pressed into the corridors. This is a triumph. As Noguchi is moving through the crowd the distinguished His addresses Manabe. "By one glance at him I can tell he is a great man." Manabe asks how. "Do you not see his hair the way it stands on end?" Noguchi is holding tight to his manuscript. The manuscript is German. He knows German, reads it fluently, writes it with skill, pronounces it abominably. He realizes how abominably and has asked that his paper be read for him.

The Germans give their attention, and the attention goes not only to the paper but to the oriental gentleman, the small compact vivid individuality propped up on a stool to one side of the speaker. The oriental gentleman likes all this, is once more looking from under, not at any person now but at the ceiling. The charm of him, the excellence of these things he has done, and no grotesqueness of speech, everybody is enthusiastic.

Friedrich von Mueller has all this while had to be in another building attending another lecture, one by the great chemist Emil Fischer. The lecture is late and Friedrich von Mueller knowing that he cannot keep the appointment with Noguchi has sent word to Manabe. But Noguchi's lecture is also late. Noguchi could not have kept his appointment either. When Friedrich von Mueller hears this he hurries over to the hall and enters just at the close of Noguchi's demonstration but cannot make his way through the crowd. Someone notes the fact. Someone calls out.

"Herr Geheimrat Friedrich von Mueller is approaching."

Instantly there is a path and along it Friedrich von Mueller moves up to Noguchi who with the help of lantern slides is still at the business of ending his demonstration. He has the pure cultures of the various spirochetes, the sections of the brains of the paretics, the pure culture of the trachoma body, the pure culture of the rabies body, the organism that he thinks the cause of poliomyelitis, truly an extraordinary array for the demonstration of one man and more extraordinary when one realizes that it is the work of less than four years, certainly one of the most striking achievements ever brought from America across the sea. There is a lull. Manabe uses it to bring the two distinguished men together. They met several years ago at the Institute in New York, but this is different.

They speak to each other in German, the German of Friedrich von Mueller being the emphatic German of Munich that Noguchi has more difficulty in understanding than other German. He behaves however as if he understood perfectly, and surely it would be an awkward moment not to understand even very easily everything in the world. Yet presently he is frowning, looks as if he were irritated at what Friedrich von Mueller is saying, the slant of his head more pronounced than it was. Manabe sees what is happening. Manabe is nervous. Friedrich von Mueller continues oblivious. The truth is that Friedrich von Mueller a middle-aged and very distinguished gentleman is addressing this young Japanese in a most humble and friendly manner. But the head only slants more and more. Something is going to happen. Manabe knows he must intercede. He begs Friedrich von Mueller to be so good as to repeat in English what he just said. Friedrich von Mueller is a little astonished but does so and Noguchi's head gradually goes back to where it was. It even bends. Friedrich von Mueller in spite of his emphatic speech is merely asking that, when the Vienna meeting is over, Noguchi come to Munich to give his lectures and demonstrations there and learn in the bosom of the family how warmly German science feels toward him.

Friedrich von Mueller steps back. Others push in. Everybody wants to meet Noguchi. Everybody is appealing to Manabe for an introduction. Manabe by the coming of this fellow countryman as he humbly says has himself suddenly got to be a well-known man. Then the crowd draws toward a table where under a microscope Noguchi has the organism that he regards as the cause of poliomyelitis. Doctors, professors, docents, one after another quietly approach the microscope, quietly look in, and as they leave place their personal card in Noguchi's hand. Noguchi's hand is full of such cards. Only one young person of the Koch Laboratory in Berlin is not impressed and does not hold his mouth either, presumes to ask a question. The question is clearly not meant for a question but for a criticism half veiled. The quiet is immediately quieter. But the young man from the Koch Laboratory knows his worth, keeps on, the quiet soon definitely annoyed. Noguchi is flushed, the curl of his hair more marked, something in his eyes, and not a muscle of his face moving. At last he bursts out. He says something about the Koch Laboratory, something general and nasty, something about the way nobody in that establishment has ever been able to see any worth in anything he has done, then he turns on the young man.

"And you, how many years have you studied bacteriology?"

He says the words slowly and adds nothing. It is

very possible that he can think of nothing German to add. But it is better so. The young man of the Koch Laboratory is ready to spring on him. Noguchi is casually hunting among the cards in his hand, presently has the one he wants and as if the touch of it offended his sense of cleanliness tears it and flings the pieces into the air. Everybody is German or Japanese. Everybody is stirred. Nobody sees anything humorous in this. Several quickly step between the two men and that ends the episode. Manabe sweats. But he is in his glory. A Japanese has defied a German man of science. A Japanese has told even the Koch Laboratory what he thinks. Noguchi's face is much changed.

When night comes there is a dinner to which the Emperor sends a prince of the Reich. Noguchi calls it a great night. He called that other a great night too, that night when Weir Mitchell presided now twelve years ago. How fast it all moves. When he gets back to his room someone has sent him her picture. A Viennese. He goes gaily to bed. Next morning one paper heads its review Japanese Victory. Another prints his photograph. Possibly a little nationalistic feeling is mixed in this, for Austria was on the verge of war with Russia when Japan gave her as she sees it ten years of peace. But the feeling is personal too.

At Munich Friedrich von Mueller meets Noguchi at the station. That is an act for a German professor. The other Japanese in Munich do not understand, write Manabe in Vienna and ask what kind of a god this Noguchi has grown to be. Noguchi stays in Friedrich von Mueller's own house as his personal guest and when the two part it is as fast friends. From Munich Noguchi goes to Frankfurt, His Excellency Paul Ehrlich wanting him to speak to the Medical Society there, thence to Berlin, thence to Copenhagen, thence to Christiania. From Christiania he writes back to Copenhagen. In fact he writes back to his old friend Madsen from almost every point he stops.

"The beautiful memories of my stay with you and Mrs. Madsen haunt me every moment and I am very happy. Sacrifice, purity, and unselfish kindness are the qualities noble and rare, with them the world becomes paradise and the atmosphere so sweet—and a weary soul revives within!" (It is a high thin atmosphere he is living in.) "The deep influence of these qualities is far reaching. Thousands of divine gospels are no match to a single real act of sacrifice and sympathy and I have received many of it from you both! Since I left you I am another man. To me the world is beautiful once more." (The high thin atmosphere of public speeches, public dinners, the belief oh so confident in the mammoth things he is yet to do.) "Be assured that I will accomplish (at least I will strive) something worthy of your noble friendship as my teacher in science and life."

He mentions life. Even in this exalted moment he thinks of that. When first he came to Madsen he would scarce have felt the distinction, has forgotten a little since he left Madsen, now remembers again, may forget once more, but will remember again and again, and perhaps that is growth.

"My shortcomings are many, but with them all, I will march forward."

March forward. He is forgetting again, perhaps. He goes on to Stockholm where he is the guest of Arrhenius. Her Royal Highness Princess Ingeborg receives him.

"She remembered me very well and said that the King used to speak of me very often."

It is the north, away from the continent of Europe, the scene of nine years ago—Princess Ingeborg in the palace of Prince Karl, princesses and princes and a king. He was so happy nine years ago but now, as he says, must be marching forward. From Berlin comes a request to address the doctors. He is wanted in London. Kossel has asked him to come to Heidelberg. He receives letters or telegrams from Breslau, from Hamburg, from Edinburgh, from Strassburg. "What shall I do?" He asks Madsen in the same way he did when Madsen was his teacher. "Just tell me ('Decline' or 'Accept')." At least he must go to London and Berlin, so he crosses from Bergen to Newcastle and addresses the Royal Society on October 20th, a big generous meeting.

"I am not unaware of the difficulty that you are put to in trying to understand my defective speech, but it is to be hoped that this drawback may be remedied in great measure by the aid of actual demonstration which I have arranged for your inspection. Besides the microscopical preparations and other specimens (cultures), I shall freely resort to projection, and this will, I hope in part relieve the speaker of the sense of guilt under which he is suffering from imposing upon your patience."

How it is plain that he regards himself, this boy, for that is how he looks to the English, as one of the great scientists of the earth. If he could not quite rise to so regard himself at that sacred moment when he received the invitation to Vienna, Europe has ever since been busy teaching him. In London he is the house-guest of the Honorary Secretary. Everybody is gracious to him. A shade of this feeling, among other shades, lies over the letter to the master Chiwaki at Cherbourg that evening before the ship set sail.

"In Vienna I lectured on the cultivation of the different spirochetes, and on the relation of tabes and paresis, and on rabies. All this roused great interest. As you know, I am the first to cultivate the spirochete of syphilis. Also of relapsing fever. And more too. Then, as to the cause of paresis, the demonstration of the spirochete is medically important. It is the conclusion of a problem that has been studied for years. By my discovery several conditions that had been assumed syphilitic are proven syphilitic. The problem of therapeutics and preventions may now be attacked. In Europe and America fifteen to thirty percent of the mentally diseased are victims of this infection. In New York state alone one million dollars are spent annually for this incurable disease. . . . The cultivation of the

213

cause of rabies has been tried since Pasteur, for thirty years, but has never succeeded. . . . Then too I have reported on the problem of poliomyelitis, and on the cultivation of that organism. This last is my independent work, but by Doctor Flexner's wish, he having been on this problem for several years, the article went under two names. . . . In Copenhagen they gave me the Royal Medal. If I add what I got from Spain, I have two foreign decorations. It is said that the Swedish Crown intends to decorate me, but I do not know. . . ." (A feeling possibly of immodesty enters him and he casts about for something.) "These honors might become a weapon to me, particularly in a place like America where anti-Japanese feeling is great. Such things will be a silent help." (But the need of a justification, if that is what it was, does not trouble him long.) "I have been here fifty-one days now. If I subtract seven Sundays and five days and nights spent on the ship, it leaves thirty-eight days in which to visit ten big cities, to give eleven lectures, to attend thirty-eight banquets as the principal guest. I was given audience by two royalties. You can imagine how busy I have been. I have sat with great men of science and become intimate with them." (Twelve years ago he sat opposite Chittenden whom he admired in silence.) "In Copenhagen I was the guest of the Royal Society. . . ."

And he is not bragging. What he says is true. But he writes the truth down. And how he writes, never in a letter corrects a phrase, says what it occurs to him to say and lets it stand. The night may have something to do with it too, Cherbourg with the sea in the air making one expansive and frank. He posts the letter. "It will probably go through Siberia." He himself is going the other way.

XL

The Mind Too Must Lie Fallow Awhile

"Dr. Flexner is trying to prepare an anti-serum against the organism (poliomyelitis or infantile paralysis) and he asked me to cultivate the organism in large scale."

Noguchi is of course writing from New York, is back about two months, is in a tempestuous, irritated, fighting state.

"During my absence two of the assistants who studied my method succeeded in isolating the poliomyelitis organism twice."

Good, but no more than further encouragement to believe that the organism that he regards as the cause of poliomyelitis is the cause, and it would have been better if the encouragement had come from someone other than his own assistants.

"One of them has also found the organism in the tissue by my method of staining."

Good too, and satisfying to dwell on, for the length of a letter. Poliomyelitis has gotten to be one of the principal problems of the Institute, more than one at work on it, a so-called group problem, naturally not too stimulating to anyone just back from Europe where everyone was praising an individual. For "howsoever ready to cooperate in any undertaking" this is a poor time to expect Noguchi to believe much can come from any group effort, that anything of importance is born outside of the silence of one. And in any case so far as he is concerned poliomyelitis is solved. Not everyone accepts his organism any more than did the young man of the Koch Laboratory. Indeed in another part of the country a fine honest worker blames an altogether different organism, but in the afterglow of Vienna Noguchi cannot be too ready to doubt himself. If his organism is the true organism what is to be got out of that discovery he has already got, and, if not, the problem is too much divided for much to be hoped from it. He is at something else.

"I have just renewed my rabies work in order to complete it—chiefly the question of the life history of the organism and immunity."

Old work too, more entirely his own, but no promise of anything big, for if the rabies bodies are the cause of rabies it was not he discovered them, and if he were to develop an immunizing substance Pasteur would have had a very good one before him.

"Besides I am asked to take up the study of Hog-cholera (Schweinepest) and I will do my best to find out the etiological agent. This work will be entirely my own and if I happen to accomplish something you may be sure that I had done it alone—no matter whose name may be inserted in the publication."

That too. But what an interesting letter.

"I will keep you informed of the progress of my work when some new facts are observed."

None especially are. None are likely to be where a work begins in fear or disillusion. Nothing especially is coming of anything, poliomyelitis, rabies, hog-cholera, and not long ago he was living in the house of Friedrich von Mueller, was invited by Paul Ehrlich, having royal audiences, and even now continues to hear rumors of the Knight of the Order of the North Star of Sweden.

In December several of his friends come to him, offer him the directorship of research at Mount Sinai Hospital. The position is to be created. "The conditions they offered me were ideal." He is to have $6000 a year. At the Institute he is still only an associate member. "Director of a Research Department of this City." That is the sweet way the offer looks to Noguchi's eye, even the City capitalized. Someone outside is wanting him. That is when one's life changes. Nevertheless he declines.

"I spoke this matter to Dr. Flexner and told my readiness to accept it. But Dr. Flexner asked me to remain at the Rockefeller Institute, promising me of Membership (permanent position), and an increase of salary (to $5000)."

And so, not without precedent in history, is his salary increased and his rank advanced. But it does not exactly help a disillusion to see how the world goes. The Institute is not doing badly either. A man with an international reputation, a young man, thirty-seven in November, a poor time certainly to let him slip. The salary is only $5000. At Mount Sinai he would have had $6000. But the bargain is fair. His prestige at the Rockefeller Institute will be greater and there will be more money behind his experimental work. The election to membership takes place in January and becomes effective in July. He writes to Madsen.

"Now you see your sympathy and actual assistance in giving me a recognition on my recent visit to you were not in vain, and I am very grateful to you. This change makes me in the same rank as Carrel, Meltzer, and Levine, Cole (Hospital head), Loeb (Biology) and Flexner himself. I will be given a suite of rooms for my work and a few technical assistants."

He found the spirochete in the brain one night on his dining-room table when he was all alone.

In July the war breaks out, overruns his Europe. It was Europe, he feels, got him his security and stood as a kind of guarantee.

"From a few months back Europe has become a bloody street. No science, no humanity, no life, and that is most sad. . . . The scientific world with Europe gone feels lonesome and seems small. . . . Before the war I used to get almost daily letters from Europe, but now only occasionally and I have practically severed my relations with my friends over there. . . . Carrel of this Institute went over just before the war, and now is at Lyon, head of a large hospital, serving with the French army."

Noguchi was happy that year he was on the other side.

"In quiet hours in my laboratory I will look back to these moments and will conquer everything that may disturb my peace in the walk of life."

Meanwhile he has once more returned to the old problem of trachoma and once more left the old problem of trachoma, without result. The work on hog-cholera continues, without result. He has been working on a new method of purifying smallpox vaccine.

"Mine far superior, this as to the size of ulcer, the number of takes, the slightness of body reaction."

Good work, but they would not have invited him to Vienna for this. With poliomyelitis he is done.

"I have gradually withdrawn myself from that work. . . . Besides, there has been an extensive epidemic of foot and mouth disease among the cattles of America and I was charged with the research of this disease."

But nothing comes of that either. Nothing comes of anything.

And a little while back at a physical examination, quite incidentally taken, he learned that he had a great enlargement of his heart and a valvular lesion.

"Through some strain of work I seem to have caused a slight cardiac affection."

His friends say that he is paying no attention to it, but perhaps he may not feel as certain as once that nothing in this world could undo him.

"I took your news as calmly as you can imagine,

because I grasp the situation very well. I will faithfully follow the course necessary for such a case."

That is what he writes to one friend. It is concerning the diagnosis. He tells Madsen, of course. "I am cautioned not to work intensely." And there is the real blow. The triumph of last year came to him in no small measure just because he could work intensely, just because he could work with total disregard of body. He knows that. He knows in a way he never knew that achievement depends not on steady drudgery but on a steadily renewed intensity. For a while he gives up smoking, then begins again. When his colleagues ask him to their houses he finds he cannot come, or rarely, but that was so before too, in the beginning making the most elaborate excuses, then quite flat about it, simply cannot come. He and Maizie leave 1 Manhattan where there is no lift and move over to 381 Central Park West. For a while too he stops all drinking, but takes it up again, never in these late years has drunk much.

Then in May he learns that he has been awarded the Imperial Prize of the Japanese Academy. This is 1915. Miura, physician of the Emperor, has proposed him, just as earlier he proposed him for hakushi. Noguchi writes Chiwaki.

"Day before yesterday I received notice from the Academy that I was awarded the Academy prize. I am somewhat astonished though I know my work has had attention. I doubt whether I deserve the prize." (One Japanese to another.) "Please go receive the medal in

221

my place and after showing it to Watanabe send it to my mother through Kobayashi, then at your convenience send it to me."

If a Japanese speaks of his mother at all he is pretty sure to speak of her not as my mother but as my foolish mother, just as she speaks of him as pig-boy, nothing-to-brag-of. But in this letter Noguchi lets himself out more freely.

"The last years my greatest worry has been my mother. I have also been spurred on by her trouble and my glory and my courage will still be owing to my mother's love. Although I would like to return to Japan at this time the journey is great and my circumstances do not permit me, but in two or three years I will return."

And yet this would be the year to return, the Academy prize fresh in everyone's mind. He has put off so long. Would Hoshi loan him the money? He writes Hoshi and Hoshi cables.

"Come any time you can. As to expenses, seven thousand yen should be enough. Whenever you are ready, cable."

So the matter of money is settled, and still he hesitates. He wonders now whether he ought to leave his work. That work has gone so badly since his return from Europe. But perhaps he ought to leave it just on that account. He shrinks from not having his laboratory near, likes when walking in Central Park abruptly to leave the side of whoever he is with and rush back to the Institute. Maybe he ought to go though. He is sick. His life is not right. He is disillusioned. His work keeps small. Maybe he ought to go. He debates back and forth, then Ishizuka sends him from Tokyo a picture of his mother. "Her eyes are very crossed, the one very very off to the side." He cables.

"Want to see mother. Send money."

And the money comes. He buys a new Tuxedo. He buys many things. He wants Maizie to go along, but she will not, not money enough really for that, and anyway he will be happier with his mother alone, and then that perpetual bowing over there. It is late summer when he starts for the east.

XLI

He Returns Home With a Brocade Kimono

September 5th. "For this memorable day even the rain that has been beating all night has ceased." Hoshi, Chiwaki, Miyabara, Okumura, Hata, Manabe, more, all have come the twenty-five miles from Tokyo to Yokohama and are waiting at the dock. Kobayashi has come the whole way from Wakamatsu. Shika would have come but thinking it over decided the villagers ought to have the happiness of being there when she meets her son, so sent a letter to the ship giving him instructions how to behave now that he was once more in his own country.

While the ship is docking he is the "slave" of the newspaper men, every now and then looking over the edge of the ship, seeing someone he knows, bows, suddenly sees Manabe. Manabe of Vienna. Manabe must be representing the Imperial University. Even the Imperial University is sending a representative down from Tokyo.

The Imperial University is doing nothing of the sort. Manabe is representing himself, but easily reads

Noguchi's illusion in Noguchi's face, leaves him in his illusion, even encourages him in it, and when later all together arrive at Shimbashi station and there is no single representative of the Imperial University even there at the train in Tokyo, Manabe promptly takes the blame on himself, says he was mistaken about the time, informed them wrong, and finds an excuse for slipping away off to Aoyama. Aoyama is head of medicine at the university, leader of the one faction, Kitasato leader of the other. Manabe says Aoyama must go at once to visit Noguchi at the Imperial Hotel where Noguchi's friends have by this time brought him.

"And why should I? A former member of the Kitasato crowd, and an inconspicuous member, and where is he coming from? From America. What is science in America? A hanger-on to the tail of Kitasato with a reputation made in America, and I should go to his hotel to visit him—why?"

Manabe tells why, talks for several hours, talks with his natural swinging pounding impetuosity, describes the whole scene at Vienna, Noguchi hailed by the Germans, an internationally known man like Friedrich von Mueller, a man greater than Aoyama, not only paying respect to Noguchi for his beautiful works but receiving him as a friend—and the Imperial University of Japan cannot send a representative to Shimbashi station.

Aoyama is convinced, says, yes, he must go, and a little later arrives at the Imperial Hotel. Noguchi is wild with excitement. Aoyama calling on him! He is as

225

he was that night at Vienna, wants to dance, does not in the least suspect that all is not as it seems. IMPERIAL UNIVERSITY—AOYAMA—PRESIDENT OF NATURFORSCHER VERSAMMLUNG — ROCKEFELLER INSTITUTE FOR MEDICAL RESEARCH. Names still have a strong grip on him. "He is such a child." Manabe says that too, said it already in Vienna. A consequence of the visit is that Noguchi is invited to talk of his work at the Imperial University, and so is the kindness of Friedrich von Mueller eked out by the vigor and good sense of Manabe reaching down even to this present hour.

Two days later, on the 7th, Noguchi starts for Aizu, goes by train as far as Koriyama, just nineteen years since that first time he went the other way. At Koriyama he is met by members of his Aizu clan, it being the gentle custom of the Japanese to board a train somewhere before the destination and to ride along the last of the way. To several in that second-class coach their youthful friendship with Noguchi is the one distinction of their lives, repays even for certain monies that at the time seemed almost mulcted. For their friend is now a man known in the world. Men are reckoned as known in the family, then as known in the village, then in the city, then in the country, then in the world—the literal is, master in the world. But there are some villagers too have talked a great deal these last days, and with an emphasis quite the reverse. "Why should we honor him? What did he do for us?

What did he do for our village? He did not give us money, did he?" To-day these hold their tongues.

A rickshaw waits to bear him from the train to the huddle of houses where he was born. When he reaches the huddle he goes afoot. It is still one street, as it was, rather a road, the houses along one side, the road spanned to-day by a great arch of bamboo under which he is to pass, beyond it the children dismissed from school standing silently in a line, and in another line on the other side the road the elders. All are in dress kimono. This is the real Japan, the world in kimono again. The mayor talks a long time, then hands his card to Noguchi and Noguchi hands his card to him. Then the mayor introduces the chief citizens, they handing their cards to Noguchi and Noguchi handing his card to them, doctors from Inawashiro, doctors from Waka-matsu. The smallest children at one end of their line, not knowing when to bow, begin uncertainly, are nudged by their neighbors, and the head-master, seeing catastrophy, gives a word of command, and everybody bows and is done with it. All a little like a memory from another incarnation.

Shika has not seen him yet. Shika knows he is in the town, but keeps behind the shoji. (She saw a man on horseback once, this in a dream, the dec-orations on him so bright they blinded her and she could not make out his face.) He is coming up the road now but goes on past, does not enter. That is part of her instructions in the letter to Yokohama. That is her wish, and he continues now to carry out the rest of that wish, visits all the houses where anyone was kind to her while he was away. It is summer, the houses are open and he needs but rest his hands on the yen and bow and mutter a few words. Finally he takes the road that leads to the temple, walks the hundred feet, enters the yard, stands there, and not a villager takes an eye off him. He stops before the middle of the temple, the sacred things before him, and prays, all still as his mother's instructions, offers thanks to Kannon because without Kannon's help this day would never have come to pass. Next the temple is the school, and next the school is the graveyard.

That night they talk and talk, he and his mother and Inu. Inu had got it into her head that he would come back looking like the village doctor big and fat, but he is not. He is short like his grandfather. "Stand up and let me measure." She leaps to her feet. He measures carefully. "Ah, you are getting bigger." She is not really. He is so droll. They all laugh. Then they eat, and mother and son kneel side by side, close, and when it comes time to sleep they lie in the same tatamied space. They talk and talk, and Inu says they are still awake at daybreak. "Each time I studied a dangerous disease I thought I might die and here I am healthy and strong." Inu hears him say that again and again.

Next day come the villagers, tell the same things, use the same phrases, till it all grows so dull, as in spite of enthusiasm it is bound to, and the day after he finds himself going even with a certain relief to Inawashiro. There he addresses the pupils of the koto-shogakko

228

ALL THE WORLD IN KIMONO AGAIN

NEVER HAS SHE OMITTED TO PRAY

and the doctors of the countryside. And the following morning early he starts for Nakata Kannon, twenty-five miles through fields of rice, walks down the aisle of ancient trees, stands where his mother stood when she prayed for his burnt hand, when she prayed and he sailed for America, when he wrote back and wanted hakushi.

And then it is time to return to Tokyo. Banquets have been arranged and meetings with distinguished men of state. His mother is to come along. Hoshi thought of that. When Hoshi first mentioned it Noguchi hesitated, was ashamed of his mother, is not of the class that is sure that whatever is is right. He was afraid also that she might not be happy, a little old uneducated woman of a remote prefecture in the big capital. But Hoshi convinced him, said he would arrange that she might not have to stay in the great Imperial Hotel, that there was a small Japanese place close by of which he knew. "And she is all right." That is the way dear kind Hoshi says it. Everyone who meets her is astonished at her, this peasant woman who wears mompe when she is at home, who has no experience of the grand world, has yet an inner quiet that carries all. Noguchi is glad he brought her. She is someone to be proud of. He takes her everywhere. It is true that she has had to remain behind in the village while he went forth into the world. It is true that he grew. But she also grew.

Much in Tokyo takes his time, dinners, meetings, interviews. He gives a lecture at the Saiseigakkusha,

229

tells how it went with one who sat on those benches (stood off to one side with his arms blusteringly folded). He visits the Imperial University and looks over the library. "Uh, still a little German colony." He is informed he is to receive the Fourth Order of the Rising Sun and goes to receive the honor, but reiterates that it is not for honors he returned. "During sixteen years I have not seen my mother and I wanted to pray for her health and therefore I returned." And if this is not quite true, if it is not quite what lay behind his decision back there in New York, he is finding that it is truer than he thought, that he is making it true. And now there comes also a tour of the whole west of Japan, he and his mother and Kobayashi and Kobayashi's wife. Hoshi makes everything possible. Everywhere the four go. Everywhere they visit the shrines and temples. They worship at Ise where the first Emperor is buried and where all the Emperors go at the coronation and where the sacred Three Pieces are kept. How Shika will tell of this when she gets back home. In Osaka they eat at the famous geisha house where Yoshiya sings and dances. Yoshiya the most beautiful geisha in all Japan. But Noguchi seems not to see Yoshiya. Odd for Noguchi. Odd no doubt for any man. He is so busy explaining to his mother the nature of the foods she is eating. She wants to know how all are prepared. The old teacher wants to know too and brings over his long head. And the old teacher's wife. So Noguchi is explaining and does not see Yoshiya, and Yoshiya watches him and weeps. "Noguchi has made Yoshiya weep." That is what they tell you in Osaka.

Then all are in Okinajima again. The prize of the Academy carries with it one thousand yen. Part of this Noguchi gives to his mother. And she gives part to Nakata Kannon and tells the goddess about her son. And part she gives to Omiyasan Choshozi the village temple and tells about her son. And part she gives to the village master so that he may give to the aged. And part she gives to the principal of the school. All this is carefully considered. She wishes she might somehow extend the memory of these days into the future, would like the coming generation to ask: "How did it go then?" She decides the thing to do is to buy and dedicate a small village farm. Hideyo agrees. When he gets back to America he will send additional money. The property is to be called the Royal Gift Farm, and a wealthy neighbor hearing of the plan offers the land cheap.

But now Noguchi must go again to Tokyo to be a little with his friends. Miyabara sleeps with him in the same room at the Imperial Hotel. They talk of many things, of that day Miyabara wandered into the temporary institute in New York, of the Lexington Avenue boarding house, of East 65th Street. One day they went together out to the Bronx to see the lion. Noguchi planted himself in front of the lion and delivered a speech. "Imitate him. If you are like the sheep you will be eaten up. That is the way human beings are. Do not be a sheep."

231

After a big banquet Miyabara and Noguchi return to the hotel and Noguchi says that he is afraid, so many high officers of the army and navy were present. It made him think of what he had forgotten in these weeks, how badly his work has been going the last year and a half. "Yes, I have had one success, two successes, three successes. They have cost me more and more energy. I do not know what the future will be." He has received all these great gifts and they worry him. "I like the small gifts more. The small gifts come from friends. They spring out of a feeling for me. If I do not have more great successes the great gifts will be against me. And anyway if I put all these great gifts into my house it will make the place so rich I cannot work anymore." The work worries him. At Okinajima when asked to write for the village he wrote in Chinese the one word, Patience. When again asked to write he wrote the French proverb, La patience est amere mais son fruit est douce. He learned his French partly out of a book of such proverbs.

He meets Yone. It is at a banquet where there are many people. She wants to speak with him alone. It is he now hesitates, thus openly. Ishizuka invites the two to his room and leaves them there to talk. They stay a long time. Yone has had a number of children, her husband is dead, and she would like Noguchi to take one of the children to America to educate it there. But Noguchi cannot. Things have changed since they saw each other last. He has gone where neither of them could have foretold and he must disappoint her. But

232

some vague spring-time feeling is back in his blood and later when he is on the way to Niigata to give a lecture, Ishizuka again with him, he suddenly turns to Ishizuka, and asks him to send a telegram on to her to be at the station as the train passes through. The telegram miscarries and a sadness lies over Noguchi, as it would no doubt over you and me.

Shika has written him from Okinajima. He is staying too long in Japan. It worries her. He ought to go back to the Rockefeller Institute. And he is meaning to go, of course, visits Okinajima for the last time. That night when he returns to Tokyo he calls Miyabara to come quick to the hotel, and Miyabara can feel in his voice how it is. "My mother is a greater person than I. She did not say much at the parting. But I was not sure I would see her again and I could not help it that I had to wet my handkerchief." His mother also was not sure they would see each other again. Some days ago she was talking to Hoshi about her son's return and the happiness that had brought her, then continued half to herself. "I am ready now. I have done my life work. Death may come any day." Hoshi relates this to Noguchi, and Noguchi agrees it will not be long, uses oddly almost her words. "And I have done my duty as a son. I am ready. Her death may come when it will." From Miyabara he draws a solemn promise to go from Tokyo to Okinajima if ever there is danger. Good he returned this year. Had he returned sooner his distinction would not have been so full. Had he returned later his distinction would not have been so fresh. She had it at its best. In his pocket he carries a photograph, his arm around her shoulder, so queer a thing for an oriental to do.

The newspapers have announced the departure. People are calling at the hotel. A great chrysanthemum is waiting for him in his room. From a lady. He lifts his eyes to Miyabara. Another lady, graduate of a woman's college, would speak with him very particularly. He lifts his eyes to Miyabara. When he and Miyabara walk along the Ginza together Miyabara carries the bag with the manuscripts and paraphernalia for demonstrations. Once Miyabara has to set down the bag. Instantly Noguchi takes it up. He feels about that bag as the samurai about his two swords. Miyabara understands. Miyabara says that any Japanese would.

[XLII]

The Selection of My Problem of Investigation Is More Difficult Now

Noguchi is at two new problems. One sprang from work he saw in Japan, possibly the other too, or it may be the other grew out of a visit to the Harvard Medical School just after his return. At least he talked there to Doctor Wolbach who was beginning his search for the cause of Rocky Mountain spotted fever, had in December sent to Washington for the wood ticks that are carriers of that infection. Early in February Noguchi is himself in Washington inquiring about ticks, someone in Washington under date of February 16th writing to someone in Boston to say that Noguchi was there, and thus does everybody know about everybody and the race for the cause of Rocky Mountain spotted fever is on.

"As soon as I came to New York (from Japan) I began working at the Institute day and night. There are many problems, mainly Rocky Mountain spotted fever, quite like tsutsugamushi disease. As to the casual agent we know nothing."

This is the way he writes to Kobayashi. The tsutsu-gamushi disease of which he speaks is very fatal in Japan.

"The reason I take up the problem is mainly because it is related to tsutsugamushi disease."

So the wish to study Rocky Mountain spotted fever may after all have been born in Japan and the visit to the Harvard Medical School simply have strengthened that wish, or perhaps the other way, and interesting either way, and no immortal difference either way, and at least no question that he would like to be having a hand in the medicine of his own country. He adds his customary caution.

"Whether I succeed or not is another matter, but the problem is worth the trying."

The second new problem is another disease very fatal in Japan, infectious jaundice. The cause of infectious jaundice was discovered last year by Inada and Ido, both Japanese. The cause is a spirochete, and when Noguchi was in Japan he saw the spirochete. So he cannot discover the cause. And he cannot discover the experimental animal because that is discovered too. And he cannot make the first pure culture. All that has been done. What is his interest then? Partly that the cause is a spirochete and he is interested in spirochetes. Partly that the disease is Japanese. Partly and mostly that he still has nothing absorbing of his own. He is back from Japan but finds himself still much where he was before he went to Japan.

Infectious jaundice occurs among rice planters and

236

miners and sewer workers. The same disease has recently broken out on the European battle fronts, the men in the trenches being for the time also miners and sewer workers. Search in the blood of the German and French and Italian soldiers has revealed a spirochete apparently the same as the spirochete of infectious jaundice in Japan. The European disease like the Japanese is carried by a rat, at least the spirochete has been found in the bodies of altogether healthy wild rats.

What Noguchi makes his special study is to find whether the spirochete lives in American rats as well —not too inspiring a beginning. He removes the kidneys of all the wild rats he can gather, makes an emulsion of the kidneys, inoculates the emulsion from forty-one wild rats into fifty-eight guinea-pigs, and in twelve of them produces a disease seemingly the same as the Japanese and European diseases. The spirochete is not only like the spirochete he saw in Japan, but if he vaccinates an animal against the European and American diseases it is safe also against the Japanese disease. All of which is good work, satisfactory to most men. In the course of the work he realizes that this spirochete is not like the spirochetes he has dealt with in the past. Its windings are more minute. He thinks there ought to be a new genus and suggests the name leptospira, which means slim spiral. So he has also godfathered the discovery of Inada and Ido, but he has had births of his own.

In the course of the winter he gives the Harvey lecture on the subject of spirochetes. He contributes an

237

article to the memoire published in honor of Metchnikoff. He starts a study of the spirochetes living in shellfish. He makes a pure culture of trichomonas, which is an inhabitant of the human mouth, lives in the tartar and does no harm there. He writes a paper on immunity to the various spirochetes, nothing to do with an immunity to syphilis in man, once his dream, but seven years now settled over that dream, his friend Kaliski reminding him now and then, some good people as lief he forgot, having protested, it is said, when he made his first effort, feared he might find a prophylactic against syphilis and the world become a worse place than it already is. The good people need have no fear. He is in no such state as makes the big discoveries.

[XLIII]

Akiramerarento Akirameta

He was thoughtful and sad that last night before he
left Tokyo, and in the months since his return has been
more outspokenly Japanese than at any time since his
first coming to America. "Take me to the noodle-
stand." That is what he said to Miyabara that last night.
The noodle-stand had seemed a disorderly mess when
he first got back, had lost its old romance. Everything
had lost, seemed rottener even than it used to be.
Tokyo had no sewers. There was no progress. The
chrysanthemums were no bigger than the chrysanthemums they grew before he went away. "It would not
be so in America." Then gradually he began to settle
again into the old. It was all a little like the recovering
of a memory. The very smells ceased to be unpleasant.
Then, finally, that last night. "Take me to the noodle-
stand." Miyabara led the way. They went single-file
down the Ginza, squeezed in and out among those
amazing oil-lit stalls where venders bargain over everything nameable from bad prints and images of Daru-
ma to singing insects and creeping turtles. Hard to

239

think that next day one will be putting all this ten thousand miles behind one. "The longer I stay the more I like it, so I am going back to America as quick as I can." That is the way he summed up his feeling. He was running away from emotions that yet might rise. "There is a peculiar interest over there too." He referred to America, of course. "Here in Japan I could never work because someone would always be calling on me." Once he said he would come back when he was old and build himself a house at the edge of Inawashiro lake. Once he said he would come if some Japanese rich enough would build for him a big institute and pay all the expenses. Then for two weeks he recrossed the Pacific. The Pacific seemed so enormous this time. He started from Yokohama the 10th. By the 13th the waves were mountain-high and in an ugly lurch the ship broke a rudder. All day and night of the 13th and all day of the 14th the crew worked desperately on. He lay there vomiting. It seemed the ship would never push through that belt of storm. An officer spoke to him. He did not answer. Near him stood a woman. "Ah, how fortunate I am to cross but once and to behold what sailors behold but rarely in their lives." That is what the woman said, and to the officer the woman seemed the remarkable of those two. When the ship put in at Seattle it was days late, Japan now enormously far away, back in the past, done. Seven trunks of souvenirs followed him to New York. *Akiramerarento akirameta. I have given up that that cannot be given up.* He wants to be in New York. He must be in New York. Yet, akiramerarento akirameta.

He overhears someone in the street say Jap. Formerly he would have passed on by. Now he stops, addresses the someone, says he is Noguchi of the Rockefeller Institute, the someone immediately apologetic, which only heats him more. Not because he is Noguchi of the Rockefeller Institute but because he is a Japanese one must not use that word. He loses his temper altogether, lectures the man with thoroughness and goes his way relieved.

[XLIV]

Akatsu

He has continued all this while inoculating guinea-pigs
with the virus of Rocky Mountain spotted fever, every
day draws a little of their blood, makes smears on slides,
studies the slides under the microscope, starts at slides
early every morning, keeps at slides all day and when
night comes is still at slides, just as when he was looking for spirochetes in the brain, only he was gay then.
Often too he takes home slides, even gets out of bed
when he is already in, examines a few more, and finds
nothing. Week after week, nothing. It follows that he
is crankier and crankier, somewhat as in the beginning
on East 65th Street, only it is not Araki absorbs the
crankiness now but one named Akatsu. Akatsu is Noguchi's first Japanese assistant. Akatsu like Araki thinks
of Noguchi as teacher, calls him sensei, is humble in his
presence. "I am not an assistant really, more a pupil."
Akatsu begins at 8 o'clock every morning and works
till 8 o'clock every night, no Sundays, just as in Japan,
but no holidays either, and in Japan one has holidays.
Then he is always getting scolded. Sometimes he knows

why, but sometimes he is very miserable. When he is miserable he tries to remember that he is the pupil and that Noguchi is the teacher, and that helps him. Yet it is hard to understand how if the teacher is truly a happy man he can behave as he does, and he ought to be happy, just back from Japan where everybody heaped honors on him. Some days he is crankier than others. He complains. He says that he wants to be working on something big like cancer but that others at the Institute are working on cancer and he cannot. Or common colds. That would be big too. Or scarlet fever. Sometimes he gets very very absent-minded, pours alcohol instead of water over a slide, thinks he can dry the slide in a gas flame, drops something quick, and that makes him laugh and the afternoon is lighter and Akatsu is glad.

On one problem the teacher works directly with the pupil, and the kind of problem shows about the teacher too. Paul Ehrlich, knowing that the spirochete that infects fowl can be made to tolerate greater and greater doses of arsenic, took it for granted that this was true also for the spirochete that causes syphilis, did not stop first to prove it with preliminary test-tube experimentation. The hope of a successful treatment for syphilis would be to find some compound of arsenic that would sterilize the body with a single dose, the spirochete having then no chance to get used to the arsenic. What Noguchi is now doing with Akatsu is that preliminary test-tube experimentation that Ehrlich did not trouble to do. Whether or not Ehrlich found his compound of arsenic has of course nothing to do with the point, which is that a large mind in its vigor simply leaps over the kind of question that Noguchi now makes the subject of a special study. He himself feels that way too. He keeps saying that he wants something big, something like that he had several years ago, and that all that he can find is the small.

Sundays he invites Akatsu to a Japanese restaurant, as he used to Araki, and three or four times to the apartment at 381 Central Park West. Akatsu looks ahead to the Sundays. Noguchi is not the same man on Sundays. He is not the same man when he gets out of that laboratory. It is almost as if he hated that laboratory. And Sundays he talks Japanese. In the laboratory he sticks to the rule made in Pennsylvania, never talks Japanese, always says, and is apt to lose his temper more and more as he says it, that a student before he dare come to America must learn English. The practical consequence of the teacher's rule is that there is no talk in the laboratory, only now and then and mostly when Akatsu gets scolded, the scoldings in an English which Akatsu always finds he can understand. Akatsu minds the scoldings less than he did because he knows that soon he is going back to Japan. And also he sees clearly how much the teacher has taught him. The scoldings were nothing really, and when Akatsu mentions them it is not himself he is thinking of but of the teacher. How can a man who is that cranky be happy? How is that possible?

244

[XLV]

The 42nd Year Is a Bad One As Every Japanese Knows

On May 24th they take Noguchi by ambulance to Mount Sinai Hospital. Perhaps they should have taken him before. Doctor Libman has been over to Central Park West and has said that the patient must positively be got out of that house. Hidey does not want to, does not want to admit he is ill, yet was strange last night, his eyes full of fever and he singing, yellow note paper scattered all over the dining-room table, writing, writing, writing, now and then shooting his fingers through his dry curly hair. Maizie must snatch his pencil from him and force him to bed. A few days ago he dreamed he lost his shoe in mud. Mud is bad. Maizie asked him whether he found his shoe again and he said he did, so things will come out all right at the end.

He thinks he has infectious jaundice. He does not say too often what he thinks but that is what he thinks. Three weeks ago accidentally he sucked some of a culture through a pipette into his mouth, washed his mouth, of course, but from time to time has inquired whether there was not some yellowing of his skin, mean-

245

while has continued eating oysters. He has been eating them night after night. "Someone at the Institute advised him to eat them for building up his constitution." That is the way one of his Japanese friends explains when Noguchi himself begins to wonder whether it may not have been the oysters made him sick. "He ate three four dozen a day." Maizie says that really he did not eat more than one dozen. "Wanted to build up his constitution quick. He, a bacteriologist, ate three four dozen oysters a day. Derned fool. He says so himself." Secretly he sticks to infectious jaundice. Doctor Libman says typhoid—and typhoid it is.

And so the oysters are to blame. Had he not eaten oysters he would not be sick. Yet one feels he was doomed to a sickness anyway, was running on one for months and even years, ever since 1913 and before, but especially since 1913, and not that he has been working too hard, as everybody thinks, at least he has worked harder, but possibly has not been working right, possibly not working happily, something besides overwork at any rate, and besides oysters, and besides spirochetes. Which is nonsense to anyone who knows exactly how the typhoid bacillus looks. Nevertheless one has the further feeling that if once he were thoroughly ill he might be thoroughly well again. At Mount Sinai they write down typhoid, of course. Noguchi's friends meanwhile are saying to one another that he has not been well for a long time. He was cranky before Akatsu. He has his enlarged heart. What they are wondering is whether with that enlarged heart he will be able to with-

246

stand this illness. Some say he will. Some say he won't. It is a popular idea that intense natures fall ill intensely when the illness is typhoid, and certainly he is critical when he enters the hospital. He enters in fact with one of the complications of typhoid, a serious complication, a perforation of the gut, and there is the immediate question whether or not to open the abdomen. When a physician is ill he is apt to have many physicians, and even if these have not been formally called into consultation they are there in spirit. Among those of the spirit there is a difference of opinion as to whether or not the abdomen should be opened. Doctor Libman says not. Several call Doctor Libman over phone. They express their doubt. He continues to say not, and the abdomen is not opened. The patient weathers on.

The day before Decoration Day is the crisis. It is generally felt Noguchi will die. One person goes down to the Battery, walks back and forth, back and forth. It seems impossible such a man should die, that God should let such a man die. A wild day, raining, thundering, Noguchi himself so far as he is aware of anything realizing that it would be easy to die now, and not much minding, things not so happy of late, but the nurses keep rubbing his legs, keep him alive almost against his will. Maizie is beside herself, every little while is telephoning the hospital. Hidey looks awful. His eyes are so big. His tongue is swollen. He is going to die and leave her alone. Where is that Noguchi pluck? She hardly knows what she is doing. She starts for the hospital once more, is just approaching his room as someone is leaving, Kaliski, Doctor Kaliski. "He is showing fight. He is going to get well." That is what Doctor Kaliski says, and what a weight off Maizie's mind. And it is true that he is a little better next day.

The news has gone to Okinajima and Shika is praying. Good, she feels, that she did not die before, else who would have prayed for him. She walks the twenty miles to Nakata Kannon and asks the goddess to help her son get well, then walks the twenty miles back again. She is sixty-five.

Doctor Libman brings another doctor. The doctor has just made a blood count, says the count has risen, talks pretty loud, enumerates the possibilities of such a rise, names the complications of typhoid. Such a fool, and a doctor, to let the patient overhear. And the patient has overheard, opens his eyes. "How do you feel?" Doctor Libman asks him and he smiles, says he is indifferent, says the word in the mildest way, knows that his doctor is worried about what he overheard and wants to reassure his doctor, asks about his doctor's eyes, says they are not well yet, are still much inflamed, begs his doctor to go on his vacation, not stay any longer into the summer, it is already late.

Araki comes to the hospital. Araki has read in the Japanese newspaper that the teacher is ill. The order is that no one is to be admitted to Noguchi's room. But did not Araki live with the teacher for three years? He pushes into the room. "Poor Noguchi lies there so pale, can hardly open his eyes, yet pets me, like a brother." The Japanese newspapers said the teacher was critical.

248

Araki does not know what to think, sits off gloomily against the wall, remembers that the teacher has not been right for a long time. It is many months since Araki called on the teacher and the teacher looked bad, Araki thinking it lack of exercise, advised the teacher to play golf, in the same moment remembered about the teacher's hand, how the teacher could never play golf with such a hand, and how the hand would be the first thing the teacher would think of. Araki wishes he had not spoken of golf that day. What has the teacher had of life? Work, work, work. . . .

Noguchi is somewhat better and allowed a pot of tea. The day-nurse comes, tidies his room. The order against visitors has been somewhat relaxed, one or two visit, one from the laboratory, and Noguchi talks a little of the laboratory, wishes he might be there, gives a few instructions. The day-nurse brings the midday meal. Maizie arrives. He is feeling so uncomfortable. "They have me here like a guinea-pig in a wet blanket." Myrtle and Jacques come. Then finally the evening meal, night settling, the night-nurse taking the place of the day-nurse, at last a free opportunity for talk. He talks and talks. He ought to be relaxing but he talks, feels he has some strength again and spends it. He tells how in his delirium he saw thousands of guinea-pigs. They walked past him one after another in an endless procession. When he is well he never seems to think of guinea-pigs. When he is inoculating them by dozens and letting them die in the vile way bacteriologists feel they must he never mentions them, yet now

249

in his delirium is seeing them, perhaps after all has felt something about them.

Presently he is complaining that his bedding is not right, then that his food is not right. He is getting better. Dr. Libman thinks perhaps Japanese food would be easier for him to digest, talks to Hori, and Hori and Tokuko Hori, who is Hori's sister, come to the hospital, (Doctor Libman observing), tripping, both so small, both so worried for Noguchi, Hori with a sheaf of arrow-root under his arm. "Please, Doctor Libman don't give my friend no rice to eat. If Japanese with fever eat rice he dies on spot." It is the old idea against solid food in typhoid. Doctor Libman does not want his patient to go along on arrow-root water and rice water, at the same time does not want his patient frightened, so asks him. "Do you think a Japanese dies if he eats rice?" Noguchi smiles, but as for eating the rice he has no appetite for that either. It is simply convalescence, the lack of appetite with the necessity to eat, the sleepiness with the sleeplessness, the bed hot and still the fear of being chilled.

Sarah Bernhardt happens to be in the hospital, knows Noguchi, met him long back, walked one day just ahead of him into Doctor Carrel's little operating room on the upper floor of the Institute, Noguchi carrying a great camera, setting it up there in the operating room, taking the divine Sarah's picture, one of the best she ever had. The two liked each other at once. There is indeed something similar in them, so much man in her, so much woman in him, so much

250

artist, actor, in both, as with genius generally. She now offers "the great Japanese doctor" her more commodious room. The great Japanese doctor does not accept. "Ah, the Noguchi, I like so much. So small this way." She indicates the height with one hand. "So big this way." She indicates the breadth of his head with two hands. "I give the Noguchi my room."

Then comes a day when he feels once more the thirst to read, asks for the Kodan. The Kodan is a collection of Japanese detective stories. "His taste in Japanese literature was always like that." So does one of his Japanese friends reflect, then adds that, really, there is no Japanese literature, wipes out Japanese literature so that Noguchi may have no weak side now when he is ill. "And, anyway, could Noguchi, a scientist, married, middle-aged, be expected to read Japanese poems?" Noguchi pages in the Kodan a while, then lets the book fall, lies there, sweats, the damp sheets close to his body. He is thin and the life is out of his muscles, but it is a beautiful body despite its not exactly beautiful proportions. It is tiny all except the head and shoulders, and not that the head is unusually large but against the tiny body looks large, the more so now that the bony frame juts through. The neck has a roundness like a child's, not immature but delicate like that, and from it rises that remarkable head. He knows how remarkable. He wears his hair carelessly but even now when he is ill wears it in such a way as to keep up the effect of such a head, close over the ears and piled up on top, is glad that it helps him to look

251

a little taller. The lips are full and not pale even here in bed. The eyes are far apart. The nose he thinks is too small and wishes there were more bridge. The whole left side of the body is more developed than the right, and as good a clinician as Miura doubts whether this could all be disuse, suspects some touch of infantile paralysis unnoticed when he was young. The left hand he keeps under the sheets except at such moments when he is holding, for instance, the rice bowl, refuses the bowl if it has a round bottom because he looks so awkward when that kind of bowl slips from him. The right hand is strong and sure.

He asks also for a Spanish grammar. That is, the old lure of learning a language is over him again. Kaliski brings the grammar. Noguchi was already a member of the Institute when he went nights to the Y. M. C. A. to add to his French. Mitsuboshi used to see him in the restaurant with his head in a French book. Mitsuboshi feels toward him somewhat as Araki and Akatsu. "I do not disturb him. After a time he looks up. 'Ah, you.' Immediately he pokes his head into the book again. He is peculiar like that." Here in bed now he goes to the Spanish with the same kind of hunger, in one mood traces each new word back to its root and relates it to similar words in other languages, and in another mood runs slipshod over the pages. He knows now Japanese, English, German, French fairly, Chinese fairly, Danish fairly, Italian not very well, and is adding Spanish.

He is beginning also from his bed to do a little

THE RIGHT HAND STRONG AND FIRM

work in his laboratory, but he is not supposed to, and that is why Steve when he slips in glances round to see that no one is there, then pulls a tube from his inside pocket and shows it to Noguchi and quick puts it back into his inside pocket again.

But most of the day Noguchi still just lies and thinks. His thoughts have had no such chance for years, not really since he was a boy at the edge of Inawashiro lake. It may be that the bon Dieu has no other way of halting a nature like this than to make the man sick, to force the man to take a rest from an activity that for his inner sake has become meaningless. And if the bon Dieu has nothing to do with it, at least there is no question that Noguchi has seen death close up and it must then be easier to ask oneself whether these last years, this perpetual addition of paper to paper, this fight for a success which of late has not even been that, whether that was wise. To some of his colleagues the idea of the bon Dieu going to so much trouble and using such an elaborate devise might seem a bit mad, but the madness would not be quite so mad in the country from which this patient comes where there are still a goodly number believe that not an elbow is nudged in the street without immortal forethought. And one of the more sensitive of Noguchi's friends does through the course of this illness discover a change more than bodily, and two others not so sensitive but still sensitive speak now for the first time of something that one of them calls the settling sadness.

On all sides meanwhile the patient is reminded of

the warmth of the human world. Flowers fill his room, messages come from persons he scarce believed had any concern in him, from the highest in Japan. And these messages he reads. When he is well he so often tosses messages unread into his waste basket. Napoleon did that too. Araki says that it is simply no use to write Noguchi, except that if maybe at New Year one were to mail him a postcard because he would not have even to open an envelop he might perhaps read it. Noguchi himself, now that he is able to, puts his pen to a few postcards. "Bad 70 days." Thus to Wani, an old one of the Saiseigakkusha, and Wani will carefully lay away the card. The master Chiwaki also receives a message, Noguchi describing his illness.

"There were nurses night and day but the patient himself on account of high fever is unconscious and peaceful in bed."

In Japan the newspapers have all along been reporting the stages of the illness and Noguchi now asks Chiwaki to put a notice in these newspapers, thanking all the many who prayed for his recovery.

Matsumoto and Yamakawa, two who lately have come to work in the laboratory, followed Akatsu there, visit the hospital. To them Noguchi admits that it is not his illness is worrying him but money. Where is the money to come from? "A terrible year. Nobody knows. The very very closest do not know." When he is well it is like wasting money to lay it aside against an illness. Now he is ill and despite messages and letters and flowers dreads a world that he has some reason for

254

thinking respects nothing but conformity and present power. To Matsumoto he says that he cannot pay his bills. He ought perhaps not to stay in this hospital where, no matter how generous everyone, he is daily increasing his obligations. He talks also to Hori, finally decides he will cable Hoshi, cables, and money comes. He pays all his Mount Sinai bills and all his other bills, and still has money. He will invest that presently in an automobile. He will also buy gifts for everybody, for his doctor a platinum watch.

By the 7th of August he is ready to leave with Maizie for Shandaken in the Catskills, read of the place in an advertisement. He lost his hair while he was sick and the new hair is coming in straight. Myrtle asks him if it will ever be curly again and in a small petulant voice he answers: "Yes." He is shaky. His muscles are flabby. Maizie rubs his calves, that look worse because they are Japanese calves and normally big. When he left the hospital he weighed ninety-seven pounds. When he fell ill he weighed one hundred and thirty. He is weak and whining, then hears that there are fish in the stream and his whole body changes. Maizie would have liked the seashore, but Hidey likes the mountains, and a stream to fish in. Shandaken is a mountain valley. They put up at the hotel. All day he is writing letters, uses so much stationary that Maizie is ashamed of herself to have to be going down into the lobby again and again asking for more. Life in a hotel would never do for him. He is too active, needs his own place, wants a cottage and has begun looking round for one. This hill country suits him, he says. He was born among hills, and all this makes him think of Aizu. Hoshi's gift would go part of the way to the buying of a cottage too. The cottage he prefers is the one where the stream flows just behind, but the house is in a bad state and Maizie is by no means sure it is a good bargain. But Hidey wants it and steps are taken. They will not be able to move in this year, of course.

Hoshi has proven a good friend, paid the return to Japan, paid part of the bills of the illness, part of the automobile, now part of the cottage. And the friendship of another Japanese is counting in another way. Hori has been after Noguchi for years to get him to paint. "Art is all. If you have not some art in your life you have not lived." Noguchi has laughed, perhaps has said Hori was crazy, was a painter and they are all crazy, and, as for his beginning to paint, he had not the time. But there is a superstition that whoever goes long enough to Hori's begins to paint and when Noguchi started for Shandaken he had a paint-box in his baggage. Hori gave him that, also a few instructions. "He would be good at anything." That is what Hori says. Noguchi does not want anyone to teach him, wants to work the thing out for himself, and the way he sets about it is astonishing. He believes in himself from the first stroke. He sets up the easel in the middle of the road. There are a few reflections and a tree. He puts down boldly what he sees, no doubt with a good deal of simplicity to anyone who knows about such things, but with the fact of his honestly liking something pretty well expressed. Those eyes that were so shut that day at San Francisco, and that have ever since been opening on so many things, do now open rapidly and widely also on the beauty of the physical earth. A stranger comes along the road. Noguchi is blocking the road but does not apologize, instead calls the stranger. "You see that tree?" He points to the tree in the picture. "That's that one." He points to the tree in nature. "Same thing, isn't it?" One friend calls his canvases masterpieces and Noguchi laughs promptly and heartily, next day.

But there are hours when he does not paint and does not look into the microscope, just lies by the river, says, yes, it is all a little like Okinajima. The river at Okinajima was actually only a rill that ran between rice fields. He used to sell fish and bought pencils with the proceeds. He may lie there hours and hours, is letting his mind lie fallow as he had hoped it might of its own accord last year. It is late in the fall when he gets back to New York to be as he says the worm of the laboratory again.

The worm begins gradually to get in motion and yet that gradual seems still too vehement. Or possibly the bon Dieu thinks he ought to have even more time to consider. At any rate there is a relapse and Noguchi must be taken to the Institute hospital and when at length he has recovered from the relapse shows symptoms of appendicitis. The symptoms are not marked and he still has not his strength, nevertheless Doctor Libman wants the appendix out. There is no fever and the blood is normal, but the patient does not look right. Again the physicians of the physician discuss the wisdom, again there is much calling of the doctor over the phone, and the appendix is removed. For an hour and a half after the operation there is water in the lungs and things look bad, but the patient once more weathers on. Back in Okinajima the old mother is walking again the twenty miles to Nakata Kannon to stay all night in the temple and the following morning is walking the twenty miles back to Okinajima. Japanese all say that the yakudoshi, the climacteric year, the 42nd, is likely to be a man's worst. If there is any illness in him it is likely to come out, and one can never be sure till the year is quite over. The dull add that anything that occurs at this time is simply laid to the yakudoshi.

XLVI

Yellow Fever

In Europe still the war, we in now too, June now, 1918, Noguchi a little shaky on his legs but bent upon a big adventure—is on the way to Ecuador to see if he cannot find the cause of yellow fever.

Fifty years ago yellow fever was only here and there regarded as a contagion. Nott in 1848 thought the disease carried by a mosquito and Carlos Finlay later thought he knew which mosquito, both guesses of course, because neither Nott nor Finlay could have proof. Proof did not come till the opening of the century and by a succession of steps taken by extraordinary men and making in the total if not the greatest achievement in American medicine certainly the most dramatic. American too from the very beginning, from the very discovery of the principle upon which all that follows rests, the discovery of the so-called extrinsic cycle of a parasite in an insect host. An insect bites a man suffering with a disease, sucks from his blood the parasite causing the disease, and the parasite now living in the insect host goes through a cycle of development at the end of which if the insect bites another man it leaves in him an infective stage of the parasite. Doctor Theobald Smith found this for a disease called Texas Fever, and the finding so astonished him that it is said he did not trust what he found, put off three years the publication of the facts. What exactly he found was that in the blood of cattle suffering with Texas Fever there is a parasite which a tick sucks from the blood, the parasite developing in the body of the tick, and the tick passing the disease among the cattle. Naturally that at first would look like a flight of fancy. It proved a great principle. The discoverer as is usual with real discoverers was not setting out to discover a principle, was only struck by certain facts of ticks and parasites and cattle.

About this time there runs a debate in the newspapers. Should or should not ships and cargoes coming from yellow fever countries be fumigated? The health officer of the port of New York has ruled that all such fumigations cease. People are uneasy, are afraid of yellow fever breaking out in New York, the protest growing and growing till it has reached the ears of President Cleveland. The health officer sticks to his ruling. President Cleveland decides that the health officer had better go to Egypt to learn what he can about the way yellow fever spreads. What the health officer learns in Egypt is mainly that there is no reason for changing his ruling. Not the cargoes and not the ships but the human beings, some occasional yellow fever convalescent, must be watched for.

The next step, a great one, is taken jointly by a group of doctors and privates in the American army. A bacterium has been seen in the blood of yellow fever patients. Walter Reed has lately restudied this bacterium, has shown that it exists widely in nature, in northerly climates too, obviously then cannot be the cause of yellow fever. It is Reed's first work on yellow fever, brings him much attention, and he is sent to Cuba as head of an Army Board that is to study especially that disease. The others of the Board are Carroll, Agramonte and Lazear.

The Board decides it will investigate Carlos Finlay's mosquito. Carlos Finlay has been breeding the mosquito in his own house and supplies the eggs. The Board meanwhile is seeking permission to experiment on volunteer human subjects. Reed is temporarily off to Washington, and Carroll and Lazear begin experiments on themselves. Agramonte describes what takes place.

"Carroll and Lazear were in the laboratory attending to their respective work, the conversation turning upon the mosquitoes and their apparent harmlessness, Lazear remarked how one of them had failed to take blood, at which Carroll thought that he might try to feed it, as otherwise it was liable to die before the next day, (the insect seemed weak and tired); the tube was carefully held, first by Lazear and then by Carroll himself, for a considerable length of time, upon his forearm, before the mosquito decided to introduce its proboscis. . . ."

Carroll falls ill. A private, William Dean, knowing the risk, lets himself be bitten by the same mosquito and also falls ill. Lazear had previously let himself be bitten, did not fall ill, but later while feeding mosquitoes on a yellow fever patient one of them settles on his hand and stings him, and on Tuesday the 25th of September he dies.

The mosquito theory is proven. The great question is answered, but many important questions remain and the thinking of this small group of men is as clear as its deeds are bold. Finally they publish their conclusions, the conclusions being immediately put to work and the stamping out of yellow fever begun. It takes some acquaintance with the past to know what that means. In yellow fever countries the greater part of the population is stricken in infancy when the mortality is low and from then on is immune, and that is fortunate because later the mortality is high. In Ecuador when the young men who have passed their boyhood on the Andean plateau where there are no mosquitoes come down into the lowlands for military service one in two dies. They know what their chances are before they come and it is strange sometimes to see the apathy of the fatalist in boys. When death seems near they will call the doctor and tell him that if he will but inform the padre so that the padre may pray for them they will not mind to die.

Henceforth it will be known that there is something definite to avoid, mosquitoes. Up to now anything might be suspected and anything dreaded. And the problem of the health authorities will be clear, kill the mosquitoes and wipe out the breeding places. One man comes to the fore with just the right quality of energy. When Gorgas himself contracted yellow fever it was at the risk of being shot for having slipped through a military cordon to enter a quarantined region. Gorgas got his training in Cuba, then took charge of the sanitation of the Canal Zone where he put to work the conclusions of the Army Board. The digging of the Panama Canal became possible. With Cuba, the Canal Zone, Vera Cruz, New Orleans, Laredo, Rio de Janiero freed, other regions are bound now quickly to follow, but what is plainer every day is that with increasing travel and with every relaxing vigilance not only will old areas flare up after they are thought put out, but the scourge will spread into new. Hence Gorgas' dream to dry up or cover with oil every swamp, puddle, creek, cesspool, in every country where yellow fever is or was or yet may be. That takes a kind of Shakespearian imagination. "I want to eradicate yellow fever from the earth." Unless all areas are cleared none are safe. Gorgas' head is full of schemes when the war breaks out and makes further work impossible. Gorgas is appointed Surgeon General of the United States, a big job till one sees again the continent of Africa and the length of South America and every breeding place in them. And Gorgas apparently sees that way too, for the war is still on when he calls his friend Arthur Kendall and asks him to hold himself ready to go to Guayaquil in Ecuador. Gorgas himself was in Guayaquil.

When he left the Guayaquilians burned his effigy in the streets. But perhaps even that is why he wants to begin there, wants to clear Ecuador first, for then certainly it ought to be easy to follow with similar attacks in Mexico, Brazil, Peru and finally and behind all Africa.

But how to get into Ecuador? Gorgas discusses his difficulty with Kendall. To Kendall it seems that it might be a good idea simply to ask Guayaquil for the use of its yellow fever material to make a fresh search for the parasite that causes the disease, the parasite, if that is what it is, that the mosquito carries, present that to the Guayaquilians as the important issue and insinuate the hygienic attack by the side. Gorgas agrees provided there is someone who fairly may be imagined to find that cause, and Kendall speaks up promptly, Noguchi. And that is why Noguchi thus toward the last of June, still somewhat shaky on his legs but animated by the chance to work at that new and big that for years he has sought and not found, is on the way to Guayaquil. He is an excuse. He is to search for the cause of yellow fever so that Gorgas may smother mosquitoes. Noguchi's fate looks a little more like that pale lady than ever before.

XLVII

This Is the One I Suspect

By the 7th of July he has got as far as the Canal Zone.

"Am feeling strong and well. All my little g-pigs are doing well, too . . . the butcher on the steamer attended to them. . . . It may interest you to hear that my 17 boxes were to be in Guayaquil when I landed here—they were shipped by the International Health Board directly, and I was not supposed to look after them at all. But, when I got on board "Ucayali" at Balboa (Panama), I made an inquiry about my boxes. The purser said there was no freight later than June, and that there was none addressed to me. So that evening at 11 p.m. I finally got the Railroad President and succeeded in getting them shipped from Colon (other end of Panama) to the steamer. Six o'clock in the morning the boat was about to sail when 15 boxes came! Two cases did not arrive."

By the 15th the "Ucayali" lies off Guayaquil. On the ship is a Senorita Maria Barrientos and her company of sixty musicians bound by contract to sing in Guayaquil but the contract broken because back at the

Canal the singer was told that in Guayaquil the yellow fever dying lay in the streets. Senorita Maria Barrientos will not disembark. Senorita Maria Barrientos cannot be made to disembark. There are also three nurses on the ship and they do disembark. Great singer, big salary, afraid of her life, will not disembark, and three nurses disembark. The newspapers are full. When the nurses reach their rooms they find them filled with roses. And the Japanese doctor disembarks. The feeling toward him is mixed.

"As you may well imagine the indignation fell upon me—in a way—because I came here to study the dreaded disease."

A senator of the republic talks to Kendall. Why does the Japanese doctor wear his puttees? Guayaquil is hurt. The Japanese doctor would not wear his puttees in the streets of New York. Puttees will not save him from the mosquitoes.

But puttees will. They will save his legs, and that will leave him freer to watch his neck and hands, and the yellow fever mosquito is not one announces itself with a buzz but floats and only when it has stung does one know it was there.

Delegates from the municipalities and from the various medical organizations have come down to the ship. Noguchi makes them a speech—in their own language. They are amazed, the more so when they learn that he studied Spanish by himself and did not begin till last year when he was sick in bed. The newspapers report the speech. They report that besides the

266

doctor and the Senorita and the three nurses there were eleven cases of instruments and five boxes of chemicals and live guinea-pigs. Fancy the Japanese doctor bringing guinea-pigs from New York to Ecuador which is the home of the guinea-pig. People laugh. The Spanish doctors laugh. The American doctors laugh too. There is in fact a law against bringing guinea-pigs into the lowlands for fear they spread bubonic plague, and the Bubonic Plague Hospital with 200 beds stands fifty yards from the Yellow Fever Hospital in a city of 80,000 as mute testimony to the justice of any law. There is likewise a law against admitting Japanese to the country, but no one mentions that either. Some Japanese laborers are indeed in the country, came in before the law.

"Dr. K's party was also on hand. I and the nurses and technicians were led to this hotel where the Commission had established its headquarters a week previously. . . . I was given a suite of rooms, bedroom, bathroom, and sitting room—rather unusual accommodation, because they themselves did not have such a pretentious suite."

When the commotion is over, the senator of the republic calls on Kendall, is worried, says that this about Senorita Maria Barrientos will be cabled everywhere and Guayaquil will have a worse name than it already has. But if now someone of the commission were to make a statement? Someone in authority? Such a statement would help the commission too. Guayaquil has no reason to feel especially friendly

267

toward American commissions. The Harvard School of Tropical Medicine was down here in 1913 and when it went back to the United States classified Guayaquil as one of the most unsanitary cities in the world.

Kendall agrees to the statement. What he says, briefly, is that though told before his arrival of the dying in the streets of Guayaquil, and of bubonic plague and other dreadful diseases, and of a heat so suffocating that only the accustomed could live, all is false. The city on the contrary is clean. The climate at this time of the year is like spring in the United States. And as for men dying in the streets, men die in their beds as elsewhere. The truth is that he has not seen so much as one dead rat. About 5 o'clock next morning Kendall is waked by a pounding on his door and a moment after in bursts the senator, falls to his knees by the side of the bed, proclaims that never has such good been spoken of Guayaquil. Guayaquil will never forget. "Hear, hear, how the newsboys are shouting in the streets!" And so they are. Kendall is invited to Quito, the capital, to tell the governor about yellow fever sanitation. That is what Kendall came for. Ecuador is being won over. Noguchi at the same time is writing that he has already started his work.

"I commenced my work July 16th, the day after my landing, at the Yellow Fever Hospital of this city. The whole hospital has been placed at our disposal, and although none of my instruments came at that time, I purchased enough equipment to start. . . . The laboratory had no shelves and they had to be put up.

268

Incubator, refrigerator, sterilizer, kerosene lamp, etc., all had to be installed in a hurry and you may well imagine the confusion against which I had to strive. But it is now getting better."

Gorgas believes that when the cause of yellow fever is found it will prove an organism very like the organism of infectious jaundice, an interesting guess on the part of an interesting man and worth noting. And Schaudinn, discoverer of the spirochete of syphilis, predicted that a spirochete would one day prove the cause of yellow fever, another interesting guess on the part of another interesting man and also worth noting. Noguchi is busy. Everybody is wanting to help.

"The Ecuadorian doctors, the director and his aides, are so eager to assist me in my research work that it is almost impossible to be alone! They are always about me. I am grateful to their good will, but I often wish I could work quietly alone."

He makes the wish felt. The wish seems strange to the Ecuadorian doctors, and to some of the American doctors too, and not the wish so much as the stress he gives it. He seems at moments like a child putting its arms and hands round something that belongs to it and frowning to frighten away whoever has the bad thoughts. As if someone might be wanting to steal something from him. One of the members of the commission keeps carefully away.

And it is true that he is wanting to work alone. It is true other times too. He has frequently spoken of it. He says that he does not want at the beginning of an investigation to talk of what he is at, wants first to have the idea a little firm in his own head. It is for the same reason that he does not at the beginning of an investigation read the literature, first works, then reads, likes to have penetrated a fair distance into his subject before he finds that there is no use, that everything is already done. Others, when they know what one is at, are so liable to speak of how difficult the thing is, to mention the many who have already tried and failed. Better to be a trifle deceived, to think one's subject simpler than it is, and not have one's enthusiasm damped at the outset.

But there may be something more than this. It may be partly as some others think. It may be partly that he is afraid and therefore secretive. For a while he seems suspicious even of the Spaniards with their fine manners. The members of the commission all eat together at the same hotel. One evening Kendall comes in late and because he does not want to disturb the others already seated at table takes a place in the next room and joins in conversation with the Spaniards there, instantly has the feeling that Noguchi is thinking there is something not quite straight, therefore goes to Noguchi and explains. Noguchi is so visibly relieved it is funny, thanks Kendall, and next morning thanks Kendall again, does it very sweetly, and Kendall is very fond of him, yet it is hard to escape the impression that the thanks is disproportionate. How sensitive Noguchi is. In a few days he begins to be easier, even of his own accord talks of what he is doing, invites the other men into his laboratory and describes to them how he sees his problem, says that he came to Ecuador with an idea, that he already half knows what he is after, that if he finds the cause of yellow fever at all the chances are he will find it soon.

Kendall meanwhile has accepted the invitation to meet the governor and has started across the mountains to Quito. By nightfall his train has reached Riobamba. Next morning in the cold, with no breakfast, in the blackness of pre-dawn, people standing in the aisle of the dirty coach, the journey is to continue. Kendall refuses. "Damned if I go to Quito like a peon." He starts instead back to Guayaquil, and the news that he is starting back runs on before him. Noguchi hears, comes across the river to meet him, takes his hand, presses it, presses it in the quietest way, imagines that perhaps Kendall is suffering as he would if he were in the same place, fancies Kendall may have been over-hasty and now is regretting.

A few days later the finest accommodations in the republic are put at Kendall's disposal and he starts once more across the mountains for Quito, this time gets there, talks with the governor, easily wins him over, then returns to Guayaquil. He is anxious to return, knows that Noguchi's laboratory is not yet according to Noguchi's wishes, and wants Noguchi started on his work as soon as possible, therefore goes straight to the laboratory when he arrives. As he enters Noguchi points to the microscope. "Look in there. That is the one I suspect." He thinks he has the cause of yellow fever already.

"I have already obtained a very encouraging result in regard to the causative agent of yellow fever. I have seen a delicate organism, not constantly, but very significantly. . . ."

The organism tapers to a fine point at each end and the ends are hooked. It is a spirochete, as Schaudinn predicted, and very like the spirochete of infectious jaundice, as Gorgas predicted. Noguchi only half conceals how excited he is. He says that he found this leptospira—for it belongs in the genus that he himself created, the same genus with the spirochete of infectious jaundice—on the 24th of July, just nine days after his arrival, and if really it is the cause the discovery was easy. He has been working on spirochetes for ten years and ought not to overlook a spirochete. He tells what he means to do. He plans his campaign, says Kendall, like a military genius, as if he had thought this all out in advance, knew what he would find, found what he knew he would find, and knows what he will do with what he has found. He has the organism. He has the experimental animal, the guinea-pig. And he has the pure culture.

"I succeeded in growing it and then producing a typical experimental disease resembling yellow fever— but I shall have to do much more before establishing the relation to the disease."

Lucky too that he brought those live guinea-pigs to the home of the guinea-pig.

"They were so useful in starting my work, as it was my very first step to transmit the disease from man to animal. If I did not have them with me I could not have started my work on the second day of my arrival. Guinea-pigs are said to be abundant in this country, but it took fully two weeks before I got about two hundred. . . . Monkeys are impossible to get here, and contrary to all the vague ideas of the abundance of this animal in all South America. I have tried most varied kinds of birds I could put my hand on. Four donkeys are coming to-morrow. Eighty wild rats and twenty-five mice. . . ."

Kendall is a hardened bacteriologist, yet it is stirring to see this man scheme and drive. He is preparing for the mosquito experiments.

"If I succeed in transmitting the germ to the mosquito and render it infective, another link of evidence will have been connected."

First thing every morning he goes into the city to see what new cases have occurred in the night. He wants to watch the disease at the bedside, is not willing simply to accept the findings and descriptions of the clinicians. To one of them it seems he doubts all eyes but his own. Doctor Pareja is director of the Yellow Fever Hospital, knows the yellow fever of Ecuador, goes with him. He is anxious to see everything, understand everything, makes innumerable notes, believes as always in writing everything down. Between him and Lebredo, Cuban member of the commission, there is some difference of opinion, possibly even some ill

273

feeling—a detail, but of some interest, and evidence that the human scene is growing naturally with the rest. And the human scene is growing.

"I do not go out after the supper but lately some doctors are coming to play chess with me. Now, I think this is a great waste of time and am thinking to give it up."

But he does not give it up, not chess. Some nights of course he stays in the laboratory, and some nights moves off into the dark of the porch to talk philosophy with Elliott, and whatever he is doing smokes the long black native cigars. The porch is screened. The laboratory is screened. Everybody is careful to close doors quickly behind them and except for the immune natives life is a slipping from one screened place to another.

"The first Sunday was spent by going out for alligator hunting on the River, and I shot at least three, but all escaped. No one else in the party hit any! So I was the great gunman! Well, it was rather hard to hit from a moving launch. The second Sunday I was taken again to hunting, this time birds as well. Seven birds—very huge one to a wee bit one—were killed by the same—the little fellow you know!"

And every Sunday now the commission is the guest of the municipality, a special steamboat, Ecuadorian soldiers at both ends loading guns so that all the huntsmen will have to do is pull the trigger. One Sunday Noguchi comes with a new gun, a shot-gun, bought it the day before, is free with his money as always, fancies he can kill alligators with a shot-gun, has forgotten about the skins. Everybody laughs. He does not mind that they laugh. He knows they are his friends. He does not mind about the gun either. He is too pleased about the gun to mind about the gun, bangs at everything he sees, nevertheless the following Sunday leaves the gun in his room. He is the only one of the party ever kills an alligator, does a post-mortem right there on the river bank. He is a good shot, is good at everything, as Hori says, and everything is his target. When he was in Pennsylvania it hurt him to think of the rabbits in the next room waiting to be swallowed alive, and he carried the old white rat about with him in his pocket, and last year when he was ill he was troubled by the unending line of guinea-pigs, yet he shoots at egrets and kills an alligator several hundred years in the making.

It has got about Guayaquil that he would like to know the smaller animal life of Ecuador, and every day now children come to the laboratory, one with a newt, another with a turtle, another with a toad. Noguchi never fails to leave his work to see what the children have brought, likes children, especially these little Spanish children, strokes their heads, suddenly may remark that he does not want children of his own. Some days he goes to one of the two big markets where there are the strangest kinds of animals. He is interested in all these animals because any one of them may be the carrier of disease, but he is interested in them also for themselves, fondles them, laughs at them, gives them names of human beings, yet shoots at egrets.

Guayaquil meanwhile follows intently what he is doing. All the earlier half-hostility is gone. Guayaquil has a hot head but a simple heart. It has seen how the American nurses stay day and night in the lazeretto. It has seen how the American doctors work. It has seen how Noguchi works. By the 27th of August the newspapers are permitted to say that the organism of yellow fever has perhaps been found. A few days later they say that this organism in the guinea-pig has produced all the clinical signs of yellow fever. In a long article *El Telegrafo* writes about Noguchi in this present discovery, in a second article about Japanese medicine and his place in that, in a third about his place in the history of yellow fever, all with easy conscience.

The nights now are made gay with dinners, long lavish Spanish dinners. Noguchi has in him something with which to perceive the Spanish quality, this fluidity so much more Japanese than American, bursts of hot emotion followed by a quiet. Surely he regards no one with suspicion now. Indeed the only persons he is not friendly with are his own nationals, those Japanese laborers who entered Ecuador before the law. The dropping of this distinguished Japanese exactly into their remote city must have had to them some of the earmarks of miracle. Yet he is cold, will have nothing to do with them. To one he seems almost brutal. Is he ashamed of them? He shows Kendall his Japanese

276

A Post-mortem on the Shore

He Looks at You from
Under

Something of an Actor

passport, would not give that up for anything in the world.

By early September the commission is ready to return to the United States. The newspapers print all the details, print again Kendall's photograph, Noguchi's photograph. There are cartoons, in one, the one that everybody speaks of, a huge mosquito is derricked up by a chain and the American doctors stand round to perform the autopsy. But Noguchi does not depart with the commission, still has work to do.

"I redoubled my efforts to find the organism in the blood and tissues of yellow fever patients and have added a number of strains, all of which are now in culture."

He has so far found his spirochete in six of twenty-seven cases diagnosed undoubted yellow fever. The guinea-pig continues the only animal subject to the infection. The guinea-pig is also the experimental animal for infectious jaundice. The two diseases do in fact have many similarities. While the members of the commission were still here the talk nights often turned to those similarities. Noguchi was fully aware of them. The members of the commission were mostly inclined to agree with Noguchi's views, only it seems Lebredo did not. The organisms of the two diseases are so much the same, the experimental animal is the same, and though up to now there has been no infectious jaundice reported in Ecuador the text-book description makes it clinically also much like yellow fever.

277

It is imaginable surely that the two might be confounded.

The time has come also for Noguchi's departure. When the fact is announced, late in October, there is a quick movement for a banquet and a movement to keep him in Ecuador, build him a fine laboratory, give him a fine salary. The Ecuadorians know of course that he will not stay, so pour their enthusiasm into the banquet. The night is the night of the 29th. The governor comes over the mountains from Quito. The commander of the army is present, the Mayor of Guayaquil, the Chief Justice of Ecuador, the President of the University, the Director of Hygiene, the Chief of Police, the Dean of the Medical School.

"Sir, by your discovery the country is once more given a future." (That is the way the principal address begins.) "Listen to the voice of gratitude of an entire nation, a nation that lives in dread because of the tragedy of the past. By your work fields will become fertile and the land rich. Once the disease is wiped away the immigrant will crowd this shore, will go out along the undeveloped seacoast, or into the mountains to look for hidden treasure. Think, when that day comes, how the gratitude of this nation will have increased. Honored Sir, the name of Hideyo Noguchi will never go out of Ecuador."

Oratory, but truth too, for it is Ecuador where the young men come down from the Andean plateau and die one in two. Noguchi has already inoculated the freshest battalions of these mountaineers with the vac-

278

cine made from his new spirochete. Whether this vaccine will protect the vaccinated cannot yet be known, but the feeling toward him is real. He seems both a benefactor and a great man. He is called on to speak, rises, with his right hand fingers the edge of the table, tips his head to one side, the body north-north-west, by some odd insistence of individuality leaning always at a slight angle to everybody else's—leans that way in the snapshots too.

"You would not take me to exaggerate if I say that in my life I have never experienced such sentiments as this evening. Your earnest sympathy, the profound kindness of to-day and the personal care which you have given me ever since my arrival, all put in me the extremity of spiritual pleasure. The height on which you have placed me is less high than the high culture of your country, and the great honor which you show me is a measure of your generous mind. I can find no words properly to express my thankfulness. I have come as a representative of the Rockefeller Institute to this city of Guayaquil to investigate yellow fever. From the day after my arrival I have worked in your hospital and have had great help from many of your doctors. Though I cannot go into my experiments now, because they must be made public after my return to New York, I may say that I think they have bearing on how we may prevent the horrible calamity of yellow fever. The results I have obtained are really the work of many scholars, and I am but one to have the happiness of trying to rescue many brethren falling victim to this dread disease. Strange fate may again put me into this land that I love. I hope you will allow me to offer my thankfulness to the many officials and friends who did not spare themselves to give me the necessary aid to accomplish my mission, because my glory, which I have now, owes very much to them. The brave army of Ecuador made me its commander, so please bear in mind that if urgency demands I will be the first to come up in haste to the call. I will wait the opportunity to serve. I pay my respects to the persons who have helped me in my labors. And at the end let me offer a word of applause to the young students of Guayaquil and Ecuador. Allow me to praise the high young men who stand in a row in a place as high as the high culture of your country, and I hope they may share with me the honor which they have given me."

That is how he feels toward the Ecuadorians. They are here in front of him where he can see them. What suspicions of Spaniards he once may have had he has no more. But how about the members of the commission? They are gone back home where he cannot see them. Who knows what they may be doing? At any rate one of them later receives a letter that must strike him as odd.

"I note that you have already prepared your paper for publication, and I shall be very much pleased to see it in print. One thing which I would like to request is that until I make announcement myself of the finding of the organism in yellow fever cases I should like not to have any mention made of it in your paper, this being the desire of . . ."

He tacks on the name of someone of the International Health Board, some director, someone in authority, and of course not impossible that it is the desire of the someone in authority too.

[XLVIII]

She Is Not Gone

When he is a few days out at sea, Guayaquil far behind, in the village of Okinajima Shika falls ill. Many in the village are ill, an epidemic of influenza. Hers is only a slight attack, but she is sixty-six, and soon they are sending to Tokyo for Miyabara as they promised Hideyo if ever there were danger. The influenza has turned to pneumonia, nevertheless Shika insists she is able yet to direct the affairs of her house, then presently is able no longer, is able only to lie there with closed eyes. Someone mentions her son's name. She rouses. The news has come that they have made him honorary colonel of the army of Ecuador. They have presented him with the sword. She is able to speak again. She hopes he will live long. She hopes he will keep his strength. She hopes he may go on and on, may push his investigations further and further. To that end she has lived even from the day when by her carelessness, as she has never ceased to think it, his fingers were burned away. And he has pushed on. He has succeeded greatly. Such success cannot come by

282

human ill alone. It is Kannon. Never has she omitted to pray. Without that help he could never have grown so great. Now she can die.

Miyabara arrives. Her lips are blue. Her pulse is quick and small. She is closely wrapped in a new quilt. Miyabara sent her that quilt a long time ago, wanted her to use it nights, but she never would. It was too fine. Only when she fell ill and the chills came then she thought she might. The shoji are drawn. The charcoal in the urori glows. Bandai and the rice-fields and the big temple and the little graveyard all are covered with snow. On the 19th of November she in her turn is ready to be sent to the fields.

Miyabara stays that night with Inu and with Inu's growing family. The old doctor Tokaku is there, and the old teacher, and Akatsu the student come back from America. They talk of many things. Last month, just a month before she died, she was able to buy a kakimono for the temple of Choshoji and another for Nakata Kannon. She had wanted to buy those kakimono most her life and just last month was able to. Was not that fortunate? Truly, her work was done. Was it not as if to finish that work beautifully that she was able to make those final two gifts to the temples that she loved so long?

Miyabara will write a long letter to Hideyo and will tell him all about this, and about the rice-fields, and about Bandai. The letter will be carried till it is frayed in the pocket of Hideyo's laboratory coat. The letter will never be answered. Miyabara knows how that is.

One can't write at such a time. The truth is that the letter would not be answered anyway. But the old teacher will write and his letter will be answered, the old teacher who carried the letters to the mother now so many years. The letter is answered at once.

"I was much moved. But since it is what we expect of life I receive it as inevitable. When I saw her three years ago she said there would be nothing left if she were to go, and the words are still in my ears. I myself think that the division between life and death is seen only from the side of life. If you think of the time before birth and the time after death this world becomes merely a temporary place to rest one's feet. So I am not confused but live in peace. I will do my best to follow her instructions and desires."

While the son is writing these words his friends in New York are worried for the way the news must cast him down. The tenderness for his mother is one fact of his personal life that he has not tried to hide. Yet he comes next morning fresh to his laboratory, glad to be back in New York, almost as if he had not heard. Finally someone asks him. He looks up sharply. "And why should I be sad? She is not gone." He says the words simply, absolutely, flatly. Yesterday when Maizie met him at the ship he took the news very calmly. They talked of usual things. While he was away Maizie had moved from the fourth floor at 381 Central Park West to the third floor, bought a number of lamps, lit them all before she went to the train. He was very pleased. He gives the feeling about certain large questions that he directly knows, directly sees, as now and then some human trait or some bit of impersonal nature. Nevertheless one of his scientist friends thinks him an atheist, thinks no doubt that he ought to be and therefore is. Another thinks something just a little turned, pathological is the word used, in his imagination. Surely the following would be a sign of that.

"On the day my mother died I was in Panama hospital demonstrating to physicians, and I know now that I was thinking of mother and of some other things and that I was quite depressed."

Paper Follows Paper

"At present I am studying the relation of this organism to organisms with similar morphology and am not at present prepared to give out any of my findings."

That is what he writes in December. It means he still has not announced his yellow fever spirochete. Later he writes Nichols.

"Certainly Weil's disease (infectious jaundice) and yellow fever are very much alike."

That "much alike" worries him. Are the two spirochetes really distinct species? Finally he has decided they are and has let the announcement go.

There follows a long series of papers. In the first he describes the patient. He begins with the general picture, then takes the symptoms one by one, how they appear, how they recede, contrasts the cases that recover with those that go to death, all very detailed and sometimes very terrible. Usually the patient comes down suddenly and is anxious to go to bed. His head aches. His loins ache. Where he touches there is pain. There is an agony in the abdomen. He is drowsy, often prostrated, and the advance of the symptoms is rapid. Vomiting occurs often as early as the first day. From the mouth comes a cadaver-like odor. The gums bleed. Great thirst. The whites of the eyes that were blood-shot in the beginning take on a yellow tinge and the yellow deepens. The skin is a light saffron that approaches at the height of the disease a gray-green. Sometimes there is bleeding from the nose, usually then also bleeding into the stomach, the ordinary vomit being replaced by black vomit, the blood in the stomach turning to a kind of tar. And if there is no black vomit during life there still may be black vomit stagnant in the stomach after death. After death the face is often smeared with blood and the mouth filled with clots. This death is most frequent on the fifth and sixth days, and if the patient survives the seventh his chances are good. As late as the eleventh he seldom dies. Beginning about the eleventh an intense jaundice spreads over the body and only very slowly disappears. The yellow fever of Guayaquil, Noguchi says at the close of this first paper, is like the descriptions of the disease in all parts of the world.

Paper follows paper. He describes the disease when the guinea-pig is inoculated with the patient's blood. A paper on that. He describes the disease when the guinea-pig is inoculated with his pure culture of the spirochete. A paper on that. The fifth paper is very important. While in Guayaquil he collected the blood of eighteen persons who had recovered from yellow fever and found that the serum of fifteen of them was able to destroy or quiet the movements of his spirochete, arguing further that his spirochete is the cause. The reaction is called the Pfeiffer and is carried out, an oddly diabolic instance of the scientific fancy, in the abdomen of living guinea-pigs.

He is working hard and happily, not as before the illness, looks healthier, comes early, goes late, as usual does not appear in the Institute dining room till the others are gone, is indeed conducting his campaign, as Kendall said, like a military genius. He treats some of the sick animals with his serum. They recover. A paper on that. He finds he is able to transmit the disease with mosquitoes. A paper on that. There has been a report of those fresh battalions of young men from the Andean plateau vaccinated with his vaccine. The great majority have passed safely through a yellow fever epidemic. So his vaccine has protected them. It is the old pace of 1910, 1911, 1912, but in a renewed human being. He begins even to look a little fat.

[L]

This Is Not a Complaint Against America or Americans

The fog is so heavy that his ship must anchor just
outside New York. He is on the way to Mexico. There
is yellow fever in Mexico. This is December 12th. Most
of the passengers are drunk. A steward is disagreeable.
How badly Americans behave. How insensible sometimes. A lone Chinaman sits on the deck and not a
person speaks to him. Why? Because he is yellow. In
the middle of the night after all the others have gone
to their cabins, in the black and fog, a woman screams,
rushes screaming through the hall, says a man has tried
to force his way in on her. There are voices, a sinister
uproar, then everything is quiet again. Through the
whole time no one has so much as snapped on a light.
Next morning, fog. Then on the horizon a black spot
—Cuba.

"431 years ago Columbus the undaunted reached
this very shore on his second voyage, and the history
of these years since his discovery is most astounding
of all human archives. To-day in the veins of those
who inhabit this hemisphere runs the blood of the new

comers and the original dwellers of these shores. . . . The very disease of whose investigation I am now on my second expedition has an inseparable relation to the early colonization of this hemisphere and it is surprising that, though the problem is no longer of the same practical importance as in earlier ages, a Japanese should have been given an opportunity to promote our knowledge of this historic scourge. Pray God he may not spend his efforts in vain though none but He alone directs as seen fit."

The black spot grows and later in the day the ship puts in at Havana. Noguchi spends the stop-over in Havana with Lebredo, Cuban member of the commission in Guayaquil.

From Havana to Progresso Mexico is thirty-six hours. At Progresso he is met by the American consul and several others, and by evening has reached Merida, where Doctor Kligler is waiting at the train. Doctor Kligler went on ahead from New York. The two have supper and then go immediately to the isolation hospital to see a patient. The patient is definitely jaundiced.

Merida has been free of yellow fever for about five years, but this year the mosquitoes have come in unprecedented hordes and the fever is back, or rather was back, at present there being only three cases. One is a soldier who if he really had the disease is at too late a stage to give any hope of finding the spirochete. The second is a fatal case, but though guinea-pigs come down with a typical infection it is not possible to find the spirochete either in the tissues or the cultures. That leaves one case. From it blood is taken daily and cultures and animals are inoculated.

"Then, on a Sunday morning I came to the laboratory first and Noguchi was to follow." So writes Kligler. "Immediately on my arrival a dead pig was brought in. It looked definitely jaundiced. It had run a normal temperature course. We had expected nothing, and I came somewhat later than usual merely to see if everything was O. K. Then Noguchi sauntered in. Immediately the air became electrified. I had been excited by the find, but not being certain had suppressed the excitement. Noguchi was certain. With feverish excitement the autopsy was carried through and the search of the organs for leptospira begun. It was not long before they were found."

After the day's work toward 11 o'clock Noguchi himself writes of the same event.

"How beautiful the three-quarter moon sending her cool silvery beams over this unusually romantic patio. . . . This dustless world of moonlight! . . . My mind is relaxed since this afternoon. Do you know why?"

He goes on then to tell what Kligler has just told. And thus in a disease diagnosed yellow fever in Mexico the same spirochete has been found that was found in a disease diagnosed yellow fever in Ecuador. Presently he is able to show that the serum prepared against the disease of Ecuador protects animals against the disease of Mexico.

So the work in Merida is done. He can be as leisurely as he likes, visits in the town, finds he is as fond of the Spaniards of Mexico as he was of those of Ecuador. Late every afternoon he goes for an automobile ride, talks frequently with Kligler of Japan, of its development, is as much patriot as at any time these last years. And evenings he goes to the Cuban Club or to the cinema or plays chess, and as always is worried when he loses.

"An old gentleman of 70 years with a youthful mind and well preserved constitution, and who had been in Mexico for over 30 years as an adventurous engineer under Diaz and who knows the country well came to my room and played chess until 12:30. We enjoyed the games, but the light went out at 11, and we had to resort to flashlight, each carrying one in his hand while playing!"

In February he is back in New York.

And by April is in Havana again, on the way to Peru. There is yellow fever in Peru. In Havana he once more spends the day with Guiteras and Lebredo—"gave them a culture and inoculated some guinea-pigs and fitted up a darkfield"—then continues on to the Canal Zone stopping at Cristobal and writing from the hotel there.

"On this trip from the very beginning everybody was very courteous. . . . I must revise my former impressions of the American travelers vis-a-vis the Japanese. Of course, many of them seem to have learned of my mission and perhaps also whom I am representing. That little bit of propaganda, 'conquest of Y-f.' has done much good, at least in arousing general interest, and naturally they think more of me because I was in it! You can see how unjustified is modesty for me. I now believe it is one's duty (at least, one belonging to a persecuted tribe like I myself) to allow any favorable press propaganda whenever an occasion presents itself. I hope you will agree with me. This world is like a child, wants to see before believing. . . . I bought a small set of oil colors in Havana and tried to paint in my stateroom, but it was impossible due to a rough sea. . . . There are two or three honeymoon couples on this trip, and many young mothers, too, everywhere I go. They are all so beautiful. Life is a miracle. . . . To-night they are having a ball at the Hotel, and so many young people seem to enjoy. The music makes me triste. Vacant life? But not for those whose hearts are happy. One often wonders the meaning of all this. Perhaps too deep to analyze! Well, I hear their hand-clapping while my thoughts are running away wild."

The ship goes on down the coast. At dinner he sits at the captain's right and everyone is friendly. When off Guayaquil, just now quarantined because of bubonic plague, he settles to another letter.

"Only thrilling near-accident was that the steamship officer at Balboa had a wrong time for the steamer, and I came some 20 minutes too late to catch it. The boat had already gone out to the sea. I inquired an American military policeman (in U. S. Army uniform) if the Chile was there at the dock. He said she was not in yet (in a haughty and arrogant air). I doubted it, so inquired a colored man at the office in the dock. He said the Chile had left the dock 20 minutes ago. I told him how important it was for me to catch the steamer. He told me to see the Captain of the Port about it. I hurried up to the office of the Captain of the Port and explained how I was misinformed of the time. He said he could not do anything for me. Then he asked me if I had any money to deposit for hiring a fast steamer to chase the Chile. I said yes. After depositing $8, he ordered one of the official launches. . . . I was glad of his assistance and finally reached my steamer after 25 minutes. The Chile was still anchored 7 miles out of the dock, but she was to send a boat for me, anyway, as they missed me when sailed. The boat man told me that such accidents occur quite frequently, and usually they make a plenty of money out of the misguided or misinformed passengers. I gave them $5 tip. The man who ordered the boat for me for $8 was not the Captain of the port, but one of the official pilots. Incidentally, if the American Military Police (this policeman is supposed to give all informations regarding the boats at the pier) had succeeded in deceiving me about the Chile's not having got in yet from Cristobal, and if I had believed him and turned back to the Hotel, I would have missed my boat altogether! An American in the U. S. Army uniform has been a curse to me. Two years ago they annoyed me with rifles, and this time by a lie! What a dishonest and dishonorable

294

lot of creatures I do meet! I dislike their attitude toward me in detail and in sum. . . . You once told me I am down on the Americans and things American in general, anyhow. Well, after having had the experiences I am having, you would not blame me getting resentful. . . . Did I write you about an American Purser on S. S. Merida, one of the United Fruit Co. boats? On that steamer Dr. Barberis, of Ecuador, sailed. I went aboard to give him my letters of introduction, but he was not yet there. I went to the purser's office, and I was met with a sneering greeting, and peculiarly arrogant young man wanted to know who I was, etc. I said who I was, and that I did not see why he should have treated any man like a whipped cur. I demanded the explanation. He tried to tell me that he knew some Japanese in New York, and they have brought many presents, etc. Then wanted to know if I cannot get some jade for him. I said I was not a pedlar. I said he was an important man on board, as he is the purser, but said it did not entitle him to insult a stranger who came to see one of the passengers. I told him I knew the General Manager of the United Fruit Co., at Colon, and that the company has been taking care of many things. This changed his attitude completely. He turned pale, trembled, and stumbled. He offered an apology, but I did not bother with him. I just smiled. He keeled over and sat on the berth and sobbed and shed a great deal of tears. He would not stop crying. I felt sorry and patted his back and told him not to worry, for I will not 'tell on him.' He stopped weeping, with occasional sobs. Well, I never saw a man behave like this young purser. Perhaps he is insane. If I had more time I would have demanded explanation from that Military Policeman for telling me a lie about the Chile—perhaps he was insane, too. . . . This is not a complaint against America or Americans, but a record of facts for useless reflection. I really believe that many specimens of human beings are like wild animals, and I am not the worst of them yet. . . . I played chess with an American, a Frenchman, a Spanish, a couple of South Americans, but I won all. . . . You must forgive and forget about my indignation over the military policeman or the crazy purser—read them as news and no more."

Payta is the northernmost port of Peru. When Kligler got here he found no water, no light, no facilities, and no spirochetes.

"For weeks I sweated at Payta with no results whatever. Cultures, animals—everything was negative. Yet there was real yellow fever there. Dr. Carter in person made the diagnosis. I blamed the animals, the culture media and the makeshift wooden hut near the beach which served as a laboratory. But the results continued negative."

Noguchi reaches Payta the 5th. Kligler has come from the foothills of the Andes to meet him, the first lap of Kligler's journey being sixty-five miles across desert, thirty hours on horseback with a police escort and only two short periods of rest. He went to the

Andes because of a report of yellow fever, got the blood for inoculating the cultures, but now that he has reached Payta is exhausted. Noguchi writes of Kligler's experience.

"He got 6 cases (one of which proved later not to have been yellow fever) and then felt headache and pains all over his body—diagnosed as y.f. and took the serum. Got well in 3 days."

Bad about Kligler, but very hopeful that the serum should have helped. Early next morning the two are already at work. A remarkable fact is that Kligler's cultures are not contaminated. They were collected under the most primitive conditions in dirty huts with the patients lying on the floor. The two begin at once to search for spirochetes. The way they do is to have Kligler go over a slide and if he finds nothing Noguchi go over the same slide.

"The first 15 minutes were tense, but after the first positive result the rest were carried on with easy mind." (Kligler writes.) "It was only after that that I really convalesced."

Spirochetes are found in cultures from three of the five bloods and guinea-pigs are made ill by four of the five bloods. Thus in a disease diagnosed yellow fever in Peru the same organism has been found that was found in a disease diagnosed yellow fever in Mexico and Ecuador. Noguchi writes that the work was a complete success.

"Yesterday I went to a nearby village called Larena by horseback. At Catacos I was thrown off the horse and badly struck on the head, hip, and thigh. But no fracture. After a little rest I continued the trip and finished the tour of 1½ hours under scorching sun. . . . There was no case of y.f., only a false alarm. . . . A doctor (Peruvian sanitary corps) felt sick since Sunday night, was quite ill Monday, showing definite symptoms for y.f. He was taken to the Hospital in the afternoon and was treated with the serum. His temp. was 39.5 at the time of injection, 9 p.m., and fell to 37 at 3 p.m. to-day. He is feeling well already, other symptoms disappearing."

So this doctor also has been helped by the serum. Noguchi reached Payta the 5th, leaves the 26th.

"I worked every day from about 8 a.m. to 6 p.m. . . . In the evening there was no certainty of electric light and many a night we had to crawl to bed for lack of light. . . . Our after-dinner hours usually useless because we formed an habit to spend much time in the dining room after supper (or lunch) by discussing various things—by the way there was always some light in the dining room, but that was not of any good to me to spend a quiet evening alone in my room."

He stops at Lima, meets many distinguished Peruvians, but something else, something possibly much more important than Peruvians, two Peruvian diseases, hunts them up in the hospital, local diseases but so peculiar that they have lured the curiosity of bacteriologists everywhere—Oroya fever and verruga peruana.

"Fortunately I saw both of them and made smears

298

and cultures and animal inoculations. . . . I am anx
ious to study them sometime."

Then he is once more at the Canal Zone and by
night writing a letter.

"This is 2 a.m. already and the night is deep and
still. The window opens to the sea and admits the ever
stirring murmurs of the sea, a sound peculiarly unbal-
ancing and disquieting. I don't see the sea but it reminds me of angry waves and I do not like them—you
remember that my boyhood was spent in hilly
countries."

And a letter to another friend, an old one, the
oldest now, Kobayashi.

"For long silence I feel quite fearful. While in
Peru from Piura I wrote you and I think that letter
must be under your knees by now. . . . There is not
the smallest moment when I do not think of you two.
Only during scientific experiment I do not have much
time to sit silent and then I feel very guilty for negligence. . . . In Peru the President offered me directorship of Peru Research Institute . . . pay me 40,-
000 yen . . . contract for five years and renewable
. . . heirs to get 100,000 yen if I die. . . . These
offers are record-breaking. . . . I have not written
reply yet. . . . Also the Department of Agriculture
of Great Britain is beginning investigation of hoof and
mouth disease and offers me directorship. . . . You
speak of last words of mother and I know mother's
spirit is staying round me and so I pass my life without
great mistake. . . ."

He tells how he carried the o-fuda all the way to Mexico and all the way to Peru, the o-fuda, the bit of sacred paper that his mother brought from Nakata Kannon on one of her pilgrimages and sent through Kobayashi the long way to America.

The offer from Peru he does not accept. The offer from Great Britain he does not accept.   But an increase of salary he has.

The Summer of 1921

And now it is vacation time, June again, but he is not thinking of that. He is reading the proofs of the last of the yellow fever papers. He is thinking too of a revision of the old book on syphilis.

"Yesterday I went out to sign the contracts with Mr. Hoeber and I took a luncheon at the Hotel Netherland."

At the luncheon the talk turned to another book, a book on spirochetes, and he has agreed to that too. Also he has been considering a book on yellow fever, rather a monograph on yellow fever. All three subjects at once. So he is very busy. And besides he has had to take a quick dip back into the serology of syphilis, someone having gone to print with a criticism of what he did twelve years ago.

"It showered heavily in the evening, and it rained all night. I went out to play chess. My work on Rocky Mountain spotted fever is getting interesting."

Rocky Mountain spotted fever too. The revision of the book on syphilis. The book on spirochetes. The yellow fever monograph. Serology of syphilis. And to-day something happened in the laboratory.

"By chance I examined one of the normal rabbits showing a suspicious lesion and found the 'rabbit pallida' in fairly large numbers!"

That now is very interesting. A German recently reported finding just such a rabbit spirochete, also similar lesions.

"I have made some cultures and will follow the further development. I am sending you a broken slide for amusing yourself."

He quickly has the spirochete in pure culture, is taking photographs of it, is inoculating rabbits and monkeys with the culture, doing experiments to find whether the disease is infectious, also to find how it is carried, also searches in the normal stock to see if any more are infected and learns that two are. "I am glad to inform you." He makes a Wassermann test, finds the blood negative. The rabbit disease is not the human disease. Meanwhile June has slipped by and he is still in New York.

"As to my getting away I have no definite idea. I want to follow up the work a little longer. Perhaps I shall go to Shandaken on Friday or Saturday. Anyhow this is unimportant."

And a few days later again.

"The work is getting so interesting that the vacation is getting distasteful to me just now."

Then he does go to Shandaken, takes with him all the data on this rabbit spirochete, begins writing the paper. Once he breaks through the writing for a quick run down to New York.

"On the train I cut up the photographs of the spirochetes (rabbit) and have them arranged for plates."

And a little later he is finished, everything, the experimental work, the photographs of the germ, the writing of the paper, all in something more than one month.

At the same time he has made a fair headway into the literature for the book on spirochetes.

"I am trying to read up these books on my desk before getting away, but there are so many of them, and I am so slow in reading!"

The chapter on classification of the spirochetes will be the most difficult to write, there being so many points of dispute.

"Spironema was proposed by Vuillemin to replace Spirochaeta. . . . But it happens that Schaudinn replaced Spironema with Treponema. . . . I cannot see why we should choose Spironema, proposed vaguely by Vuillemin, for the type of organism still unknown to that time but definitely shown to have a flagellum by Schaudinn, who purposely created a spiral genus for this type."

This book on the spirochetes is to be the proof of that mastery he set for himself so many years ago, spirochetes reaching over the whole of his scientific life beginning at Watanabe's microscope and ending with his discovery of the spirochete of yellow fever.

The chapter on classification continues to seem hardest. He thinks it is because he has so little natural history. "Still nothing is difficult, you can learn at any time."

The cottage at Shandaken is a summer place and things get out of order.

"The water supply was found completely ruined by a pollution of the well. The putrefactive odor of the water was such that it was not possible to touch it or even live in the house unconcerned. . . . The garage man came and said he would dig up a new well. . . . The lighting system is O.K., but the coal and wood left last summer are mostly stolen (?). The villagers greeted me cordially, but my humor is none the better."

Several days pass. He goes to the post office for his mail and finds a letter telling him, odd coincidence, of certain large spirochetes living exactly in water having that kind of putrefactive odor.

"Oh! I am sorry that I have not kept my old polluted well undisinfected for the study of spiral flora. It must have been wonderful, but now I had it filled with chlorinated lime and ashes, etc., that there can be nothing left of interest! What a stupidity! All through excitement to have a well dug, etc."

There is one spirochete for all his work on spirochetes that he has not seen, and it happens it is the first ever seen by any man, by Ehrenberg in 1832, its structure said to be easily made out in stained preparations and on it based the theories of the structure of all the spirochetes and the guesses as to how they move. He would like to see that one.

"I have never seen any real Spirochaeta yet, and I must find one soon somewhere. I just examined the well water, but nothing living seems to be left there!"

Then some days later.

"This morning I went down to see if anything was in the well, and, to my disgust, I found a wild rabbit drowned in it. I am getting the water disinfected and then covered with a board to prevent another accident."

Apparently anything may suggest spirochetes to his mind, for the letter goes right on.

"There are many rabbits around the bungalow, but I don't know whether I can examine them for spiros or not, it will be interesting."

He examines earthworms, grasshoppers, trout, his own teeth.

"The improvised darkfield was too feeble to be of any use, so the direct sun was tried, and with perfect satisfaction! Lucky that the day is sunny. I examined the scrapings of the deposits on the back of teeth of lower jaw and found rich flora of spirochetes."

And again some days later.

"This is a warm day, and I have been working under the direct sun (for darkfield) for many hours studying the oral flora of spirochetes."

He is much struck by some observation of a friend also interested in spirochetes, writes his friend a letter, expands his friend's idea, sees the possibilities, makes a number of suggestions. "Here is your great opportunity." He rushes along, then suddenly stops, realizes

305

that if he keeps on in this way it will soon be as if the idea were not his friend's but his own, and he knows how it feels to have that happen to one's idea.

"I hope the mere mention of these things will not take off the edges of your conception or idea already in execution. I just felt to write this down."

He lays aside the chapter on classification to paint a picture, copies the cover of Ibanez's *La maja desnuda*. "Finished it in one day." Sometimes he finishes three in one day, but sometimes works many days, especially on one, a portrait that his friends say was very good when he finished it the first time. He is always taking that portrait down from the wall, insisting that it is not quite right, touching it here and there and then putting it back on the wall again. When he paints hardest there is paint even on the dog.

And the next time he lays aside the chapter on classification it is to fish. He goes just back of the cottage. If he does not return in the first fifteen minutes he will stay a long time. The fish must bite in the first fifteen minutes, otherwise, no, he has not the patience. When they do bite he comes with fish in all his pockets, his pants pockets too. He owns a fish basket, but you can't catch fish, he says, with a thing like that. Of course he does his fishing nights. And of course the night must be moonless. "The fish see you!" Some nights Maizie goes with him. "It is you and that dog —you sitting there lighting cigarettes—how can one fish?" It is terrifying to watch him. The stream is swift. He begins carefully enough, steps carefully from rock to rock out toward the deep water, seems conscious of the precariousness till the moment he casts the line, then gets very excited. His mother used to say that when he was a very small boy he would sit at the edge of Inawashiro lake and his eyes follow the movements of a wren and a crazy look come into them.

He leaves Shandaken a second time, goes down to New York, stays three days, each of the three days from morning to night bends over the darkfield microscope examining spirochetes, takes photographs of spirochetes, runs through a large collection of samples of stagnant water. And a little later still the summer is gone. When next he returns to New York it is to stay. A few days after his return he writes Nichols.

"I wonder if you have a strain of yaws in rabbits?"

Yaws is another disease caused by a spirochete. He fancies he is going right through the winter working on his spirochete book, but he is not. It is not yaws comes next but Rocky Mountain spotted fever.

[LII]

I Must Do Something About It

It is many years since Ricketts, then not long out of college, went to the Bitter Root Valley of Montana to study Rocky Mountain spotted fever. The valley is the valley the old Indian chief said was visited at certain times of the year by evil spirits, and no wonder to think of evil spirits when on one slope of that valley nine in ten falling ill with the disease, if they are past middle life, die, while on the other slope the disease does not occur at all. Ricketts worked with speed and brilliance. Soon he was able to announce that the guinea-pig and the monkey were the experimental animals. Soon he proved correct the earlier suspicion that the carrier of the disease is a wood tick, proved it by having the tick feed on guinea-pigs sick with the disease and then on healthy guinea-pigs and make them sick. He showed that the particular tick lives in nature on the dangerous west slope. In fact he touched every side of the problem. He appears even to have seen in the blood of the animals that very organism that was later to be thought the cause.

308

But he only saw the organism. He could not get it in pure culture, consequently could not produce the disease in animals, consequently left the cause still an open question. And that was why Wolbach and Noguchi in 1916 both set out to see what they could do, Ricketts then dead six years, dead of typhus in Mexico City whither he had gone to try to prove that a louse is the carrier of typhus. Wolbach began very early in 1916, Noguchi a little later, and already in the spring Wolbach was able to announce an organism having certain peculiar characteristics. He could not get the organism in pure culture. He saw it in the tissues of the experimental animal, later saw it also in the ticks and in the tissues of man, but still could not get it in pure culture. So Noguchi could not but regard the cause of Rocky Mountain spotted fever as somewhat an open question. And he has so regarded it year after year. The suspected organism belongs to the class known as Rickettsia, named so after Ricketts.

"The Montana ticks were full of the Rickettsia, but none was infective this year. It is still a question to my mind how much of these bodies are pathogenic and what difference between the infective and the non-pathogenic."

That is the way Noguchi writes now in 1922, continues not convinced, but has nothing more convincing of his own, and this work he has been at since summer is a search not for a cause but for a serum.

Ricketts also tried to produce a serum but never was able to get one potent enough. That is Noguchi's difficulty too. What he does find, however, is that if a guinea-pig that is convalescing from a first dose of infected blood be inoculated two or three times during its convalescence there is a fair increase of potency. But the guinea-pig is too small to make even a potent serum useful. Some larger animal must be found. He tries the horse. It will not serve. The rabbit is better. It is bigger, and its serum does definitely suppress infection in guinea-pigs if given before symptoms have appeared. That would mean that a man out hunting on the dangerous west slope would have to know that he had been bitten by an infected tick and take the serum at once. If he waited till there were symptoms the serum would do him no good. If a laboratory worker were accidentally infected the matter would be simpler because he would ordinarily know. Yet saving laboratory workers from accidental infections certainly would not seem far to extend a serum's usefulness, nevertheless Noguchi regards this as very important, has even an oddly strong feeling on the point, the oddness a little less when one learns that every year some worker in spotted fever dies of spotted fever.

So he has the serum. He tries now for the vaccine, works at that for months, later will carry it with him to Missoula Montana to attend a conference on Rocky Mountain spotted fever, nine Japanese at Hamilton and all the Hamilton laboratory force volunteering for the vaccination. Noguchi's hope again is that even if the vaccine may not come into wide use it may yet make the work of laboratory workers safer.

310

Some years ago he had a helper, Steve by name, the same Steve who slipped into the room at Mount Sinai and secretly drew a tube from his inside pocket and let the sick Noguchi see. Steve handled the spotted fever virus all the time Noguchi was at Mount Sinai and continued to handle it, more or less because he had begun, after Noguchi got well. Steve knew of no accident, yet he fell ill, showed symptoms of spotted fever, and after he died his tissues were the tissues of spotted fever. Doctor Wolbach himself saw the tissues. Doctor Lambert sent them to him. They could be the tissues of nothing but spotted fever or tsutsugamushi disease or typhus, and Steve had of course not been exposed to the latter diseases. So there must have been some accident of which he did not know. Noguchi was terribly shaken by the death, felt young Steve as much a martyr as if he had been investigating the disease he died of. Steve had a wife and baby. As one who went to the funeral said, Noguchi could not have been more stricken if Steve had been his son. Steve has since remained more or less constantly in Noguchi's mind. Noguchi handles the virus himself. Nobody in the laboratory is allowed to touch it. To Maizie he says again and again that Steve died for some reason, calls him *my boy,* and is very likely in the next moment to say that something must be done about Rocky Mountain spotted fever. Had there been a vaccine Steve would have been vaccinated and might never have been infected, or with a serum might even have been cured after infection.

Steve's death is of course only part of the urging behind Rocky Mountain spotted fever. The obscurity of the disease and Noguchi's pride also are part. Then there is the hope that if he pure-cultured the cause of spotted fever the fatal tsutsugamushi disease would follow, and typhus too. "We might resolve many similar diseases." Whoever works hereabout knows that the untying of one right knot may undo a whole bundle of discoveries. But instead of untying that knot someone else has untied it for him, or seems to have. That is not pleasant. He has worked six years on spotted fever and has not published a single paper. Why? Because there has been nothing to publish.

Meanwhile everything that touches the subject continues to excite him. He visits an old friend of Pennsylvania days. The old friend has a country place with a valley and a stream, the dogs never allowed to go to the stream because they are sure to come home covered with ticks. Noguchi is told the fact, not a remarkable fact, but remarkable the way he receives it, begs that the dogs just this once be allowed to go to the stream, he himself will be responsible for every tick. His friend does not understand but lets the dogs go, and Noguchi keeps his promise, carefully picks off the ticks, carefully bottles them, carefully corks the bottles. He is most excitedly happy all the afternoon. All the morning he was genial and dignified. Several days later his friend receives a report that the ticks are in no way dangerous either to man or beast.

312

LIII

That Tour of America

Chiwaki has arrived in America. This is that tour all expenses paid of which there has been talk almost since the pupil himself arrived in America. Chiwaki no doubt smiled more than once at the thought of Noguchi ever at one time having money enough to pay all expenses. But on Noguchi's enthusiasm, on whatever change in his pocket, on a big banquet, on his hours, those hours that he gives less and less to anything outside his work and his intimate life, on all that Chiwaki knows he can count. Chiwaki still wears his hair close-cropped, is not so different really from when he first came for a summer month to Wakamatsu, is tall for a Japanese, has big ears. Noguchi now travels with the master from one American city to another, spends the best of a month, arranges meetings, dinners, railroad reservations, goes as far west as Chicago. From Washington on May 26th comes a letter.

"Everything went all right so far. Had a fairly restful night on the train. Hope Mr. Hori got rooms for Dr. Chiwaki. . . . We will reunite at 11 a.m. and

313

get ready to be presented to the President and Mr. Hughes. Must hurry up now."

Chiwaki's practical reason for this tour is to learn what he can of American institutions and to find what moneys he can for the upbuilding of the old college back in Tokyo. So Chiwaki is interested in dentists and receives from President Harding an introduction to his Cleveland dentist who it turns out is also Mr. Rockefeller's dentist. There is a meeting with Mr. Edison. Small wonder if Chiwaki feels that he is moving at once in celebrated American society. There follow dinners, weeks of dinners, meetings, interviews, the party moving westward, at length a letter from Drake Hotel, Chicago.

"The trip to Cleveland was pleasant and eventless. . . . Doctor Casto, dean of dental school of Western Reserve, was there to meet us. He drove us to Dr. Stephan's office, where we were greeted by Dr. Stephan, a young man of 49 and a very pleasant man. He showed us some of his skillful works, and then photographs of Mr. Harding, of J. D. R. Sr."

The first day in Chicago also is eventless. The second day the party calls on Doctor Johnson and on Doctor Brophy.

"Both about 75 years old but as vigorous as young men. . . . These both venerable old men are really lovely, and I appreciated their friendliness to the Japanese in general."

In the evening there is another banquet and next morning, the 29th of June, Noguchi at last parts with the master of Takayama nights and days. The master says he has himself paid all the expenses.

LIV

The Summer of 1922

And by the 1st of July Noguchi is in New York and at work again. He is at herpes, a new problem this year.

"I am still making experiments to determine the filterability of the herpes virus. I will cut short my experiments and go to Shandaken by Friday of next week. . . . To-day about forty rabbits are being inoculated."

He goes to Shandaken. This summer is not beginning like last. His mood is different. Furthermore, there is to be so much less freedom this summer. There is so much that is definite, partly left over from last summer, partly accumulated during the winter. The revision of the book on syphilis is still not out of his hands. The book on spirochetes is no further than it was. The yellow fever monograph is where it was. Finally there is this vexatious subject of herpes. He has been at it through most of the winter and spring. Several are at it, again a group problem like poliomyelitis, and he apparently about as happy at this as he was at that. It is ten years since poliomyelitis, but he has not changed, still squirms under any collaborative scheme, regards it as in the end always a dilution of the one self that can do the work. The winter and the spring hang over him. It is not as easy to get himself under way this summer as it was last. He starts one thing, lays it aside, starts another, tries all the old external sources of stimulation.

"Yesterday I found a Spanish gentleman from Cataluña who plays chess with me. . . . No fishing or painting yet, except I have tried, but there is lack of inspiration in these directions this year. I hope my mind gradually be relaxed in time to enjoy the stay. When one has so many things on his mind, he is apt to be worrisome and unproductive."

He tries to do something to finish up the book on syphilis, is considering the arrangement of the chapters and the indexing and is writing a preface, still does not understand why his modification of the Wassermann has got so little attention, still lays it to the inertia of the doctors, meanwhile himself continues as listless as before.

"Up here everything is dead, and I spend much time in looking over some literature on septicemia. Quite interesting to see that Dr. Smith had already done so much in immunity work as early as 1890! Somehow, his work is model of precision and foresight. . . . The old Spanish has met so many reversals in the chess games that he does not come often to play. But a young Cuban boy beats me as a rule, and he will come again."

A few days later he is once more at the herpes data.

317

He complains that as the labor on this group problem was divided he could not carry his experimentation into the brain and it had to be carried there because the disease led there. One cannot break up a disease into convenient organs. It goes where it likes.

"It was wrong from the beginning to restrict my work in that way, as no one can discover anything with such a restriction. . . . Then for a few hours I have tried to paint a lily out of the garden. . . ."

He continues moody, tries chess. "Won all—they are not very strong." But his moodiness does not change.

"I often think that zoologists, botanists, chemists, and physicists enjoy their lives better than the less scientific medical men because of their broader preliminary scientific training and their complete absorption in their chosen research work. Their regards are not 'worldly,' but their own satisfaction in finding the truth."

A few days later the mood is less general. He is doubting himself now.

"Somehow I am getting conscious of my incomplete preparation to go on with the research work—in other words, I need rejuvenation. Where and how can I get it? I had a spare time to peep and read some articles in the J. of Gen. Physiology and other journals and was amazed to see the rapid progress in all the fields. I could have done some fine works too, but the vague indefinite bacteriology kept me from progressing."

And in another week he is only worse.

"I have never felt so lonely and depressed as in these last few days. . . . I went out to fish at night with such success, played chess, with some gains, tried to paint, without much success, speculated for future and many other things—usually my spirits seem to flag. Why?"

He complains of the rain and chill, and continues to complain through the next two weeks, not his way when he is right. He says that he has lost track of the date in his restlessness. It is August 4th. By August 7th he is still the same, says that he remained out fishing until 3 o'clock in the morning and fell in the brook. And two days later he says that he feels frozen out of life.

Six weeks of the summer are gone. So little is accomplished. He takes a run down to New York and on his return has a spurt of energy, starts again on the herpes, is determined he will not break up at Shandaken till he is through with that work.

"I am now about to finish up herpes work, to analyze how far I have gotten in the study of its nature."

And he continues at the analysis day after day, ever so often recalls how in the spring and winter his work was restricted and his temper rises afresh. He says that the evidence for the filterability of the herpes virus is simply inadequate unless the brain is used to test the filtrate. But——

"Anyhow, I did the experiments with brain emulsions and proved the filterability in my last experiment (in June) . . . . A great waste of energy it was for me and for everyone concerned."

All that, however, makes no difference now. Now he has himself once more in full control.

"Last night I worked a lot, till quite late, but I am feeling better than ever. I am getting stronger, and my mind quite active. I am hoping to finish several sections to-day. It is getting interesting!"

By the 9th of September he is only busier.

"I work straight through the whole day and well into the night, but the task is a frightful mess."

Then a relapse.

"Yesterday it rained pouring and thundered from the morning. . . . To-day it is so chilly that fireside is not a bad place to sit. Then, it is drizzling and windy, and I have a cold. . . . I often find myself confused, and I am seeking to see my way through out of this uncontrollable entanglement of circumstances. I often wonder what all this means—a phenomenon of life—and where we are heading to, and what, if any, is the purpose of life. It seems we are life itself and only a part of a larger force. We are brought out here to play our parts as completing that greater system of force. I only feel the smallness and weakness of man. . . . Each is endowed with a given amount of energy, and this is so variable in different individuals. Those who are fortunate to have more energy may break through these external forces, but not always, because the latter may be proportionately too great to overcome. Or, an individual with less energy may come out triumphantly if the external forces be relatively weaker."

The next day he is better again.

"This morning got up at 6:45 a. m. and started the herpes analysis. My head was clearer, and until this moment I continued to work (except breakfast of three eggs and a glass of milk). The work progressed to a stage where I may start writing something systematically. Anyhow, my courage is coming back." (Remembers again.) "I still detest anyone's hanging on my heels when I am trying to accomplish something." (And feels what he felt about collaborative schemes.) "I am getting less tolerant as I see that such combinations will never do any real good to science—much waste of energy on my part, at least."

And now it is time to return to New York. "In looking back I have done so little this summer that I am ashamed." The book on spirochetes is no further than last summer, begins to go as the venom book. The yellow fever monograph is no further either. "At least I have finished the herpes paper." But that, a work of his maturity, a work of a spring and a summer and winter, never sees print.

[LV]

Hori's Flat

On and off he visits at Hori's flat, Hori still at 1 Manhattan. They may expect Noguchi any hour. He rings the bell, and the door opens and shuts quickly behind him, and there may be a laugh. It is another world. When that door shuts it shuts on New York, on America, on the occident. Americans say he is so very American, but a good deal of Japanese there is left in him no doubt.

Hori's flat is a different place from what it used to be. Tokuko Hori, who came that day with her brother to the hospital, has made over that bachelor citadel. And such a bachelor! Tokuko loves her brother, says he is a ve-e-r-y gifted man, not like her father, but ve-e-ry gifted in his own way. What things he collects though. Heaps them up. Pictorial supplements of the *Times* as far back as—Hori himself does not know how far back.

The men play chess. It seems they would not get done their game all night. Games! Hour after hour. Tokuko sits in the next room and wishes they would get done. Hori is often wishing it too. "One o'clock." Tokuko calls in to them. But Noguchi has not won his share of games yet and does not want to stop. He is a man all power, this Doctor Noguchi. Tokuko goes into the kitchen, makes them tea, always fresh tea, many times in the course of a night, and never green tea, but ban-cha, the old tea, the cheap tea, too much stimulant in green tea. Noguchi likes ban-cha. But it must be fresh or it is nothing.

Some nights the men do not play chess. Some nights the three just talk. After a time Hori gets sleepy and dozes off. Noguchi never gets sleepy. He talks and talks. He does all the talking. Wild sometimes. Sometimes ve-e-ry interesting. What things he says. He is a genius, that man. But he is not like her father either. Tokuko thinks often of her father. He was so gentle, a painter, and his father a painter before him, painters for generations and generations. Poor, oh yes. Her father was always proud he would do nothing to make money, and never had in his life. He painted and by that lived as best he could. He was a samurai. Everything about him spoke of samurai, of the best of that best of classes. And if her father was a samurai, so must she be too, and her brother too. But Noguchi is not a samurai. He says he is not. He says he is not like her and not like Hori either. Sometimes that is the first thing he says when he comes into the room. And on those nights he talks rough. Tokuko has boiled soup, Japanese soup, fish soup. He likes fish soup. All the time he eats he talks. Sometimes he tells terrible things.

323

Sometimes he brags. He is a very vain man, this Doctor Noguchi. He says that the samurai class has the manners and he is not of the samurai. His class settles things with their fists. And when he says that he beats the table and everything flies.

But he would like to have fine manners—that is the truth of it. Not of late so much as when Tokuko first came from Japan. He was feeling that way then. He has changed again since, a good deal in the last year, perhaps is not so gay. But when she first came he used to be so careful about the suits he wore, and the ties. He would come with a new suit on and march up and down the room in front of her and Hori, so funny he would be, like Charlie Chaplin a little. Suddenly he would stop. "How do you like this?" And he would slap his hands on his hips. "A cra-a-a-zy suit. Such big checks in the cloth. Too bold." She would say it straight out to him. "It belongs to a circus man." When he heard that he was ve-e-ry sad, but cheered up quick. He said he would buy another. It was only money. Money made no difference.

He is sweet like that. Then again he is not sweet. He scolds. He growls at everybody who comes into the apartment. He says he does not like anyone in New York and he does not like anyone in Japan either. Someone in Japan has written his biography. "It is a bad book. No man is perfect like that book and no man would want to be perfect like that book. That is not a human being. Life does not go in a straight line like that. It goes up and down. It is only in the story

324

that it does not go up and down." He gets happier all the while he talks. All of a sudden he laughs rough. He says he is not like Tokuko. He says she is not even able to understand him. He says it is hard for any man or woman to change. He is of the lower classes and always was and always will be and the lower classes settle things with their fists.

Yet he is gentler than that really, and gentler and gentler of late. He has changed much in spite of what he says. Sometimes he does not seem happy, and sometimes he growls, but he is gentler. Now and then he talks of cats. He likes cats. He likes them better than dogs. He talks and talks. While he and Hori talk, maybe she bakes chestnuts. He loves chestnuts. Most everybody loves chestnuts in Japan. He loves toasted potatoes too. He talks and talks. He says he did not paint so much this last summer, but the summer before he did, and the summer before that. He did not have time this last summer. When he is happy he has time for everything. When he is not happy, then he has no time. He is always talking of how fine his paintings are. Perhaps he does not boast to Americans but to Japanese he does. It is nice when he boasts. When he paints best he says he gets spots over everything in the house. He says that is bad. But he says he does not care.

Sometimes she tells him of her father. Her father was a poet and loved the night. One night she remembers better than all other nights. It was at the time of the harvest moon and the moon had been up but a while ago had gone down. It was dark. Yet it was not dark either. There was a light. From where it came you could not tell but it lay just on the top of the rice. Her father thought that very beautiful. She thought that very beautiful too. She can see it all now. Her father lifted his hand to the light. His hand was beautiful too. "You know we have fine fingers we of the samurai class." That is what her father said. And that is why he had to make the holes in his flute so small. He made his own flute out of bamboo, and played ve-e-ry well.

No, Doctor Noguchi is not like her father. Doctor Noguchi is a genius. That is different. He is all power. He does what he wants. He has his own way. One night he takes her and Hori to the Institute. He shows them the chimpanzees. She has to look but she does not like to. She tells him that he kills too many animals and has all his life. She does not even want to think of that. She is a Buddhist. Doctor Noguchi is also a Buddhist. He is a ve-e-ry religious man. But sometimes, yes, he makes her sad. He cannot help it. She cannot help it. And when she is sad she always paints, decides she will be a painter and paints hard. At such times she goes to bed thinking of paint and when she wakes she paints, paints and paints. And so she forgets she is sad. And so she makes herself happy again.

LVI

I Am Not Fond of Traveling

"There are two expert chess players, and they are chums from Rio (though American business men). I cannot beat them. Then, there are a few less skillful players whom I can usually beat."

He is bound for Brazil. This was written on the 15th, three days out at sea. By the 18th the effects of the sea are worn off.

"For a few days past they started a chess tournament. I also entered the competition and to my surprise I have defeated them all. Even those two men who used to give me handicaps in the first days can no longer beat me in even matches. So after all I was not so weak as we all at first thought."

He plays chess a while, then goes to his cabin, works a while, has brought a manuscript along, then writes a letter, writes in fact a good many letters, takes to wondering how he will be received in Rio. "I am so uncertain of the Brazilian people." He is on the way to Brazil because there is yellow fever in Brazil, but he is also on the way to Brazil because there is criticism in Brazil. That criticism he is told began in Cuba, Lebredo having done some experimental work on the basis of which Guiteras wrote an article that has much affected South American opinion, which, if true, makes an odd footnote in the history of opinions—a tiff in Ecuador heated in Cuba getting so hot in Brazil that it brings Noguchi from New York. It turns out that the Brazilian people receive him very warmly.

"The papers have been making much fuss about my visit all in friendly and earnest spirits."

In Bahia, where he is to work, everything is ready, at least as ready as Doctor White and Doctor Scannell could have it. There is a big room to live in and the Institute Oswaldo Cruz to work in.

"My room faces southwest on the 2nd floor and has a double bed with mosquito net, a dresser, washstand, an enormous table of 4 feet by 8 feet in the middle of the room. Besides, there is a room adjoining for four trunks. You can imagine how large a room it is."

There are windows at one end, so that the room may be converted into what is nearly a porch. Screening is unnecessary. Noguchi praises Scannell and the others for their excellent anti-mosquito work, but no denying that that work is cheating him of what he came for, cases of yellow fever. There were three in September and not one since, and this is very serious because it means men will have to be sent to the interior and that will be slow and add to the uncertainty of the diagnosis. The last is a worry, but the slowness is the chief worry. Everything is slow. The slowness is in himself too.

"Somehow the climate is not very inducive to a quiet thinking or writing; we are more or less stretched out and no latent energy left. No wonder they don't produce too much here."

Promises are made and not kept. Doctors say they will come and do not. It is a hot part of the world and the Portuguese have their own tempo.

But even if there were yellow fever he could not begin work. His boxes of equipment are lost somewhere between here and New York and though there are daily conversations about those boxes no one seems to have any idea of how to go about finding them. And the place he is to work is turning out a disappointment too.

"Fine looking buildings marked by libraries or museums, but they are not open."

The outside of everything is right and he must work with the inside.

"The buildings were most faultlessly built for laboratory, but no water, no gas, no instruments. They must have been astonished to see how complete and sufficient our materials are."

So important a piece as the sterilizer cannot be connected with the electric current. About this too there are daily conversations. Good he brought a certain amount of sterilized equipment with him, else he could not have worked at all, and he is beginning to work a little.

He speaks to Doctor White about chess, and Doctor White says that he does not know much about the game but is willing to play, and plays, and wins, the first game. The second is a stalemate. The third he loses and he never wins another.

Noguchi is disappointed because he has no darkfield microscope. His own is in the boxes.

"To one who is accustomed to use darkfield for routine examination of everything fresh it is a big blow not to have one."

How do these men do their work? He speaks to whomever he meets. Finally he learns of one darkfield microscope, then of another, then of a third, but they are not in use nor fit to use. He nevertheless brings all three to the laboratory and tinkers with them.

"Thus, by combining parts of three men's microscopes I was able to demonstrate a fair darkfield effect."

The fact disgusts him. Among these are the men who have criticized his yellow fever, and they cannot so much as set up a darkfield. And his spirochete cannot even be so much as seen without a darkfield and must be seen because it does not form visible colonies on the culture medium. "After a stay of a week I am sadly disappointed."

He catches sight of the British consul sitting on his porch, sees in that gentleman somehow a game of chess. "Two games were played, even results." It will not be even results long.

And still there is no yellow fever. Maybe there never will be. He had better begin working on some-

It Will Not Be Even Results Long

thing else. In the out-patient clinic there are infections with flagellates, minute animal organisms. From these flagellate ulcers he makes microscopic smears, injects a rabbit and two baboons and inoculates media. There are also other diseases, a disease called granuloma venerea which occurs among the natives and is believed to be caused by an organism. He says he will try to cultivate the organism. He is considering working on smallpox virus, then learns there is measles in the town, has always wanted to study measles. Perhaps he has come from New York to Bahia for measles! But by the time he has got permission from the professor of pediatrics he finds the case is already in the fifth day and useless. The last days he has been teaching the boys in the laboratory to take the temperatures of the animals, and the boys are so slow. "I feel that if things are going on at this rate we will never accomplish anything." He calls several Bahian physicians, talks to them, and they feel his earnestness and promise they will telephone other physicians. What he is wanting is samples of blood from persons who have recovered from yellow fever, as many samples as possible, because then he will be able to do Pfeiffers and at least find whether the blood in the yellow fever of Brazil is like the blood in the yellow fever of Ecuador and Mexico and Peru. "Perhaps I can get enough cases to do the Pfeiffers before the end of the month." As always his hopes go right up and as always he does not rely too much on them but whips things along where he can, and the Brazilian doctors begin to move with him. "He makes us all believe in him." At one of their meetings they elect him honorary chairman. "From their enthusiasm they mean it."

He has begun on their language, says that he is going to need it, that he will get along better with the people. Last summer it was Russian. His Russian, he says, has got to a point where an amateur linguist should stop. One of the doctors has found him a Portuguese teacher and on the 9th of December he takes his first lesson. Presently he is writing a poem about the city of Bahia and the moon and the bay, all in Portuguese. A newspaper gets hold of the poem. Of course he cannot speak Portuguese, and he and the Brazilians up in his room every now and then laugh loud because he cannot find a word, has begun a Portuguese sentence and got lost in it, is making gestures of searching for a word in the air, has tried to substitute a French word, but no one has understood, and then a Spanish word, then someone suddenly has understood and everybody laughs. After one of his lessons he walks up by the side of the bay, sits for a time on a magnificent portico, has a "nice Lipton tea and many sweets which others enjoy." The sweets he has to be careful about because before he started for Brazil he learned that besides his bad heart he has diabetes. Now and then he remembers the fact.

And still there is no yellow fever. But there is a rumor. Doctor White surprised everyone at supper last night with the news of a case at Pernambuco. Pernambuco is where Doctor White wanted Noguchi to work, knew that there was yellow fever there, but Noguchi preferred Bahia and Doctor White even from the very beginning felt that Noguchi ought to do just what he wants to. Doctor Scannell has that feeling too. Only Noguchi's money matters, those it is hard to keep straight for him, as it was hard for Kligler in Peru. "Noguchi had no idea of the value of money, his own or the Foundation's." Kligler in Peru had assumed the impossible task of keeping Noguchi's accounts straight for him. "They never balanced. He never could say at the end of the day what he did with the money he received in the morning. He just put it into his pocket and handed it out again. I am not sure that on several occasions he did not hand out five dollar notes instead of ones. At the end I gave up trying. I gave him smaller sums, paid for him when I was about and let it go at that." Here in Brazil it is the same. When there is any particular undertaking he is given a letter of credit and asked to keep a list of expenses but he always returns the letter of credit with whatever balance and no list of expenses. Almost as if he did not understand what they meant by making a list. As for that yellow fever at Pernambuco it seems the rumor came from one physician via another who had not so much as seen the case. So there is no point in going to Pernambuco. And anyway Pernambuco does not want the fact of its having yellow fever spread about and the health officers promise not to be very friendly.

But a good thing has happened. This morning an

Englishman called at the Institute and said he had had yellow fever and was willing to give his blood. Unfortunately there was no one to receive it, but the Englishman said he would come again. And this afternoon there was a German, said he had had yellow fever in May, and a sample of his blood was quickly drawn. If things continued this way it would be easy to give the physicians a fine demonstration. To-day too the boxes came and in the boxes the darkfield microscope. "A great joy." And at 6 p. m. the telephone rings and two cases of measles are reported at Vermello. Immediately Noguchi hurries with one of the doctors to Vermello.

"A humble colored family living in a small hut. A girl of about six years was lying with a high fever and some rashes. Attempts to get into veins all failed and a small quantity of blood was drawn from finger tips."

The blood was drawn from the big toe of the other case, and both bloods were inoculated into guinea-pigs and rabbits, and examined with the new darkfield. So on all sides things are beginning to move. A tall vigorous medical student, a native, comes so often to the laboratory that it seems Noguchi ought to be warned about her, she is so obviously making for him and he is so innocent and does not understand. And more than the tall medical student are interested in him. Everybody is, even the housemaid, Eremita, very pretty, does for Doctor Noguchi everything she can think of, brings him great pots of tea when he works late into the night, and he is working later and later and later. He is al-

334

ways saying funny things to her. She laughs so hard. She kneels on the floor close by him.

Every day now yellow fever patients are coming to give their blood. There is an unexpected number. Noguchi is quite able to set December 19th, Wednesday, 4:30 p. m. as the time of the demonstration. He has invited the physicians. At 2:30 p. m. he himself goes to the Institute. All is ready. He has the sera of nine patients who said they had had yellow fever or whose physicians said they had. He has four strains of the yellow fever spirochete got in Ecuador and Mexico and Peru. He has three strains of the spirochete of infectious jaundice. He is letting the Bahian physicians themselves make the tests, mainly members of the faculty of medicine of Bahia University. There are two darkfield microscopes. If the Bahian physicians do not know exactly what this is all about, they are at least having a hand, and that should not lessen their interest. The results are clear-cut. The nine sera from the nine yellow fever convalescents give positive Pfeiffers with his yellow fever organism and negative Pfeiffers with the infectious jaundice organism. Everybody is impressed. Yellow fever in Brazil is serologically identical with yellow fever in Ecuador and Mexico and Peru. Noguchi cables the United States. The truth is that there were some slight discrepancies in the tests, but these he feels were really a good thing because they will remind certain of the Brazilian doctors that it is easier to criticize a man's work than to repeat it. The injections into the guinea-pig's abdomen, the withdrawal of

335

the fluid, the use of the darkfield, all that takes skill. This demonstration has won round many. The doctors are asking why anyway there should have been such antagonism to Noguchi's work. Why should Brazil have been so influenced by criticism originating in Cuba? That is the way one puts it to Noguchi. On the 25th Noguchi works till 5:30 in the morning. On the 26th he works the whole night through.

And now those who were sent to the interior return, report they have found yellow fever, have inoculated cultures, and one of the men has examined his cultures with the darkfield and seen the spirochete, and is getting a good deal of credit for that. The first to discover Noguchi's Spirochete in Brazil. Again Noguchi cables the United States.

All this business does not mean that he has not kept up his interest in measles. He is also working on malaria. He has been gathering material for the study of hoof and mouth disease. He has not stopped working on the flagellates either. One morning he spends at the university looking at specimens of live snakes, never lets go anything he has once touched, talks long to Doctor White of his dream to do something in the treatment of syphilis, that dream of 1913, wants to make a serum, as he expresses it, that might be used as simply and positively as the anti-toxin in diphtheria. All yesterday he was feeling ill, to-day too, but does not stop work—has found a case of trachoma! He takes smears and makes cultures from the case, and only feels more ill, then has a spontaneous rupture of the ear drum, and feels better. The experiments that are interesting him most are those on hoof and mouth disease. It is the same disease the British Government wanted him to investigate for them. He thinks he is on the track of something. His experimental animals are showing swellings and ulcerations of the feet. How thrilling it would be to have gone to Brazil to round out yellow fever and come back with the cause of hoof and mouth disease. The Brazilian doctors feel how thrilling. When now they say they are coming next morning they come. There are even too many visitors. Noguchi shows three priests his spirochete, and a Franciscan, a professor of biology is amazed at what he sees in the laboratory, stays and stays, learns all kinds of things, things a professor of biology should have done with his own hands and not studied from books, in the opinion of one who has quite forgotten Wakamatsu where he studied all things from books and did not think it ridiculous in the least.

One morning Doctor White wakes at 3 o'clock, sees a light shining on the wall opposite, goes to investigate and finds Noguchi awake, scolds him, thought Noguchi always went to bed when he was done with chess. Noguchi promises he will go right away. He seems to have no more idea of hours than of money, appears at the Pensao for a game and cannot grasp why the place is dark. And once he rises from his big table thinking it time to stop for the night and looks into the sun. Two cats slip in through the window, fight. Little Eremita brings tea. He notices nothing.

337

The time is spent and he must go back to New York. While packing he continues the experiments. The yellow fever work he feels has succeeded. He has obtained in pure culture one strain of the flagellates. The work on malaria is indecisive. The measles is indecisive. So too the trachoma. So too the hoof and mouth disease. That is the way he knew it would be before he began. He casts, casts, casts, many lines, has always known that that is the way to catch fish. In point of time the expedition has cost something under four months. On Sunday the 24th of February the Governor sends his aide-de-camp to the ship and many distinguished Brazilians are aboard to see Noguchi off. Everybody is sorry. Eremita is miserable. In the Oswaldo Cruz Institute he made use of a good deal of expensive equipment which Doctor White and Doctor Scannell provided for him. Now as he is leaving the Institute, the Brazilian physicians standing about, one of them asks him what is to be done with the equipment. He waves his hand: "Take it!" It belongs to the Rockefeller Foundation.

LVII

Kingston

He got back to New York in February and now in July is out of the country again, at Kingston, in Jamaica, is reading two papers at a conference on health problems in tropical America, the one on flagellates, the other on the yellow fever of Brazil.

The doctors of the conference listen quietly to the one, for that matter to the other too though that other has just this afternoon had a kind of anticipatory rough handling, an address on yellow fever prophylaxis by Aristides Agramonte of Havana Cuba. Agramonte is the same who was member of that original Board to study yellow fever, friend of Lebredo, Cuban commissioner at Guayaquil, later resigned. What Agramonte said this afternoon he said as a man of energy may. He said the serological differences between the spirochetes of yellow fever and infectious jaundice are "not greater than those we find between organisms that form part of a single group, showing them simply to represent different strains." He referred to those who followed the "savant's" instructions, said he was willing to be convinced of the savant's organism, hoped he would be in the near future, but that "an organism that in such expert hands had piled up such an amount of evidence against itself, I declare I cannot really accept as the leptospira of yellow fever." The doctor was speaking out of his conscience, of course.

Formerly Noguchi would have lost his temper. The moment is not unlike that other, Vienna 1913, when the young man of the Koch Laboratory also spoke out of his conscience. But this afternoon Noguchi only rose, talked a while, as usual was not well understood, sat down. Yet it was not an afternoon of triumph.

"Agramonte read his paper and attacked my work as insufficiently proving the etiology of yellow fever. I was called to discuss. I mentioned the fact that the experimental evidences upon which Agramonte bases his opinions are those furnished by Lebredo and Hoffman who decidedly were dealing with a secondary contamination. . . . He (Agramonte) further pointed out that the amount of patient's blood required in injecting the guinea-pig was too large whereas a single bite of an infected mosquito is enough to produce infection in man. . . . Of course his criticisms were not seriously accepted by others who all realize that from transmitting human disease to animals such is always the case."

The criticisms were not seriously accepted, he says, but goes on.

"The air was filled with a kind of gloom, only a few daring to come out for or against."

This was not a demonstration to physicians of Bahia.

"Castellani came over to me and said that he has accepted my work and cannot be influenced by these arguments."

Friendly of Castellani, and honest, but only the expression of opinion of one man to another, for Castellani did not take part in the discussion. Henry Carter did, talked of Noguchi's yellow fever vaccine.

"I have vaccinated a number of people going into the Tropics—and I shouldn't think of allowing my daughter to go into the Tropics without being vaccinated—but that is only evidence of my belief in the value of vaccination, and not evidence of such value. . . . In the first attempt at vaccination—in the case of the battalion of the Vincedores, about 500 men from the Andean plateau—some 300 were vaccinated, and then the others came down and were vaccinated also but with smaller doses. Among the first group there was extremely little yellow fever; among the second slightly more. But it cannot be said that there was any real control. If Dr. Noguchi had broken his flask of vaccine after the first group came down, he would have had control."

Carter's discussion was friendly, stated in general his belief in Noguchi's spirochete, but did not and could not accept unreservedly. Not so Nichols. Nichols is Noguchi's friend.

"Nichols stood up and stated the U. S. Army Med-

341

ical School has accepted L-icteroides as the cause of yellow fever."

A sweet moment. Noguchi will not forget it, but what he keeps thinking of is Agramonte's criticism.

"Certainly Agramonte succeeded in creating some hesitation in those who were more or less undecided. Later I invited Agramonte to see the slides (sections). He said that he had no idea that such typical lesions and fatty degenerations could be produced in animals. . . . He wants to do human experiments in Havana (with volunteers) to produce yellow fever in man. I answered that such a proposition may be justified about 25 years ago when every non-immune was dying in Havana, but to-day we are in position to prove the same thing in appropriate animal experiments!"

In the printed discussion he says very little about his yellow fever organism.

"One point, however, that I wish to emphasize is the importance of proper facilities and technical training in this rather specialized branch of experimental research, a point that I believe cannot be over-emphasized."

He has given himself that technical training. Perhaps he is wrong about yellow fever, but until another has worked as he has worked, either has found a new organism or knows about this one as he knows, it will be difficult for that other to say. That is what he means.

342

LVIII

Flagellates

His second Jamaica paper is on flagellates. In Brazil
he learned the curious fact that lumbermen cutting
timber in the virgin forests are likely to be infected
with flagellates. He saw the ulcers those mornings when
he visited the out-patient clinic disappointed because
there were no cases of yellow fever, took one strain of
the Brazilian form of the flagellate back with him. As
soon as he got to New York he wrote to several he
knew interested in flagellates, among them Nichols,
asked them to send him some of their materials, got
his own pure cultures of a number of strains, inoculated rabbits, tested the rabbits against his pure cultures, and found that he had a very good method for
classifying one kind of flagellate. That is the substance
of the second paper.

"My paper came off in the evening of the 24th.
The room was crowded and hot and the movie was not
so good as ought to have been."

The doctors are all students of tropical medicine
and this paper on flagellates is drawing him still fur-

ther into that field, the work on yellow fever having already drawn him a good way. He began his career with venoms, the venoms took him to serology, serology to syphilis, syphilis to the spirochetes, the spirochetes to these strange and little studied diseases of tropical medicine, diseases where science has made least inroad, where treatment is still in the hands of the miracle workers, horrible diseases, fatal like the diseases of the north a century ago, causes unknown, carriers unknown, the human being never certain from where the malevolence will strike, but romance in the study of them.

He came to Kingston to read his papers, but also for a holiday. The holiday turns out like his holidays. He talks to a doctor from Venezuela who suggests that the local plants may be infected with flagellates. Noguchi hears the suggestion somewhat as he heard that about the dogs gathering ticks if allowed to run down to the creek, sets to work right here in Kingston, examines more than a dozen local plants. None are infected. But he is not satisfied.

"I heard that there is a plant in Honduras which contains a flagellate. I am thinking going over there to carry it back to New York."

And he does go, quits Kingston, pushes on to Tela, examines many plants and this time is rewarded—five varieties are infected. He starts for New York.

"I have just left Tela, Honduras, where I stayed for six days to study the flagellates."

He has the plants with him, has his bathtub on the

ship filled with them, meets David Fairchild who writes of the meeting.

"I discovered that he was almost panic-stricken over the difficulties he would run into with the Federal Horticultural Board Inspectors in New York, and as I knew that the plant had already become common in the gardens of the South, I was able to offer him my assistance in clearing the plants into the country."

Later when he gets to Shandaken he searches the countryside, sees a milkweed on the other side of a farmer's fence, hurries to the farmer's wife, asks to pluck the weed. She has heard the word infection, says no. He complains to Maizie. Maizie tells him that of course he cannot enter a farmer's lot if the farmer's wife does not want him. He writes a letter to the farmer's wife, apparently gets no answer, but apparently gets the weed.

Finally by one strategy or another he has nine strains of this second kind of flagellate, and again is able to classify. But who will care? Even among bacteriologists, who can be imagined to read four thousand words on the serological individuality of a flagellate? Only some crony caught by a similar fancy, and there are not many such. Yet the work is right, inwardly right, feels right. Years ago when he was working on trichomonas living in the tartar round teeth the work seemed small, to him too, and yet he is bigger now and from a trichomonas living round a tooth to a flagellate living in a milkweed is no great step. It is not the subject but the man has changed. Flagellates fascinate him

345

and he follows his fascination. If mankind is benefited, good. If not, good too. If scientists pay attention, good, and if not, why, good too. He is able, that is, to go with somewhat the same feeling toward a so-called big and a so-called little problem. He no longer complains of not being able to work on common colds or cancer. He is able to shrug his shoulders, and says repeatedly: "Who knows, perhaps I am wrong." He always worked with intensity, but now the intensity seems less forced. "My methods are all flowing." He seems far from Vienna 1913, far even from the morning when he returned to the laboratory after Guayaquil and brought out the sword and the medals and told Matsumoto how fine they treated him down there. He was inclined a few years ago to be a little fat. He is less inclined again.

And then, he has ceased reading the newspapers. He gives a definite outward reason for not reading them, the occasional anti-Japanese jibe, but has perhaps also an inward reason, as he had an outward and an inward reason for going to Copenhagen, an outward and an inward for describing the burning of his hand one way to one person and another to another, for not telling all about his intimate life to everyone to whom he seemed to be telling all, for so much that may now and then have been thought double-dealing. His inward reason has become a subtle thing, no doubt, as it ought to be, hardly explicable to anyone. And as for the newspapers, these he says he will never read again. Back at East 65th Street he dreaded them because they might pry into how he lived. He has learned that at least they do not pry as freely as he thought. Now his reason for not reading them is that news does not change and that it is foolish to let them carry off his mind. Someone asks him if he is not often embarrassed because he does not know what they say. "Oh, yes, I talk of someone who is dead as if they were alive."

LIX

The Summer of 1925

All winter he kept at flagellates, the book on spirochetes waiting, the yellow fever monograph waiting (he perhaps glad after Kingston to have it wait), and now Rocky Mountain spotted fever again pushes to the fore.

"I am doing experiments on Rocky Mountain spotted fever, but it does not always come out as we expect."

That is what he wrote in March. Now in June he is more hopeful again.

"I have been able to bring down g-pigs with I and II generations of B. C. 7."

To bring down guinea-pigs with a first generation culture does not mean much. The second generation is better. The third better still, and so on.

"The pigs inoculated with III generation have not had enough time to show up."

If they would it would have been thrilling. Perhaps after nine years he is still to have the victory, in fact is dreaming already on the other side the victory. Heart Water fever, tsutsugamushi disease, typhus, all belong in the class with Rocky Mountain spotted fever, and he is wondering whether the ticks that are the carriers of Heart Water fever could be brought in from Africa by someone coming from Africa.

"I know that Doctor Cowdry himself will not attempt cultivation and will not object to my trying it after I *finish* my R. M."

So he is thinking of Heart Water fever while he is working on spotted fever. He is thinking also of typhus because he adds that yesterday he tried to get blood from typhus guinea-pigs, immediately tacks on a characteristic caution, warns that though typhus, Heart Water fever, tsutsugamushi disease and spotted fever are generally believed to have a similar cause, that had better not be taken too confidently for granted.

He is working plungingly. A death interrupts, the wife of the old teacher. The old teacher had written him some time back and he did not immediately answer as he should have, then answered, with the answer included three poems, said he composed these useless things the other night when alone and very deep.

Uki kumono yukiki himanaki
fuyunosora tokarazame tatsu haruno himo

Floating cloud
coming going
winter sky
spring day could not be far

(meaning that the old teacher's wife
who has been ill is recovering)

349

Yoshi tatoi konoyono chirini miwayamuno
yamanu kikotsuwa imamo mukashimo

> Even if this world dust suffer
> spirit does not change

Torutoshino tamano kazumasu
masugotoni hikari iyamasu chichino shirogami

> Heaping year
> pearls increasing
> light and white hair increasing

Along with the poems he sent cakes and a hundred
dollars, also a promise to write Miyabara and thank him
for having gone from Tokyo. And Kobayashi's wife
did make a recovery but apparently not so complete as
was at first thought because here now in the middle of
an experiment, on the tenth of July, he receives the
cable announcing her death. He is much cast down.
"She was very good to me when I was in my birth-
place." He writes a long letter. "It seems that I always
have the ill luck not to see my beloved people before
their departure from this world." He was so full of
a young poet's condolence that night when he wrote
from Hamburg to Chiwaki about the death of Chiwaki's little daughter, was younger but full of a warm
fanciful philosophy when Kobayashi's mother died,
and that day Maizie met him at the ship to tell him of
his own mother's death was so calm and next morning
so brisk, but now seems able to call up none of that

350

vitality that draws even from death increase of life. "I am hungry and very tired this evening and everything appears gloomy."

He plunges back into the work. What brought Rocky Mountain spotted fever to the fore this time was a fresh supply of ticks. He is making a systematic study of seventy-four of them.

He starts for Shandaken, stays a week, fishes, paints, many paintings, one after another, the second before the first is dry, like Coney Island, Maizie says, and all from the dark of the porch, cannot be got into the sun even while painting. Then he is back in New York once more.

"I just had to come down to examine all my cultures and g-pigs inoculated. . . . I came down here to make new sub-cultures and test out the IV and V generations which are just 10 days old. . . . I started to work this morning at 3 a.m. and have prepared all transfers, examined cultures by Giensa, and at 10 a.m. I am ready to put ticks on the culture g-pigs. Boys are all here and busy helping. I had breakfast at 7:30 this morning at a restaurant on Madison Ave. and 59th St., so I do not feel any fatigue. The day is beautiful with gentle breezes."

It is one of his big wonderful days following on a night of little sleep, time enough for everything, time even to take an excursion far from all this, to write a letter to distant Copenhagen.

"Really I am ashamed to write you after such a

long delay in expressing my appreciation of the beautiful greetings from your graceful family. Of course I always appreciate any messages from my old teacher and his family. I am keeping these lovely letters from Miss Madsen, Torben, Trugve and young Steve, not to mention one from Mrs. Madsen.

"It was a great pleasure and a pride to have you visit this Country last fall for your old pupils. Though the calendar reminds us that more than a dozen of years had passed since I saw you and your family over in Copenhagen you have not changed a bit. You are always the same Doctor Madsen I knew and such a feeling as this makes life interesting and worth while. The reason why I could not write you before is that my brain or rather my mind was severely overtaxed with my ambition to isolate the causative organism of Rocky Mountain Spotted fever. Having had sufficient materials (ticks, etc.) for the first time in many years I tried every imaginable method to cultivate the organism. At this moment I am obtaining more or less promising results and am hoping that I shall definitely get it before very long. Of course, this is only my wish which may not materialize. The other day a beautiful card came and it was fine to recall that famous Skodeborg. The whole Institute Staff used to go there when Famulener and I were studying now twenty odd years since. I envy my young compatriots out there to be associated with these leaders in medicine as appear in the card. I can't get younger, but my memories are still young.

"To-morrow I will start my vacation in a nearby mountain village, so I am writing this note to ask you kindly to beg forgiveness in my apparent discourtesy to your family."

[LX]

Oroya Fever

A tube of blood has been brought from Lima. A kind of madness, to bring a tube of blood from Lima, Peru. The blood was kept on ice, but it was twelve days on a ship and through the tropics and sixteen days since it was drawn from the dying patient. The patient was diagnosed Oroya fever. So he is not to continue Rocky Mountain fever as he thought. He is to go to something new. He starts at this tube with a vehemence unprecedented even in his vehement career. What he means to find is whether two strange diseases are really two.

It is an old debate whether Oroya fever and verruga peruana are one or two. Some impulse to the settling of that debate he had five years ago when he stopped in Lima en route to New York, hunted up the diseases, made animal inoculations both with Oroya fever blood and verruga warts. But that was simply a thrust into the dark, and nothing came of it.

As far back as the conquest of the Incas there was this mysterious disease that attacked the Peruvians, covered them with warts, often great misshapen bloody warts, the warts sometimes accompanied by a fever, or the fever came without the warts, a fever that blanched the blood, and that, as the old historian says, was almost as destructive as the plague. It was a superstition that to avoid being stricken one ought to leave the mountain valleys and go to live at the edge of the sea, at least leave certain valleys, for persons in one valley were stricken while in another a few miles away they were not. In 1870 when the railroad was building across the Andes between the cities of Lima and Oroya thousands of laborers died of an acute fever. Forty sailors deserted a British ship, came to work on the railroad, and in less than a year thirty had died. When it was decided to have the workmen stop work before sundown no more were stricken.

The Peruvian doctors, most of them long believed that the two diseases were one, that Oroya fever was the acute and verruga the chronic form of the same cause. The doctors knew of patients who had escaped the fatal fever to come down with the warts. The doctors knew of patients who had both the fever and the warts at once, the fever in those instances light. Finally a Peruvian medical student, Daniel Carrion, thought he would settle the debate by doing an experiment on himself, would inoculate both his arms with juice squeezed from a verruga wart. Several days after the inoculation he developed a fever, blanched, died. That looked like proof, and from this on the disease was

355

called Carrion's disease, for the deed's sake. Carrion's bit of experiment was done in the summer of 1885.

In 1913 a great expedition proceeded to South America, doctors of the Harvard School of Tropical Medicine, and the task it set for itself was to collect pathological materials in South American countries and to investigate several forms of tropical disease, especially verruga. The Harvard doctors made a lengthy study of verruga and their findings are part of a lengthy book that describes that expedition. The Harvard doctors came to the conclusion that the two diseases were two, the one caused by a definable parasite and the other by an indefinable virus. The Harvard doctors showed that the occurrence of both diseases in one individual did not necessarily mean one disease and that the statement about the same valleys was perhaps not absolutely true. In 1909 a Peruvian doctor, Barton, had seen in the red corpuscles of an Oroya fever patient bodies that looked like bacteria and inclined to the belief that they were protozoa. The Harvard doctors inclined to the belief that these bodies lay somewhere between bacteria and protozoa. The Harvard doctors gave a name to these bodies, called them Bartonella bacilliformis, describe in their book exactly how they came to the name.

"Upon investigation, however, we have found that the use of Bartonia as a generic name has been applied by Cossmann to an eocene mollusk, *Bartonia canaeliculatum,* hence we have given the generic name "Bartonella," retaining the specific one, "bacilliformis" (*Bartonella bacilliformis*)."

And these Bartonella bacilliformis can indubitably be found in Oroya fever, as Barton discovered, but the Harvard doctors thought that those investigators who saw the bodies in cases of verruga either were wrong or were dealing with individuals suffering with the two diseases at the same time. Indeed this fact of Bartonella bacilliformis not being found in both diseases the Harvard doctors believed one more reason for regarding the two as two.

The Harvard doctors pointed out that monkeys could easily be infected with a verruga wart, but that even large amounts of blood from even a severe case of Oroya fever did not produce any noticeable effect —another reason for regarding the two as two.

The Harvard doctors even had the opportunity to repeat Carrion's experiment and inoculated a human volunteer with verruga and he did not develop Oroya fever. As for Carrion, the Report of the First Expedition to South America of the Harvard School of Tropical Medicine says:

"Although it has been stated that Carrion during his illness kept notes, and gave a minute description of his symptoms to his companions, unfortunately it appears that none of these were preserved and published. No accurate record of Carrion's case and of the necropsy is available. It has been suggested since that he died of typhoid fever or of a more acute form of septicemia, and it is also quite possible that the patient from which he infected himself was suffering with Oroya fever as well as verruga at the time."

Obviously then it would not be appropriate to call the disease Carrion's disease.

After this expedition there was a lull of about four years. Then an American entomologist living in Peru, Charles Henry Tyler Townsend, thought he would try to determine whether or not an insect was the carrier, and which insect. The superstition about going down to the sea suggests an insect, insects not thriving at the sea because of the winds. The diseases occurring in some valleys and not in others again suggests an insect, and the danger of the night air suggests a night insect. So Townsend went to work. He blundered, no doubt, was working part of the time in experimental fields where he had no experience, and yet what he did must have taken a fair enthusiasm. For some of the work certainly he needed no very complicated equipment. The laboratory was much in his own head. The Harvard doctors speak of his transmission experiment.

"The account of this experiment first appeared as an article signed by Mr. Townsend in one of the daily newspapers during our stay in Peru, and the public was invited to inspect the dog and to examine the lesions described."

Invite the public, is scarcely what a university doctor would do. Then too Townsend thinks one thing in March and another in July, changes his mind, in March thinks it is a tick is the carrier and in July a phlebotomus. To the phlebotomus he sticks. How he came to that is interesting. He found what were the blood-sucking insects in all the valleys between 9° and 15° south latitude, the latitudes between which the diseases occur, and, yes, a certain enthusiasm that took. There proved to be fifty. When he had them he summed them under twelve heads. From this list he then struck every one that occurred also outside these valleys, for obviously such could not be the carriers. When he had done that there were left three, the phlebotomus and several species of horseflies and buffalognats. But the buffalognats and the horseflies bite during the day. "This leaves the Phlebotomus as the only agent present, capable of carrying the disease." Neat. A phlebotomus is the carrier. His particular choice of phlebotomus he calls phlebotomus verrucarum. And he is right. No, not precisely. Later an entomologist will be sent from New York and several jointly will undertake the problem and will prove that the female phlebotomus which Townsend discovered is not the exact female but that it is another female indistinguishable from Townsend's.

And now, September 1925, Noguchi strikes into the problem. He is not too well, but mentally enormously fit, and everything about him is fit. His laboratory through the years he has gradually ordered to a point where it is free of all irrelevance, and he can focus his gift at whatever spot he wishes. At the time the tube of blood was drawn in Lima several culture tubes were inoculated, but they are contaminated. Only the tube of blood remains. Good so.

359

With this blood he inoculates a large variety of cultures, proceeds at once in the old mass way, incubates, waits. No growth. He inoculates a second mass. Growth!

He has succeeded. The thing was easy. He has succeeded in getting in pure culture the bodies that Barton discovered and the Harvard doctors named and that no one was able to obtain in pure culture before. This is the first step.

With the pure culture he now inoculates large numbers of animals, rhesus monkeys, green monkeys, dogs, rabbits, mice, rats, guinea-pigs. Nothing happens except in the rhesus monkeys and what happens in them depends on how the inoculations are made. If the culture is injected into the veins there results an irregular remittent fever, and the Bartonella can be recovered from the blood. If the culture is injected into the skin of the eyebrow there comes a nodule rich in blood vessels, a bloody wart, and from the wart as from the circulation again Bartonella may be recovered. It was late September when he received the tube. He has been working with a straight, an almost terrible intensity, already in February is able to announce his first conclusion.

He will settle this old debate. He sees, as now someone much duller might, where his results are leading. The two diseases have one cause. He does not say that yet. He waits. But he knows.

By June his strain of the Bartonella has had a number of animal passages—has been inoculated into one

360

animal, recovered from its blood, inoculated into another, recovered from its blood—and has had its virulence so increased that it produces not only the remittent fever but also the anemia that gives the blanching of which the historian of the Incas speaks. That is, he is producing the disease as one meets it in the valleys, the degrees, and in this succeeds further and further, is able to say that those degrees are probably due to differences in the virulence of the strains and in the resistance of the persons. He can now almost at will recover Bartonella from the blood, also is finding it inside the corpuscles of the animals as Barton found it inside the corpuscles of the human beings.

And all this from a tube of blood brought on ice from Lima.

What could he do with a few warts from a case of verruga? He has as a matter of fact long since sent for warts. They reach him April 7th. It was arranged they should be cut from the patient the same day the ship left Lima and should be brought to the Rockefeller Institute the day the ship arrived in New York. Even so the warts have had to be at refrigerator temperature fourteen days. He examines them, then macerates them in salt solution and inoculates two young rhesus monkeys. In each there results a remittent fever and from the blood of each he cultivates an organism indistinguishable from the Bartonella that he cultivated from the case of Oroya fever.

Thus then he has produced warts from the blood of a disease with a remittent fever and a remittent fever

361

from a disease with warts. That would seem to be pretty much both sides of the story.

Monkey 5 is inoculated with his pure culture of the Bartonella. Then the blood of *Monkey 5* is inoculated into *Monkey 18,* and *Monkey 18* develops a severe verruga. What makes this interesting is that a monkey will develop just such a severe verruga when inoculated with human verruga tissue. And *Monkey 18* is besides a case where Oroya fever and verruga occur at the same time as they sometimes do in the human being. And something more. Nature when she inoculates does not produce nodules only at the points of inoculation, and in this *Monkey 18* nodules appear at points remote from the point inoculated. So he has the nodules like nature. The same in *Monkey 34.* This monkey was inoculated April 10th, had a rise of temperature April 24th, cultures from the blood on April 28th, May 12th and May 27th, yielded the organism, and early in June in the middle of the monkey's tail again spontaneously a wart.

He has all then. The irregular remittent fever. The anemia. The different degrees of the disease. The Oroya fever from the verruga. The verruga from the Oroya fever. The spontaneous wart.

"The data obtained justify the conclusion that verruga peruana is caused by *Bartonella bacilliformis.* They also definitely establish the fact that the inoculation of blood or sanguineous exudate from lesions of verruga peruana is capable of inducing in susceptible individuals a severe systemic infection, such as that to which Carrion succumbed. The designation 'Carrion's disease' is therefore the appropriate one for both forms of the infection."

No doubt he gave some time to the shaping of those three fatal sentences. No doubt too it was with satisfaction that he looked down on them. The editor when he received them very possibly reshaped them, the idiom not exactly right, a word or two taken out, three or four put in, but no matter. The sentences remain clear. They are the gravestone placed by one on a controversy that he has himself buried. They are also the shining narrow top of an extraordinary man's career. The work goes on. In May he takes a hurried westbound train and writes two papers on the train.

"It is a pleasure to work on a train, being continuously shaken, but comfortably undisturbed by worldly affairs."

He returns to New York. He works. Summer comes. He goes to Shandaken. There is some difficulty about fishing licenses for foreigners. He likes to fish but the difficulty is not worth the circumventing. He works.

Malaria and Carrion's disease occur in the same regions and are likely to occur in the same individuals. A monkey in the animal house happens to have malaria. Here is his chance to study the effect of the one disease on the other. There is none.

He has in pure culture an organism that has nothing to do with the verruga but that was present in the warts first sent from Lima. It is a new species. He has discovered it. He studies it, names it, describes it.

He compares the Bartonella of Carrion's disease with a similar Bartonella that appears in the red corpuscles of rats when their spleens are removed.

But the astonishing paper is the tenth. It is there he explains to the previous workers how they made their mistakes. It was not their fault really. One simply had to have a way of culturing Bartonella from the blood before one could know it was there. See it in verruga one could not. And yet one sees it so easily in Oroya fever. Why then think the two diseases one? Furthermore, having a way of culturing Bartonella from the blood it is possible to study different strains of it. That is why later he sent to Lima for more blood and from twelve samples got nine strains of Bartonella. Under the microscope these strains differed little. Some were coarser, some finer, some had two flagella, some four. Where they differed strikingly was in virulence, and, knowing that, it becomes imaginable how the same organism might cause the two diseases, a very virulent strain giving Oroya fever and a less virulent verruga. It becomes understandable how Carrion might die and the Harvard volunteer might not. It becomes understandable how the previous workers made their mistake. When blood from the nine samples was inoculated into the skin of monkeys no one of them developed a local lesion, yet when the nine pure cultures from these same bloods were inoculated into these same monkeys every one gave a local lesion. This is striking and unexplained, and no wonder that the Harvard doctors, knowing how they could get local lesions with even small quantities of verruga tissue, and no lesions whatever even with large quantities of Oroya fever blood, no wonder they were led astray.

"The fact that in the first mentioned condition the microorganism is incapable of inducing in monkeys anything more than a slight transitory blood invasion, detectable only by blood cultures, explains the negative results obtained by the Harvard Commission with blood from severe Oroya fever, results which seemed unmistakably to indicate a totally different etiology for Oroya fever and verruga peruana."

So the old debate of one disease or two diseases he has settled. He has done more. He has shown that not only did the previous workers not settle it correctly but they would have had to discover something they did not before they could have avoided the mistake they made—the artist. The artist finishes his work. And a beautiful work beginning to end it has been, and like the beautiful swift and relentless. One thinks again of Carrion. He did his job with two inoculations into his own arms. One thinks again of Townsend. He did his practically by a subtraction. A tube of blood and a few warts were enough for Noguchi.

Trachoma

When writing those two papers on the westbound train he was on the way to Albuquerque to gather materials for a fresh attack on the old problem of trachoma. That is, in the middle of Oroya fever he is adding trachoma. In the middle of Rocky Mountain spotted fever he was adding Oroya fever.

Chance this time is allied with a gentleman. But it is chance, for when Doctor Proctor starts to Kayenta Utah to prepare for a trip to Rainbow Bridge Arizona he certainly is not thinking of trachoma. See trachoma he cannot help, the Indians are full of it, and soon they are coming to him and having him look at their eyes. Hundreds have been operated on, and the results are bad, and Doctor Proctor wishes earnestly something might be done, the disease struck at anew and from the bottom and the organism found. He talks to the doctors at the reservations, later discusses the question with the Surgeon General, asks why no one has tried to interest Noguchi, and learns that someone has but that Noguchi was unwilling. Doctor Proctor starts for

New York. It is late morning when he approaches the stone and steel at the head of 66th Street, is just a little uneasy, does not like to disturb, is more sensitive than some others with less reason might be. And those round Noguchi are also taking good care of him, know he is not well, that he is often worried, feels that there is much he does not speak of. Visitors are frankly told he cannot be disturbed, but Doctor Proctor would speak with him only a few moments. The name comes garbled over the inside phone. Noguchi thinks it someone else. Then the man who enters he does not know. He is surprised and a little formal, but when he hears why Doctor Proctor came the formality melts. Doctor Proctor is brief. Noguchi asks a question. "Are you sure these Indians have real trachoma?" Doctor Proctor says he could show him several thousand cases. "Then I will go there and start the work." He says something about a new method, something he discovered since last he worked on trachoma and would like to try on trachoma.

Advanced and untreated trachoma is not common in a country like ours, but taking the total earth millions are afflicted. Among our three hundred thousand Indians thirty thousand have the disease, and in the Indian hospital it is possible to study every stage from the earliest granular lids to total blindness. From Albuquerque Noguchi writes enthusiastically.

"There is no limit to good wonderful cases of trachoma here. After having seen these cases I am getting uncertain as to whether or not I have ever seen a true case of trachoma in New York. Of course, a few cases I saw years ago at Ellis Island may have been true trachoma, but you cannot get the real idea of what trachoma is and does to those poor Indians and some doctors in the Indian service."

The disease begins with a watering of the eyes that may go on for months and years. A small ulcer first brings the patient to the doctor because such an ulcer is painful. If now the lid is turned back there may already be the granular look. If the granules are really due to trachoma they break down and pour out their contents then heal and with the healing scar, the scars drawing on the lid, the lid shrinking, the lashes often turned in toward the ball making a condition exceedingly painful. Such late stages are of course easy to diagnose. But the early stages remain difficult, the criteria so far from agreed on that two of the most gifted eye doctors, one the great Fuchs himself, have been known to examine the same case, the one to call it trachoma, the other to say it is only the trachoma-like. It follows that the bacteriologist unless he selects nothing but late cases may not be too sure even of the materials with which he begins.

The hospital is a ramshackle building with a sort of laboratory and Noguchi's belongings quickly fill the place. He is ready at once to work. Doctor Polk Richards, who knows the Indians and their diseases, has come from Fort Defiance to assist. Doctor Richards brings the cases. Not a pleasant disease to look on. An Indian with a firm fine body not older than twenty,

368

blind, led by a boy whose eyes shrink from the light. Eleven such cases are brought and examined. All are late trachoma, at least of two years standing, and all have gone to scar formation, are deliberately chosen so, of course. Pieces of diseased tissue are removed from five cases and the eyes of four rhesus monkeys inoculated. The remainder of the tissue is sealed to carry back to New York or is used to inoculate the culture media brought along. Those who stand by and see Noguchi are dumbfounded. He has had but little previous experience in the handling of eyes yet lightly takes up the eye forceps, turns back the lids, scans the granules, quite as if he had been at this all his life. He works all the first day and far into the night. Everybody notices how late his light burns. Everybody notices too that his trousers are bagged and that he lets his hair run wild and has an absent look. In New York no one speaks of these things.

One of the nights Doctor Richards has a patient with an appendicitis. It occurs to him Noguchi might want to see. The operating room is just the other side of an open door. But Noguchi shakes his head, says he had better not, is unwilling even to pass through an open door, is not interested, or rather is interested in something else and has learned how not to be interested in two things at the same time. The head of the Indian school would like him to visit the school, the school is only a few hundred feet away, and finally too Noguchi comes but almost immediately excuses himself and is gone again. And there ought to be a dinner, Noguchi so distinguished a man, and the night is set, Noguchi arrives, is very lovable, when anyone speaks to him smiles and answers, nevertheless shows clearly he is nervous, so soon as the food is in him apologizes, charmingly, but has risen before he began to apologize, has pushed his chair forward under the table, says that now he feels he must go back to his work, and goes.

The many tubes are packed to take to New York. As always he wants every detail to pass through his own hands.

"We got through this evening, packed up and are ready to run back to-morrow morning. I expect to stop over at New Orleans to get some material of Granuloma inguinalis from Johns." (Is thinking of another disease!) "I got his telegram this evening informing that he has two fine untreated cases. This is getting after 2 o'clock (a.m.!), so I must stop to get some rest before going on another long train journey."

Next morning he leaves, and there is an emptiness behind him. He has been here less than a week, but has put something intense into the air. Many things will be said of him. One day the question was raised whether sooner or later it might not be advisable to inoculate human eyes, and since so many Indians are doomed to trachoma anyway certainly there would be no difficulty to find a volunteer, especially as the volunteer would be carefully watched and the danger to his sight therefore not great. Noguchi had instantly said no, did not like the notion. Furthermore it might make trouble for the Institute and he is very sensitive about what may make trouble for the Institute, always has been. However, he went on to say, if the work did one day reach a stage where the issue could not be otherwise decided he would inoculate his own eyes. And Doctor Richards would inoculate his eyes, only there would not be much use in that because Doctor Richards has had trachoma already and not much could be learned from his eyes.

The cultures when they reach New York are overgrown with a number of organisms. Noguchi's feeling is that something very common has been overlooked, and he means therefore to pure culture every organism he can find and try every culture on animals. It turns out there are five, three are well known, and the way they behave in the human body well known, nevertheless he injects all into the monkeys, chimpanzees, ourang-utans, wants to make sure that no organism that he thinks he knows has not powers to infect of which he does not know.

"With one notable exception, the cultures produced only fleeting reactions or acute inflammation, which soon subsided."

The exception is a bacterium never described before. In this he sees a hope. But trachoma is a chronic disease, slowly developing, therefore, since the animals are inoculated, he may as well go to Shandaken. He has been exhaustingly busy. From Shandaken on the 18th of August he writes Doctor Richards.

"You may be interested to know that the Albuquerque material is still keeping me busy. At a time I worked day and night for many weeks. Now, I am just watching the results of animal inoculations. . . . If it is anything like trachoma the condition must last for months and years. Please do not misinterpret me as saying that I isolated the causative organism."

Two months later.

"I am collecting for you the preparations of various organisms, leptospiras, flagellates, etc., and will send them on as soon as I can. I am afraid you will think that I have forgotten."

Two weeks later.

"I had no idea of trying any direct transmission experiments with the culture I obtained from trachoma material, because monkeys seem so far to satisfy all requirements."

Before many months he is wanting Richards' opinion. The winter has marked great changes in these monkeys' eyes. The condition is more and more like human trachoma. The organism too has been passed from monkey to monkey. His confidence is growing. He writes again on February 10th.

"I wish you were nearer so that you could come and see some of the monkeys. The conjunctival condition in the chimpanzee, which was inoculated from a second passage *rhesus* monkey, is particularly interesting. I wonder if there is any likelihood that you will come east in the near future?"

And in less than two weeks again.

"Several monkeys, including both Macacus rhesus

372

and chimpanzees, have been showing a granular conjunctivitis. . . . These lesions are so much like the trachoma I saw there that I am inclined to believe the organism has something to do with the condition. I have even observed the formation of scar tissue. . . . While I am in no great hurry to form a final judgment about the lesions being real trachoma, I am, nevertheless, anxious to have competent opthalmologists and pathologists look over the lesions and sections. . . . At any rate I have an organism which produces a chronic granular conjunctivitis in monkeys and is transmissible from monkey to monkey."

Doctor Richards is not able to come to New York and Noguchi writes him on the 23rd of March, and again on the 30th, and on April 12th is sending him paintings of eyes made from pencil sketches while in Albuquerque.

"I have not attempted to make a picture of each separate case but to reproduce the impressions which I brought away with me in a composite way."

The following month, he reads a paper at the meeting of the American Medical Association, gets to Washington just in time for the paper and leaves immediately after. He has tubes in his pockets, meets a lady, pulls the tubes from here and there, is excited, explains that these tubes contain sera from cases of trachoma in the Kentucky mountains. These Kentucky sera react positively with the organism isolated in New Mexico, strong evidence that the trachoma in the two places is the same disease and that he has the right cause. At the meeting he spoke only of what is indubitable, that he has a possible organism and that time will tell, but when he writes to the old teacher he lets out freely how he feels.

"Please accept my apologies for the long silence. Spring worms are gradually breaking through the winter's hibernation. Even in this place man's spirit is floating between cherry and azalea. The fact that your illness is finally conquered is great rejoicing for small son at great distance. Please at this advanced age be very careful. My health still glowingly good." (He is writing to the teacher.) "Day and night I strive. I have just completed trachoma." (Still writing to the teacher.) "I am planning to give my first report May 16th. From a sample gotten from western America I have isolated an organism and injected into chimpanzee and have produced perfect trachoma. (Still to the teacher.) About this many scientists are much impressed and think it probably the organism. If this is true it will be a great rejoicing in the world. It will probably open new lines for treatment and prevention. I am hoping for this. It is due to praying to Kannon that you have constantly done for me. As you know, trachoma is often the cause of blindness and in the world there are 30,000,000 infected. China and Japan and Egypt are the worst sufferers. With increasing personal hygiene the cases are fewer. You find only in the poorest localities in this country. Recently I have begun again with Rocky Mountain fever study and I think I will succeed. As I grow older my methods become more fluid and I do what I could not ten years ago. If I succeed it will be a noteworthy discovery. Without doubt prevention and treatment will follow. I am quietly waiting. If this proves true, typhus and tsutsugamushi disease will have the road to their causation opened. At any rate these four or five days are most important for deciding this, one of the greatest problems.

"For the living there is no boundary between life and death. No division between happiness and unhappiness. The rich are not necessarily happy. Even the sick may be in a paradise that others do not know. If we glance and sweep this world from different points it is mugo muga, no boundary no I. What is the object of man's life? That question I ask myself. The bright moon which has been admired these four thousand years is the same that today makes me think of my far-distant home. Time has no limit and what looks so long is after all so short.

"If the discovery of trachoma were decided then perhaps in a few years there might be chance to go to the orient for investigation, and I should have the great pleasure to worship your face again. For this I am hoping."

[LXII]

He Goes to Shandaken

Certain journals he carries with him, has let them stack through the Oroya fever and the trachoma, knew what was in them, did not want them to muddle him. He is starting for Shandaken weary. Someone notes him, remarks he has come to be a little old man.

The criticism of the yellow fever was already heavy at Kingston. "The air was filled with a kind of gloom." And since Kingston the gloom has only grown. Doctor White came to him one day in the laboratory, that is a good many months now, suggested to him that perhaps he ought to go to Africa to study the yellow fever there, also asked him, gently, if he was prepared to face the possibility of his yellow fever being wrong. "Yes, I am prepared." That was Noguchi's answer, and it was not given gaily. He added that he would go to Africa when the right time came.

It might have been harder to face being wrong when he was young. Those fourteen years since the Versammlung deutscher Naturforscher are a lifetime. Yet a fastidiousness has grown in him too, a cleanness

376

as bacteriologist and artist that would make a great awkward wrong not easy to look at. The recent rounded perfection of the Oroya fever would not make it easier, nor the trachoma, though he is by no means sure of the trachoma. To begin to think the yellow fever an equally perfectly rounded failure might make him squeeze tight his eyes even in the dark. "If I could but have those three." He says that many times. He is referring to yellow fever, trachoma and Oroya fever.

As for the character of the criticism it is what from long back he knew it would be. He does not have to read the journals for that. It is being said that he confused yellow fever with infectious jaundice, the possibility discussed there in the dark of the porch in Guayaquil. He was aware from the beginning. "Weil's disease and yellow fever are very much alike." Odd if in spite of his awareness he should have made the mistake, made it among the spirochetes and among those serological reactions at which he has worked most of his life. But it is possible. The greatest of bacteriologists have tricked themselves. Perhaps, though, it was humanly that he tricked himself most. The more generous of his critics are indeed saying that the fault is not his. They are saying that it is the fault of those clinicians down there in South America who told him something was yellow fever that is not, gave him bloods from the wrong disease or from the right and wrong indiscriminately. In some of those bloods he found a spirochete —naturally, because they were bloods from infectious jaundice. In others he could not find a spirochete—

those were from true yellow fever. Many of the bloods were got from convalescents who simply said they had had yellow fever, or whose physicians said they had. Some bloods were brought from the interior of the countries, collected under conditions that he could not know. He was aware of all this but perhaps not sufficiently.

In Brazil opinion was early against him. A personal thing may have been at bottom, and opinion did change when he himself went to Brazil, but there was perhaps also something impersonal. It was in Brazil that his serum would not help. It was in Brazil that another worker got nothing but negative Pfeiffers and he got nothing but positive. That may mean that there are two yellow fevers, and that Brazil has both the disease called yellow fever in Africa and the disease called yellow fever in Ecuador, and that he hit only on cases of the one and the other worker only on cases of the other. It would be easy to imagine the African disease occurring in Rio, Rio being connected with the African coast by steamship, and the evidence increases that the African disease is a distinct disease. It was a bad day last March when one worker who went out from the Institute to Africa came back unable to find Noguchi's organism. It was a bad day, a black day, and several remember very well how Noguchi walked about.

Still the criticism need not be taken too finally either. His critics may be as mistaken as he. The fact that the number is growing makes no difference. Truth is never simply an addition. At Shandaken someone notes him, a little woman who passes the cottage, has not seen him for a year, remarks almost as did the other, "You know, the doctor has gotten old looking."

There is an oddness about all this too. Doctor Jordan of the University of Chicago has asked Noguchi to prepare the chapter on spirochetes for a new book. Certainly he will have to know his own spirochete and the criticism of that spirochete if he is to write that chapter. And that chapter is really the volume on spirochetes talked of in the summer of 1921, drafted that summer, puttered with again the next summer, then touched year after year and still not finished, and now that volume, that unfinished volume is turning on him and directing the course of his life, forcing him to put off no longer. So he is taking the journals with him to Shandaken. He is taking also his stereo-camera, Doctor Proctor having urged him to try his hand at stereo-photography. The fishing tackle goes, and the painting material, and the cat. The Studebaker is heaped. It always is when he and Maizie go to Shandaken. Sometimes Tom drives. Tom is Maizie's brother. Sometimes Hidey drives, is a better driver than he used to be, does not stop short and half throw everybody out as he used to, or just miss going over the edge of a steep place and be saved by Maizie grabbing the emergency, is quieter, is older, a good deal of gray about his temples though the mass of hair remains a beautiful black.

If he would only let up working this one summer. If he would only take this one vacation. He has not had a vacation for so long, the last when he actually did as he liked being that happy summer of 1921, that summer he regretted so that his old polluted well had been treated with chlorinated lime and all the spirochetes killed. There was a playfulness again in the summer of 1924 when he returned from Kingston and went to Shandaken and searched the countryside for flagellates. The other summers all have had definite problems, happy intensities in them, but driven, driven, driven, work that had to be done and that carried him as far into the night as ever in winter at the Institute. "No vacation should be for more than a month." He said that even many years ago. "The mind can't stand it. The mind gets too far away. It is too hard to bring the mind back." This present vacation he works from the first day. "If I had but yellow fever, trachoma and Oroya fever." He says it again and again as he sits there on the broad veranda. "This is a beautiful work that I do, you will know some day." And once he says it differently. "The name of Noguchi, you will see later on." Formerly he used to say that a man must do his best work before he is forty. Now he says by the time he is fifty. He adds that afterward he can take it easier. "At sixty you may as well be dead."

Among the journals is a Dutch monograph by Achmad Mochtar. Noguchi wants particularly to read that monograph. He respects that critic. He has brought along a Dutch grammar with a glossary and exercises in conversation, says he will spend a few days learning Dutch. His way of learning is to read straight through the grammar, so many pages a night. On the fly-leaf he has written *Bought on Aug. 22, 1927,* on page 50 *Finished Aug. 22 midnight,* on page 136 *Aug. 23 midnight,* and he is through with his study *Aug. 24th at noon,* two and one half days for the language. Then he takes up the monograph of Achmad Mochtar. That afternoon he is sitting on the back veranda facing the river with the hills on the other side. He looks steadily into the hills. He has forgotten to light his cigar. Maizie asks him what is the matter. He says: "Nothing." Maizie knows better. Then he says something about a Dutch book and Maizie wishes the devil had hold of that Dutchman. Hidey continues to sit. When night comes he paints a picture, all shades of blue, the moon on one side, a star on the other, dark hills between, the picture sending the gloomiest feelings over one. The next day he is no better. He says that the yellow fever work is not right. When his old friend Madsen wrote a little while ago that he was going to South America Noguchi answered quick.

"Those people down there will certainly appreciate your visit and you. My experience there has always been the most delightful."

And if now he should prove to have cheated those people, not wilfully, of course, but nevertheless have accepted what they gave him on trust. In Ecuador they treated him like a benefactor, like a great man.

He writes another letter to Doctor Proctor. A number of letters have passed between the two. They are playing with the idea of an expedition to Egypt to study the trachoma there. He writes some other letters. He does a little work. He reads a while in the journals. He lights a cigar, walks back and forth and back and forth the whole length of the veranda, forgets to smoke the cigar. He is planning to return to New York the 7th of September, advances the date to the 1st, and when he does reach New York peremptorily announces that he is going to Africa.

LXIII

I Just Want to Finish This Piece of Work

His friends are in a panic. To Maizie one day at Shandaken he said he might go to Africa, but never came back to the subject again, perhaps because she had been so frightened.

He reached New York the 1st. On Labor Day Nichols dies. Nichols has been stationed on the Canal Zone, dies of an appendicitis, the report in the evening papers, but Noguchi does not read papers. Someone else does, is uneasy all night long, next morning comes to the laboratory, is not sure how to begin, at last brings out the name of Nichols. Noguchi grows pale. Later in the day someone else comes to the laboratory, also has seen the report, asks Noguchi if he is too busy to talk a little. Noguchi says he is not. The man tells the story again, and Noguchi apparently allows him, the whole again, only at last lets his head drop, pushes away what is before him, says he can work no more to-day. "I must go out-of-doors. I must go to myself." In the weeks that follow he carries with him Nichols' book and reads in it now and then, seems to draw comfort from that. "What will we do without him?" He says that to everybody.

"I shall always miss him because of his brother affection that he has accorded me throughout our long standing association."

That is what he writes to Mrs. Nichols. Nichols rose up at Kingston and spoke out squarely that U. S. Army Medical School accepted L. icterioides as the cause of yellow fever. Yet Nichols sometimes wondered why Noguchi loved him so.

The preparations for Africa are already under way. There is more reason for going even than there was. Reports have come these last days. Yellow fever has been transmitted to monkeys and leptospiral diseases cannot be, neither infectious jaundice nor that disease he studied in South America whatever it was. He seems to have anticipated this because nearly a year ago he himself thought that the workers in Africa ought to be trying the monkey for the experimental animal, and if he felt any hope in that must have felt proportionately less hope for his own organism. It is Adrian Stokes who recently succeeded in the transmission, and a very important step. Certainly it looks less and less as if the African disease could be the same studied in South America. The possibility remains that the South American disease is not infectious jaundice either, that there are three diseases, African yellow fever, South American yellow fever, and infectious jaundice. Or his whole work may be the perfectly rounded blunder that he has begun so overwhelmingly to fear. He must go to Africa.

His friends know he will do what he says he will. It is wrong for a man as useful as he to go out to that black hole that has swallowed up one good man after another. Let younger men go. At the Institute they argue with him but of course cannot forbid him. He is at the Nippon Club. The news has reached there. They argue. He laughs. He meets Doctor O'Connor at a dinner. Doctor O'Connor is of the Rockefeller Foundation that is to finance this expedition as it has the previous. Noguchi leans over to O'Connor and asks him to "put in an oar" for him. Kaliski talks seriously with Noguchi. Kaliski thinks Noguchi ought not to go. "But I am not afraid. I just want to finish this piece of work. I have been put into this world to do something and I want to finish it. I am enough of a fatalist to know that when my time comes I must go."

On the 19th there is word from Africa that Stokes has died. This falls with a hideous quickness on the death of Nichols. Noguchi was not so close to Stokes, of course, but Stokes was young and Noguchi was in part responsible for his going to Africa. Odd about Stokes' death, done with his work, the date of his sailing for England set, and he seems to have changed his mind, put off the sailing two weeks and in those two weeks was stricken. "If Stokes had only left on the ship before." Noguchi returns many times to this, yet when Stokes is used as an argument against his own going smiles. "I know yellow fever. Do not worry

385

about me." To Maizie he does not mention the death. Maizie has never heard Stokes' name. Maizie has heard nothing more of Africa either.

His friends continue to remonstrate. He is fifty-one, they say. He is not well. His diabetes seems a little better. He himself mostly makes fun of his diabetes. "Only the three bowls of rice that every Japanese should accept I cannot anymore." Other foods he eats in quantity, roast lamb (Maizie tells how he likes it), cabbage, corn beef, smoked sturgeon, hard boiled eggs. (Why soft? They go to the same place.) And never any food hot. For so small a man he eats enormously, but irregularly. He also sleeps irregularly. Since his return from Shandaken he has been up night and day. He has always been irregular about everything that concerns his body. He has always both lived and worked, and both at the same time, and both with fire. Which should make him last ten years longer than he otherwise would, but his friends, who are timid, who love him, who must stand by and see him, cannot regard it so, say he is reckless, say he does not take the most ordinary precautions, that his work is dangerous enough in itself. And then they always mention his heart. He learned of that in 1914, and who knows how long it was bad before that? He does not say much about it, but possibly thinks of it, as a doctor with an imperfect organ may. Sometimes the speed and concentration with which he worked these last years, always as against time, makes one wonder whether he may not have been thinking about his body more than he gave out. He has long said he would not live past fifty. Changed greatly he has. Some feel the change is more mental than physical. Some say he is worried by things outside, that he is always getting himself into trouble. Some say he has nothing really to live for. They say he has the kind of vitality that would go far to cover what he wants to cover, would go far to cover an unhappiness. But the change is physical also, there is no doubt, especially since last summer. Certainly he has looked more continuously gray since then. Doctor O'Connor has seen him, on and off, and it has worried Doctor O'Connor how often he must sit down and rest. His breathing is bad at times. Such a small flat nose, it is hard to see how he gets enough air through it anyway. Nights when he is tired his jaw drops and his mouth stands open. He insists that that was so even when he was a boy. "Close your mouth," his mother used to say. "Only fools keep open their mouths." Little things are noticed now as they are when someone is going a long way.

"What would you have me do! Would you have me sit here in the laboratory and perform test-tube experiments on bloods that somebody else collected five weeks before? No, I must go. I must work with my own bloods, fresh bloods, from cases that I know about. I must satisfy myself." There is no answer to what he says.

The preparations for Africa continue. Noguchi was gloomy at Shandaken. He was gloomy when he first got back to New York. But he is not gloomy now.

He may not be happy either. He is something like happy though, busy. He is studying methods of tissue culture with Doctor Carrel, thinks the knowledge may be useful to him in Africa. He serves as chairman to greet the Japanese naval training squadron, gives all day of the 29th to their visit at the Rockefeller Institute. He spends a number of nights helping a Japanese prepare an English paper. He pays a call or two. The date of the sailing for Africa is set. He is completing his own papers on trachoma. He would like as much as possible out of the way before he sails. The buoyance is not dead. He looks better. He is sometimes unbelievably relaxed, talks, talks.

Maizie has lost the sense of foreboding in which she lived the last months at Shandaken. She has dismissed the idea of Africa. "He will not go down there." Then one night just after the 1st of October when they are already quietly in bed he says that he is going in three weeks. She is frightened naturally. She points out that the territory is English and that the English ought to take care of their own diseases. He says that the preparations are so far along that he cannot possibly change anything now. "I'll only stay a little while." He says again what he said at Shandaken, that he must get the yellow fever right. "Be a strong woman. You must help me." She asks how she can do that. "Keep me in good spirits." He asks her too to pray for good work. She is not consoled, but what can she do? What can anyone do? Next day she is sitting at the window at 203 West 107th looking into the street. "What are

388

all those old women going to church for?" He moves over to the window and looks too. "Think they're going to die, Maizie."

His friends keep at him. Suddenly he turns on one, stares strangely into the man's face. "Do you think perhaps I am not coming back?" The man stammers he meant nothing of the sort, Noguchi going on quite as if a question had been put to him. "Oh, yes, I will be stricken with yellow fever." He says it quite as if it were a settled fact, as if he knew, then leads the conversation somewhere else. At the Institute meanwhile a friend has the idea Noguchi ought to sit for his bust before starting out there. The sculptor Konenkov has done the bust of someone else at the Institute and would do it well, but Noguchi does not want to. Certainly he cannot want to now in the midst of all this. But it would have to be now because the Konenkovs are going to Italy and will not be in New York when he returns from Africa. Even so, he does not want to. He cannot afford the time. He cannot—perhaps there is something else, something vague, sit for a bust just before going out to the place where Stokes died. However, it is the kind of thing about which his friends say he is very like a child, had some unpleasant thoughts, they say, but easily put aside. It is always hard for him to refuse anyway. He goes to the sittings, is very prompt for them, quickly loves the Konenkovs, as they love him, and such a head too for a sculptor, the hair like a flame, the face so smiling, and so much artist in the man that he never interferes with the artist just as when he was ill there was so much doctor that he never interfered with the doctor. When he talks it is with great animation but when he sits it is with pugnacity, and that is the way he wants to look too. He wants to look just a little fierce. That is his idea of himself. And he is quite right about himself, something fierce under the smile, making one remember somehow the quiet boy of the koto-shogakko suddenly throwing himself on that one who happened to ask about his hand. He has had his way with the clay too. The sculptor sees him well, the strong right hand so emphatically there, the body light and loose (he wears the short laboratory coat), the face definitely old, something that has suffered, something that is sick, would have been more sick if the sculptor had been allowed to do freely as he pleased, something surely weary. A friend goes along to the sittings and remarks that the clay is very stern. "But look at him." And, yes, there is no doubt, what the sculptor has done is quite true.

Noguchi says many things as he sits there. He speaks sometimes of his mother. The Konenkovs are Russian, so he tries his Russian on them, laughs about that, but grows very serious when asked about Africa, says he must go because he is responsible for Stokes, then says he would have to go anyway. "I will win down there or die." He has looked bad other days but this day looks very very bad, explains that he was up till five and then it was not worth while to go to bed. The

SOMETHING FIERCE UNDER THE SMILE

Konenkovs say they are sorry he did not break his appointment. He says he made it and did not like to.

The preparations for the departure are at their most intense. If one does one's work with the whole of oneself one cannot feel that one can leave any of it for anyone else to do. He wants to plan what will go on during his absence, has a scheme for restudying the insect responsible for the carrying of Oroya fever, has arranged for the examination of the eyes of the trachoma monkeys. Then there is the equipment for the expedition, the tubes, the syringes, the sera, the viruses, takes along the virus of Rocky Mountain spotted fever so he may have it if there should be any free time down there. The knowledge gained in previous expeditions, the mistakes made, are helping him now. Finally there is the buying of the personal things for Africa. When one starts for Africa one carries all, like the soldier, even one's tent. He likes the buying no less than he liked it long long back there in 1904 when he was so young and came back from Copenhagen to buy his equipment for the new great Rockefeller Institute of New York, only this buying now runs into thousands. He has one gay day when he buys all day. But he is wearier and wearier. He looks worse but he keeps on, is even alert. There still remains that report to be made on trachoma to the staff of the Institute. He is to sail the 22nd. This is the 19th.

One of his Japanese friends to-night is having a party and has asked him to come. He would not promise. He may. He may not. He has gone nowhere for a long time, to some single individual, yes, but to parties not for years, yet he will drop in if he can. And he does. It is late. The others have been there for hours. Whenever he comes into a room everybody feels it, but now when he is so pale they feel it more. He comes, sits down, says nothing, or almost nothing, remains a little while, then rises, bows, without ceremony is gone, is already half down the stairs when his friend runs after him. His friend has looked into that pale face and what he has seen worries him, he hardly knows why. He calls to Noguchi. But what is there to say. Noguchi smiles.

He does not reach home till 4 o'clock, sleeps an hour in a chair then goes to the Institute. The next night, the night of the 20th, he does not come home at all, not till 7 o'clock in the morning and immediately goes to the Institute, says he came only because he was afraid Maizie would worry. Late the afternoon of the 21st he gives his report to the staff. Several remark upon how much easier to understand his English than it used to be. That night at 11 o'clock he is still at the Institute. But now he is drenched with weariness. This is the end. This he could keep up no longer. At home Maizie is waiting. Myrtle and Jacques came to say good-bye, have left. Africa! Maizie is full of apprehension. He is so worn out and he is going so far away. He drops into his chair, the rocker that he likes, all wood, no cloth or leather, the seat very low, he so small, the top of the table so high. "Maizie, get a little wine. Let us not go to bed to-night." She says he must. He has got to be on the ship to-morrow. He has been up two whole nights already. Well then, yes, since she wishes it, he will. She takes the small crippled hand. He falls asleep.

Next morning he is much refreshed. He dresses, does his last packing, then goes to a drawer, takes out a rice-paper scroll, a tracing of the inscription on his mother's tomb. He wants that with him. It gives one a strange feeling. Maizie begs him not to take such things, and he puts the scroll back, asks her not to weep. "Do not send me away like this." He goes. He is down there in the street waving from the taxi window. He has forgotten the o-fuda, left it in the laboratory, the o-fuda he carried in his pocket all the way to Mexico and Brazil and Peru.

Two of his technicians see him off at the ship. No one else. There was to have been a party of friends but he asked them not to come and they did not press him.

LXIV

The Sea

The ship is the *Scythia*. He will change at Liverpool. The boy brings him a wireless, has brought him several, but this one especially pleases him.

"I was surprised to receive bon voyage message from Dr. Vincent, so unexpected as I thought he might be rather disgusted with me."

Disgusted with him because after seeming for eight years to have discovered the cause of yellow fever, after having spent great sums of money, after having had his serum and vaccine sent all over the world, he seems not to have discovered the cause. A big relief to find Doctor Vincent thinking kindly of him even when it looks as if he had failed. Doctor Vincent is head of the Rockefeller Foundation that allowed the money.

Noguchi sleeps and sleeps. He was never a very good sailor but of his sleep has had most perfect control, for that reason has got along on so little and been able to work so hard. When he wakes he reads Tolstoy's Kreutzer Sonata in French, does not like it.

Maizie read it to him in English just after they were married, those nights when he worked over the microscope at the dining-room table. It is a nasty book. Realism in a novel is like an autopsy, ugly at best, he says. Now and then he lays aside the book and brings out his Russian dictionary, continues the Russian that he practised last month on the Konenkovs. He writes the Konenkovs a letter, says how happy he was sitting in their studio among their beautiful things and how he will live again those moments "in a clear moonlight night along the coast while sailing down southwards." He recalls the luncheon they had together. It was at a French restaurant. When he comes back they will eat Japanese at a Japanese restaurant.

"How time flies! And I am about to reach England within a few more days and this means that a one-third of my sea journey will have been finished by next Sunday morning. Then I am to take another boat down to the tropical coast of Africa. I am not fond of traveling."

He sleeps. He sleeps wherever he puts his head. This does not make one think of the journeyings to Mexico and Peru. "I am losing interest in cigars." He has given up cigars many times. It is different to be losing interest.

There comes another wireless, from Lagos, Africa, the Rockefeller Foundation having its station at Lagos, Noguchi not yet absolutely sure whether he will work there or at Accra which is farther up the coast. This wireless also relieves him. He has not felt altogether easy about the way things were shaping themselves down there. He is too sensitive, especially of late, but even in full health and youth it is one thing to go forth feeling the world behind you and another to feel that men no longer believe.

In Liverpool he quits the *Scythia,* will continue on the *Appam* of the *Elder Dempster Line.* The weather is bad in Liverpool. He talks of the weather. It is never a good sign when he talks of the weather, talked of it also that summer of 1922, commonly must be told when to take an umbrella. On a rainy night he writes a dismal letter, blames himself for many things, speaks of himself as if he were one of the hardest men in the world to get along with. There is much to look after in Liverpool. He likes himself to oversee the moving of his equipment from one ship to the other. He buys a few books. As usual he sends a number of cables, plenty of greetings in them, one to Carl Hagenbeck ordering three monkeys to be shipped as quickly as possible to West Africa. The weather continues bad. He continues weary. He seems still not to have made up his mind whether to work at Lagos where the others are or alone at Accra.

Finally the *Appam* puts out to sea. During the first six days there are gales and rains and life is not much, then the ship draws near the Canary Islands and everybody sweats and seems to wake up again. He is not reading Kreutzer Sonata now but Lyddeker's Royal Natural History. The first volume has to do with the primates, and there is much in the volume that he did

396

not know, that he feels he really ought to know, that will perhaps help him better to understand how his inoculations act. He grows more and more interested in the book, thinks he may do a great deal with the primates when he gets to Africa. There has meantime been an answer to the wireless to Hagenbeck's saying that the order has been received and the monkeys will be sent, but the wireless does not say when. "I hope they will hurry up." He thinks Hagenbeck's ought to have a catalogue of available monkeys, wonders whether they have. Why is one not able to buy the monkeys of Africa in Africa? Ridiculous to be sending them from Africa to Germany and then from Germany to Africa. He wonders whether Mr. Buck has sailed from New York with the monkeys and chimpanzees. He talks over all this with Lieutenant Governor Rushton of Nigeria who happens to be on the ship. Lieutenant Governor Rushton has lived on the West Coast thirty years and to him it seems that it ought to be possible to have even a gorilla or two. That would be interesting. As for chimpanzees, according to Lieutenant Governor Rushton, they can be bought on the streets from the natives at any time. "I hope he is right." A few monkeys have already been shipped to the West African laboratory but the big shipment including fifty rhesus monkeys will not reach Accra till the 24th.

"The total capacity of the animal house is fifty. So I may have some trouble for a time being."

The rest has done him good. His buoyance is back. But what has done him most good is that he has begun

397

in this new environment to busy himself with the coming practical problem, is soon as busy as it is possible to be on a small ship crossing the equator, is not so bright as on the way to Bahia, is still not the chess-playing traveler of those days, but at least is a different man from a week ago. Fifty monkeys are a good many. Clearly he is thinking in the old mass way. And clearly too he is thinking he will deal with a new disease, not what he dealt with before, a new disease with an unknown cause.

What begins to worry him is where he will get the fresh bloods. There is always yellow fever somewhere along the West Coast, but distances are great and transportation difficult. His big reason for coming is that he may be able to work with his own strains of the virus got by his own inoculation of the animals with the fresh bloods of the patients. So it is a great disappointment when on the ninth day at sea he receives a wireless saying that there are no new cases. It means that he will have to work with strains already running in the animals at Lagos or will have to begin with old preserved bloods. What makes that a little easier is that he feels sure that they at Lagos have the right strains. "To my mind there is no doubt." He said that even before he sailed. It was on one of those days when he had practically given up the hope that African yellow fever and the disease he worked with in South America might still prove the same.

However, no need quietly to accept the fact that there are no new cases. If they at Lagos who are making the arrangements cannot find any, why, perhaps he can find some on his own. A ship has a wireless. He appeals to the Inspector General Medical Service at Dakar and that gentleman immediately responds offering any help he can give, promises to send samples of blood as soon as there are cases. But as to the rumor of two hundred cases, that was only a rumor. The Inspector General positively states that the latest case was November 5th. A passenger comes from second class to talk with Noguchi. The passenger lives in Accra and knows the laboratory where Noguchi will probably work, says that yellow fever may be found in Accra at any time. The passenger is exaggerating, of course. Another passenger comes from second class, talks about Adrian Stokes, says that he was Stokes' teacher when Stokes was still in Ireland. In short, the passengers are limbering as they do when the smell of the destination gets into the salt air. To-morrow the ship will put in at Freetown, the first port of call, and to-night is passing Dakar. The captain wires the Elder Dempster office at Dakar to ask that help be given the Inspector General in securing and transporting the samples of blood that Noguchi has requested.

The weather is clear, the night beautiful, a full moon. One would be happy if beauty made one happy, but it as often makes one sad. Him it has always made sad, or strange, in Woods Hole twenty-five years ago, in Okinajima twice that long ago. But he is not so melancholy that he cannot laugh. He is the one man on the ship who does not come to dinner in a dress

399

jacket, and he laughs at that. He has no dress jacket. Someone says he will have to have one made at Accra. "What a ridiculous idea."

After Freetown the ship calls at Sekondee. Two of the doctors of the Rockefeller Foundation at Lagos have come to Sekondee, will travel with Noguchi the last of the way. From them he learns what preparations have been made for him. After Adrian Stokes' death there was trouble about a place for breeding mosquitoes, but now a place has been found in a small screened laboratory, and that is ready. Doctor Mahaffy has been especially detailed from Lagos to Accra to be there during Noguchi's stay, and that is good news because Noguchi knows Mahaffy from Brazil and likes him. A younger man, Batchelder by name, is to assist in the laboratory, and he too is waiting in Accra. Noguchi is to live with the Mahaffys in a small wing of their house, screened, a separate entrance, a place where he can be quite alone if he likes. What is disappointing is that there are still no cases of yellow fever.

He seems less buoyant again, at least writes less buoyantly. One reason is that he has entered an atmosphere where yellow fever looks the only problem in the world, where he is reminded of his failure and not reminded that if he count nothing but his achievements of the last two years he has done more than would justify the careers of most bacteriologists on earth. He talks with an almost incomprehensible humility of what there is still left for him to do. The experimental animal, the small five-pound Indian monkey, has already been found. The virus is known to be filterable. But the organism is still unknown, and of course no one can have pure cultured what is unknown. "After all my trip may not be in vain." One would think he were meaning to be humorous did one not know he was exactly the reverse, discouraged. Has he then given up all hope of his spirochete? He is wanting only more and more monkeys, and monkeys cannot be infected with his spirochete. Nevertheless it is just now that he writes that the French at Dakar are using his vaccine and serum with good result. "The unvaccinated die in large numbers." So some hope must remain.

The ship is moving along a desolate stretch of the African land. The one doctor of the Foundation is to disembark with Noguchi at Accra, the other to continue on to Lagos twenty-four hours farther. Noguchi has finally decided to work at Accra, which is on the Gold Coast, the principal city, and the reason he gives is that there have been more cases of yellow fever there, as many as fifty cases in the epidemic of May and June, but possibly he has reasons of his own, possibly wants to be alone, does not want to work where the others are. Mr. Fraser one of the kindliest and strongest men on the West Coast is present when Noguchi comes ashore. Noguchi is introduced. He is introduced also to several of the doctors. Mr. Fraser is struck by what he says. "Gentlemen, I shall do my best. The results— I cannot say—they are not with me."

[LXV]

Iimoriyama

William Alexander Young is head of the small institution for research which the British have here at Accra. Young gives over a good part of his space for Noguchi's use and himself pitches in to get things started. Noguchi looks tired. Yet he wants to hear all Young can tell him of the climate and conditions along the West Coast. While they talk they unpack. There has been but one accident in the shipping. The kelvinator was badly crated and is smashed. Noguchi says he will work nights. The nights will be less disturbed. Young will help where he can, and Batchelder will assist directly in the laboratory. There will of course be a native staff.

Noguchi wants really to work alone. Young feels this immediately and strongly. It may be as it was in the beginning at Guayaquil, and Young keeps away but is not easy about Noguchi. "Noguchi seems unhappy and worried, and I feel quite sorry for him." That is what Young says, says it a number of times, then one day it is different. "Noguchi is happier to-day.

He was looking tired and worried, and I said: 'Doctor Noguchi, if I can do anything to help you, I shall be more than delighted. Is there anything I can do?' Noguchi's face brightened and in a gratified voice he said: 'Thank you, I shall be very glad to have your help.' " From this on the two grow closer. And something else happens. "Noguchi was annoyed with me to-day." That is the way Young begins another time. "He asked my opinion on a certain experiment, and because I could not honestly agree with him (not having seen the thing myself) he was annoyed. I said: 'Doctor Noguchi, you ask for my opinion. I give it to you. I cannot say I agree with you on this point which I have not seen, and to give my honest opinion I must see for myself. Please do not think it presumption on my part, and please do not take it as against yourself personally in any way. For, do you know, Doctor Noguchi, you have a most charming personality.' " Noguchi takes Young's hand, thanks him fervently, tears in his eyes. He is so weary. It makes him more sensitive than he otherwise would be.

He is living with the Mahaffys, and the Mahaffys are very kind and doing all they can, but that does not make their place any bigger than it is. There is a living room, a dining-room, a small room to one end, then a small room to the back, tacked on, for a while occupied by Scannell who was with Noguchi in Brazil. This is now Noguchi's room. He has been told there is no other house available, but walking one morning to examine a poisonous snake that the natives have killed he

403

sees the spacious inside of a bungalow of one of the doctors. He wants a place like that. He appeals to Young, and Young without much difficulty finds a way. Noguchi is not only to have a bungalow but the British officials will make a special effort to have the screening done quickly. Two days later he is in. He writes that he will have a native cook, the same who cooked for the Prince of Wales when that gentleman was in Accra, and several native servants. Fortunately Young and he are by this brought closer still, already are occasionally heard in heated talk over the work.

Noguchi has made a great many cultures from the blood sent from Lagos. So far nothing has grown. And by the end of the month he has more than thirty monkeys going. The supply of monkeys is adequate. There has been a shipment from Hamburg, some have come from Lagos, still others are ordered. He has also a chimpanzee, and a horse for bleeding, but up to now there has been no fresh case of yellow fever. Now however word comes of an epidemic in French Togoland. Men are to go about a day's ride from Accra and bring back samples of blood immediately they are drawn. So things are really started. Nevertheless Noguchi often looks troubled, is a very different man from day to day, one day leaps out of his Dodge and has disappeared into the laboratory before anyone can see exactly how the thing took place, another day climbs out like an old man. Young is fond of him, has some understanding of him.

After dark one evening Noguchi starts up the road

404

to speak to a man he would have go to Dakar to get samples of blood. He enters the man's place, explains why he came. The man asks whether he is to take monkeys with him when he goes to Dakar. Noguchi thinks that would hardly be necessary, whereupon the man says something about men out here knowing how to inoculate monkeys without Noguchi coming to teach them. Noguchi is too sensitive, but at any time it would have been difficult for him to brush aside a tone of disrespect, and this now is like jeering, for the man has gone on talking, something about taking six monkeys and inoculating them as he chooses, also something about Noguchi's spirochetes, about Noguchi finding none of those down here. Noguchi leaves, goes out into the African night. It is a lonely place, this Accra, and perhaps no less lonely if one is the one Japanese, the others all British or American or black. Plainly some about him do not believe in his spirochete. He knew that, does not really believe in it himself, but to be jeered about it is another matter. The night is perhaps not unlike that when he painted the moon and the stars and the blue-black hills. He tells his friend what has happened. His friend sees the thing in the right light, says that the man up there in the bungalow has been drinking, possibly. "Men say what they think when they are drunk." That is Noguchi's answer.

Weeks pass. "The old man." He is quite often spoken of that way now. The climate and the long hours are too much, and perhaps also the native servants there in the bungalow are not taking good care of their master. He treats them as equals and they do not understand, is forever giving them chits, orders for a pound sterling written on any scrap of bibulous paper that happens to lie about. "He big man in your country?" "Yes, plenty big." "Is he black?" "No." "White?" "No." The natives are puzzled.

Christmas eve he has dinner with the doctors. He cables greetings to America, says he is fine, nevertheless on Saturday does not appear at the laboratory, and late Sunday when two go down to the bungalow they find him ill. He is admitted to the hospital for a mild attack, as he thinks, of yellow fever. "Fool, he won't get back alive. What did he go to that damned place for?" Apprehension makes one of his friends speak that way. Then it is reported he is inoculating monkeys with his own blood, so he must be better. He is not an easy patient. With a look he frightens all but one of the nurses away. Her he cannot. She scolds him, says he must eat. He says he won't. She says he will. "All right, if you feed me." She agrees, for one spoonful, after which he must eat the rest himself. She cuts his bread—she is an English woman—calls one piece the Colonel, another the General, another the Admiral. "Ah, now the Admiral is gone." But there are hours when he will not play. Several times he weeps, says that if he could only finish this piece of work he would be satisfied not to live any longer. Suddenly he will be afraid he has been rude to her, says he has no breeding, then asks how it was when she was a child. Did she have a garden? He had no garden, nothing like that, came of the very poorest people. Then again he will be stubborn, will not do anything she asks. "I am Noguchi!" "It makes no difference who you are, even if you were the King of England and he is the highest man I know." Noguchi laughs. "She is cruel." He points her out to the other nurses.

Odd sometimes how his hair behaves, just like his moods. He will be very depressed, half-sitting in his bed, motionless, not saying a word, his hair lying flat, then Doctor O'Brien will come in and talk to him and his mood will change entirely. He will get excited, shoot his fingers through his hair, the hair will literally stand up, and he will be a different person. Of course he is wanting to get out of bed before he has had permission. His nurse says no. He is immediately fierce, but stays. Then Doctor O'Brien leaves an order that he should get up for a little, and he will not. His nurse must almost bodily take him to the porch. She tells him that she never had so bad a patient. He sits sullenly in his chair, says he knows just what terrible things are happening inside him. She says she does not care to hear. He says he will die. She says he will not. She says he has nothing more than a bad indigestion from eating that old canned goods that he prefers, crab-meat out of tins and after standing several days, things from the refrigerator where he has been keeping his dead monkeys. She puts the *London Illustrated* into his lap. He says he will not look at it, keeps his eyes straight in front of him, but the next thing she knows he is laughing, has found some pictures of Japan. She must come and see. He talks and talks of Japan.

The Youngs visit him, find him bright and encouraged to know that his health is improving. On the 7th he slips from the hospital without leave and does not go down to the bungalow but back to the Mahaffys. He realizes what the Mahaffys meant to him, and henceforth Mrs. Mahaffy can see to it that his native cook and house boys do well by their master. Before the end of the month he has gained much in health and is vigorously at work, lays the mildness of his attack to the vaccine taken before he left New York. That was the vaccine against his spirochete, so plainly he must even now have some hope in his spirochete. Did not Stokes die? And Stokes was not vaccinated. One day too when in the laboratory a guinea-pig comes down with something very like a spirochete infection Noguchi nods his head. "Maybe Noguchi no such fool." Of late he speaks of himself often in the third person.

Young wants him to rest more, to work less intensely, to take some minimum of recreation. Young plays chess with him, and there is also someone in the town with whom he plays, a good player and victory by no means assured. At each full moon there is a bathing picnic, and Young always invites him, and usually he accepts, comes down to the beach, chats for half an hour, then goes back to the laboratory for the night. But sometimes when one of the others wants him to go he does not accept. "No." "Oh, come." "No, let me

408

alone, you disturb me." Nevertheless presently he is asking where they are bathing. "Right down here at the beach." It turns out to be a party with all the nurses of the hospital. He is the life, has them all laughing, he so tiny in the midst of these women. When the party is over he wants to take everybody home. Some live far to the other side of Achimota, but he packs them into his machine. It is late when he returns. His friend looks in at the laboratory toward 2 a. m., uneasy because he got him into this. "Yes, it was far some of them lived. But then, we had a good time."

It is February now. Young is more and more involved in the work, accordingly sleeps less and less. Noguchi can rest mornings, does not come till 10 or 11 o'clock, works then for several hours, usually over the animal lists and protocols, then lunches, then rests again a little in the afternoon, then works on into the night and, as the weeks advance, further and further into the night. Often now it is 5 a. m. that he marks the letters that he writes, the cocks crowing and daylight, as he says, but an hour away. It was 5 a. m. when he was drug-boy at Wakamatsu. It was 5 a. m. at Pennsylvania. It was 5 a. m. in Brazil. So the hour in itself is not remarkable. One letter runs on and on. He ought to be going to bed but he lets the letter run on and on, as it is so easy to do when dark and silence lie all around. And then too the early morning is cool. Before this the weather was dry, but now the rains have begun. The heat is not so great yet, and he does not mind heat, even likes it, says that too much has been made of the

409

bad weather of the tropics, that he sweats and that that helps him, nevertheless he is grateful for this chill of morning. He makes a pot of tea to refresh himself, finally starts for the Mahaffys, is driven through the African dawn toward the rolling plains of Achimota. But there are mornings too when he forgets, falls asleep over his bench with his head in his hands and when the others come at 8 o'clock decides he may as well start the day.

He is impatient about some monkeys that have not arrived, wants to cable for them. It is explained to him that the ship is already at the cape. "When then will the monkeys come?" "To-morrow." "Ah, that is good." The next morning at seven the monkeys are not there and he wants to cable, is reminded that it is still early, and that it takes time to bring the animals ashore. Presently he is at the beach seeing whether he cannot hurry the boatman along.

Young by now has made thousands of examinations of tissues of dead animals. Lately when an animal dies in the night Noguchi sends his car for Young, and Young helps at the post-mortem. This is more and more frequent. Young is so much involved in this work, is so anxious Noguchi should make no mistake this time, should be absolutely sure. His hopes rise and fall with Noguchi's. "We have discovered something but we are saying nothing meantime." That is the way he speaks one night, the next is discouraged.

The number of native helpers has risen to thirty. Their work is not flawless, but Noguchi trusts them, is interested in them, especially in their language, says that before he leaves he means to learn something about that language, will take back dictionaries of the various dialects, if there are such dictionaries. And the number of monkeys also has risen, more than five hundred now. That one weary human being should drive it all seems impossible. "He looks as if he were caught up by a great cause." That is the way one sees him. "A child with power." That way another. As for himself, he sees the thing before him. "No place else in the world can accommodate and take proper care of so many monkeys." When he gets a new specimen of blood he may inoculate as many as a half dozen. Only two of the half dozen may take down, but the other four cannot be used because it is impossible to be sure that something has not been retained in them. Then the blood of the two that did take down is inoculated into a half dozen more. Thus the number is bound to mount and the number is indeed stupendous. They constitute a good-sized and steadily growing hospital. He sometimes deals with them in batches of as many as twelve, the natives keeping them outside the door till he is ready, then holding them for him while he works. He is as free with them as he might be with guinea-pigs. No wonder some in the world beyond Accra who know the numbers and not much of the work are frightened. Noguchi has heard something of what is said of his lavishness. He is incensed. He is often incensed. When he is incensed he writes cables, puts down anything that strikes him, orders the cables sent, and next day is glad they were not.

He has found something—a suspicious organism. The organism is very fatal to the animals into which it is injected, black vomit in their stomachs and great destruction of liver and kidney. He has already five strains of the new organism. Young keeps insisting that before it can be trusted it must have been passed through at least half a dozen generations and the animals into which it is injected go down with the first injection. Noguchi wants this too, nevertheless argues. The five strains are all from samples of blood sent from Dakar, and the point of view with which he has gone to work is apparently the same with which he went to work last year on trachoma—that the previous workers have overlooked something very common. And what he has found is something very common. A man enters the laboratory. He calls the man to the microscope, asks him what the organism looks like. "Looks like the ordinary hay bacillus to me." "Ah, but you don't know. . . ."

So all hope in his spirochete is gone. He seems hardly to have looked for it. He is convinced that African yellow fever is not the disease he dealt with in South America. Whether the South American disease is also not infectious jaundice, but a third disease, who can tell? Not likely that he went altogether wrong, yet he may have, and if he did, and if he finds the right now, it makes no difference. But suppose he does not find the right now? Sometimes in the dawn he looks

412

gray and sick, and in the snapshots he makes no effort to hide his crippled hand, lets it lie there staring. It proves how tired, or how indifferent, or possibly even how done, how through with the last vanities. Once he is speaking passionately and ends: "The sunset of Noguchi, and perhaps a bad one."

There is a report of yellow fever in Matadi. Matadi is in the Belgian Congo. Noguchi appeals at once to the Belgian authorities, also to the French Inspector General, and the French Inspector General gets in touch with Matadi and urges that Noguchi be helped as much as possible. There is an instant promise of specimens and soon too the specimens arrive. It pays to take things into his own hands. It has all his life. It pays to throw in his whole energy. Where he gets that energy is harder and harder to see. It is always past daylight now when he leaves his laboratory. Sometimes he burns through the whole night every light in the place, makes everyone wonder, makes this or that one think him strange.

Remarkable that even now, even in the midst of this he should be considering Egypt. It would be only briefly, only long enough to gather materials for a further study of trachoma, a continuation of that plan talked of in the letters from Shandaken last summer. What is thought yellow fever in South America is not yellow fever here, and what is thought trachoma among the American Indians may not be trachoma in Egypt. Better make sure. But for the present he must keep his mind to this before him.

413

Young continues close. "I must see the whole of these experiments now. Doctor Noguchi has taken me so completely into his confidence, it is a great honor to work with Noguchi." And Noguchi needs Young. He needs the man, and he needs the worker, wants him to know everything, about the new organism too, a common organism, spore-bearing. In order to be sure Young's judgments are wholly unbiased it has been agreed between them that he shall make all his diagnoses of tissues without knowing from what animals they were taken. Working in this way it is found that it is impossible to distinguish animals that died of the new organism from those that died of yellow fever blood. Noguchi begins to say in letters and cables to New York that he has discovered the cause of the yellow fever of Africa. "My work is so revolutionary that it is going to upset all our old ideas of yellow fever." Some days he is very sure. Some days he is not so sure. The results are by no means constant. The susceptibility of the monkeys varies unpredictably, a succession of positive results, then when he begins to feel confident of positive results, a negative. The whole must be very guardedly interpreted. This time he must not be wrong.

But what is left to do, right or wrong, can be better done under the more deliberate conditions of his own laboratory. There is no absolute reason for staying in Africa. He allows his sailing to be set for the third week in May. Possibly he will go to Egypt, possibly not.

Mrs. Mahaffy invites the Youngs and Noguchi

to a farewell dinner. Noguchi is very tired, but his kind and almost courtly manners remain. He insists that Young have the place of honor at the table. It is one of those beautiful African nights, clear, the stars so bright. After dinner all five stand together to enjoy the immensities of the heaven—the kind of half hour one remembers.

Noguchi spends most of his time from this on making ready for departure. He is haggard. Two American artists moving along the West Coast stop at Accra, drop in at the laboratory, have been to Japan and know the country well. Noguchi begs them to stay, seems almost to cling to them, and they do stay for several days. Once or twice the talk turns on his work. "Oh, yes, I have got something." But the words sound as if he felt he had failed. It is only an impression, the impression of strangers, but to those two Americans there is a gloom coming from him that pervades everything. One of them sketches his picture, gives it to him, asks him if he would not send them a photograph of it some time later. He says he will, but the way he says it makes the artists think that nothing will ever be done about it, that nothing will ever be done about anything.

Last night, Tuesday, Noguchi played chess till 11 o'clock then went to the laboratory and stayed the night, did not reach the Mahaffys till 7 o'clock this morning, rested an hour, then went aboard the *Aba*. He has all along spoken of wanting to pay a visit to Lagos before sailing finally from Accra. He will reach there to-morrow morning, Thursday. Lagos for a West African city is big and has a port. To the men at Lagos he seems in good health. He stays the day, sleeps the night, and in the morning, Friday, has a chill. He thinks malaria, but a hasty examination of the blood reveals no parasites, and he goes to the ship for the return to Accra, is cheerful, but in the night has another chill. The sea runs high. At Accra there is no port. Passengers must be taken ashore in surfboats. There seems an almost malicious casualness about the surfboat crew. The boat lies by the steamer for nearly twenty minutes, and when it does get under way a tarpaulin shelter is made by the wind into a sail and there is little headway till someone impatiently tears that off. Before the boat has reached the shore a heavy rainstorm breaks and the sick man is hideously exposed and wet through. This is no malaria. He is taken to the Mahaffys, wants to get into bed immediately and, immediately he is in, falls asleep. Doctor O'Brien comes to see him at 5 o'clock, and at 6 o'clock, Saturday now, he is admitted to the hospital. He is quite able to walk. Mr. Fraser is leaving the hospital as he is entering, bows, does not realize that the distinguished Japanese doctor is a yellow fever patient or for that matter a patient of any kind.

This time his nurse does not scold him. This time he is fearfully ill. By morning he realizes he has yellow fever. The two Americans would like to go to him. He seemed so lonely to them, but it is thought best to keep him quiet and to allow no visitors other than certain of the physicians.

He knows yellow fever, but he does not as in January talk of what is going on inside him. Perhaps though he marks the days. Monday morning he is bad. By evening the temperature has dropped. That is taken for a good sign both by those about and by those in New York whither the dispatches are going, yet one who has seen much of yellow fever is not sure. "Remission of symptoms. I don't like it." Tuesday he is better and continues better Wednesday. Wednesday he asks for the electric kettle that all along he has had near him for his tea. The fifth day comes. The fifth day goes. The sixth and seventh days are bad in yellow fever, and after the seventh deaths are rarer. Mostly he lies very still. It might be a poor time to die. If he is convinced that he has found the cause of yellow fever, what he knows of that cause is locked essentially in his own head. There are notes, sealed tubes, and Young has followed step for step, but the power to push through to the meaning is perhaps buried in himself. If on the contrary he is not convinced it might be easier to die than to go back and face friends. "It is the end. And I want it to be." Now and then he talks of his mother, now and then of Japan. He gives the feeling of not quite daring to close his eyes. Yet several times when he is wide awake and hears someone coming he quick closes them. He might be dead for the way he lies there. The doctors approach the bed, stand round a while, then go. He calls. "They are gone?" He smiles.

"We fooled them. Talk to me." Once or twice he asks whether he ever says anything in his sleep.

Friday afternoon he seems much better, wants to know about the laboratory, but on Saturday morning has an epileptiform seizure. That seizure is a shock to everyone. He is drowsy after it and seems distinctly to weaken but does not lose consciousness. "Everything takes so long with him. Not like us." That is what one says. On Saturday evening Young comes to see him. He recognizes Young and talks to him, among other things asks: "Are you sure you are quite well?" "Quite," answers Young with no foreboding how ghastly short a time he will be. And Noguchi says: "I don't understand." He seems to mean he does not understand how he was infected. There were mosquitoes, and there was always the powerful virus that goes through the unbroken skin, ways enough to be infected, and though he worked with the precautions that workers in Africa and elsewhere have learned he worked always with great speed, was weary, was unhappy, and then breaks occur. That evening he falls asleep. But is he asleep even now? He lies there just as he lay before. And the unconsciousness too takes so much longer than with others somehow. Once he clutches his nurse's hand, but not like one in convulsion, more like a child afraid. She remembers how he would say "funny Noguchi." He always said it as if it had been said of him, as if he had heard it many times and knew what to think of it. "One feels one would do anything in the world for him." The next day at noon, the 21st, he dies.

The body must be embalmed right away, the heat is so great. Then a box must be made. One of the men makes the box. The body is laid in. "A man isn't supposed to show much feeling at a time like that but I can't help it." That is what one says. Several go to play golf. Later one takes the body in a surfboat out to a Bull Line Steamer. Young locks the laboratory door and will see to the disinfecting. "Doctor Noguchi's death has upset me a lot and I am utterly fagged out." Young has worked so hard, so many months, has helped so many nights at the post-mortems—if there were infected mosquitoes he was as exposed as Noguchi himself.

Scannell shortly makes ready to leave Accra. Mrs. Mahaffy goes down with him to the ship. "She needn't have done that. Nice of her though. When I reached Dakar they were saying: 'Scannell is dead.' They got it wrong, of course. They didn't mean me. It was Young was dead." Young too. Noguchi's body is out at sea.